AADCU PUBLI
WWW.AADCU
INFO@AADCU

ACKNOWLED
This publicatio
help and coope
institutions. Gr
David Raponi
support in the
AADCU book s
practices in th
based architec

PROJECT DIRE
COORDINATO
CURATOR/ED
BOOK DESIGN
EDITED AND P
Asia Art&Desig
IN COLLABOR
Lab&Internatio

ISBN 978-7-56

编辑与出版：亚洲
协同合作：HOV\
零度事务\美国

主编及学术项目总
国际总协调：罗小
书籍设计：°C Of
翻译：顾澎雯\清

※美国亚洲艺术与设
究和实践，由于诸多
最大程度参阅相对应

HOV

综述 004 Mission Statement, David Raponi

HOV 006 HOV

他最终会成为一位“评议员” 011 He Will Eventually Be A “Senator”, Cesare Maria Casati

MULTIVERSUM 013 Multiversum, Luigi Affuso

HOV: 科学的雕刻家 016 HOV: S-culptors Of Science, Luigi Centola

GLOSSITY

GLOSSITY 023 Glossity, David Raponi

殖民化程序研究 025 [Colonization] Programme Of Research, 1999_2000

强化再生中心 034 [Intensive Reproductive Centre], 1999_2000

反射隔离区 042 [Reflective Isolation Field] 2001

孵卵器 050 [Incubator], 2004

我的花朵 056 [My Flowers], 2006

与DAVID RAPON的访谈 060 Interview With David Raponi

HOUSE

体块住宅 064 [Block House], 2003

枕头住宅 076 [Pillow House], 2004

BUILDINGS

塔楼	085	[Towers], 2000-2006
金融学院	096	[Financial Institute], 2003
Bozen宫	104	[Palast Fur Bozen], 2003
神秘宫	108	[Mystery Palace], 2004

COMPETITIONS

意大利卡斯特费达尔多项目	117	[Project For Castelfidardo - Italy], 2000
情感博物馆	122	[Museum Of Emotions], 2001
星野富弘博物馆	126	[Tomihiro Museum Of Shi-ga Azuma-mura (Japan)], 2002
城市休闲生活加油站	134	[A City-leisure Activities Generator], 2003
安科纳城，亚得利亚海灵魂大门	152	[Ancona, Soul-gate Of The Adriatic], 2003
雕刻－随机表面的生成	182	[Carving — Generative Outline Of Random Surfaces], 2006

INSTALLATIONS

画廊	191	[The Gallery], 2004
幸福岛	196	[Happy Islands], 2004
时尚画廊	200	[Fashion Gallery], 2004
时装展示场	208	[Scene For A Fashion Parade], 2003
黑暗之光	212	[A Light In The Darkness], 2001

DESIGN

永恒的服装	217	[Timeless Clothes], 2002
Kix椅	222	[Kix], 2002

有机－数码 未来的建筑	226	The Architecture Of The Organic-digital Future, Emanuele Piccardo
建筑师年表附录	228	HOV Bibliography

MISSION STATEMENT

HOV was born as an answer to the need of emersion from clandestineness of some personal passions of mine, first of all the love for sculpture and then for quantum physics, mathematics and cognitive biology.
These disciplines are sometimes close to architecture, but they are certainly as far from professional practice as from research activities. Nevertheless this discrepancy is not a real one since hypothesis such as Maturana's multi-versus and Bohm's holographic imagery are definitely more courageous, daring and creative than most of modern literature or art.
The awareness of participating in a change in architecture is a subsequent one: it appears when one reaches the belief that it is impossible to amplify the yet numerous reference models giving way to uneasiness, which is a typical feature when the limit has been reached and the system has run dry.
Conclusions – such as the radical change in the notions of reality and organism – are then collected after the interdisciplinary convergence of reality into sciences. A reality which does not belong to all human beings anymore and which is not out of living organisms anymore. It is only one of the results obtained by the integration process materializing in between the different sciences, for which the classical reference model – united within the logic of relation between parts based on the correspondence of input-output – seems not to be up-to-date.
Since the time of that awareness, HOV has extended such basic conceptions to the research, has investigated the spaces of life within the paradigms produced or imagined by the most different circles of disciplines, offering a series of pre-figurations. The possibilities of social transformations linked to the various shapes of collective intelligence led, for example, to the birth of the Glossity Project, where to a previously defined imaginary social model, spaces and settlements were subsequently associated.
However, beyond Glossity, the hypothesis of a complex society assuming the shape of the external perturbations that model its structure, always maintains HOV activity as a not oriented one, without any preferential observation points.
The aim is to produce a series of hypothesis enclosing some variations to the basic conceptions in order to experiment their consequences. Such an attitude has not a recognizable order and it is very close to an emotional state of mind which appears as a familiar one when observed by those who write in abstraction, but it still remains hardly definable. In the best moments the sensuous relation established with images originating from ideas does not cancel the continuous experience of creation-revision, but even trying not to leave functional questions unsolved – especially in contextualized projects – one belief stays firm: amongst all animals, man is undoubtedly the most adaptable one.
The experimental works are characteristic of a freedom of mind which – I admit – cannot be shared all the times by all individuals, but, even if a new idea reveals itself to be wrong, the fact that we were not able to conceive it before proves the possible existence of a future which is much different from the one we expect.
The flow of ideas can also be dissociated from occasions or references. The elaboration of a project is an opportunity revealing itself independently of a contest or a client, sometimes showing itself just after the call perceived from the surrounding milieu and its primary elements.
Thus the project does emerge from the relation between the organism and its milieu, in the same way as – in Maturana's words – "walking is generated by a movement of legs during their relation with the ground."

David Raponi

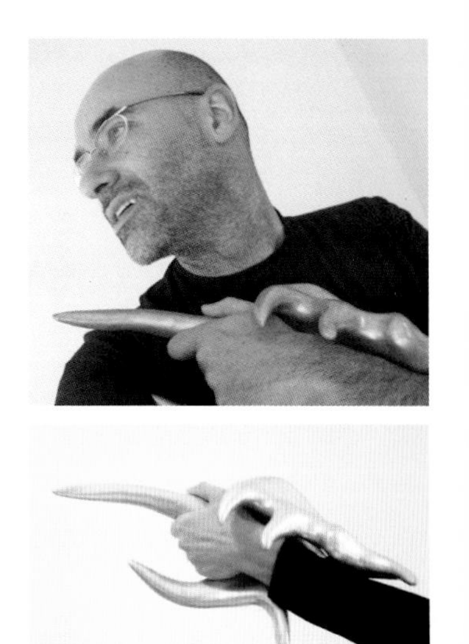

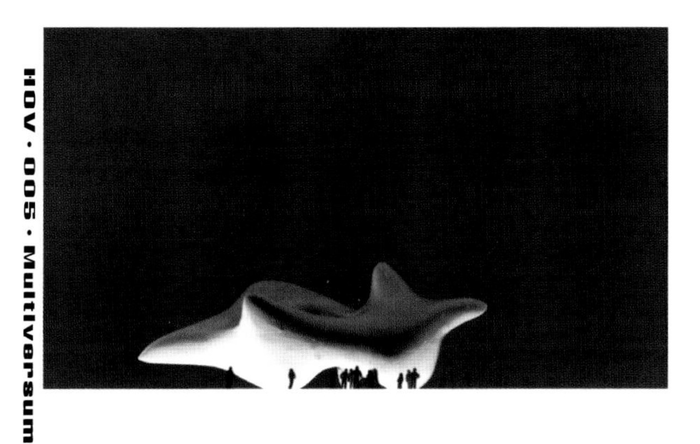

综述

HOV的诞生源于我对雕塑、量子物理学、数学和认知生物学的秘密的个人爱好的热情涌现。

这些学科有时候和建筑颇为相近，但它们距离职业实践和研究工作都很遥远。然而这不算是一个完全的矛盾，如Bohm的全像式模型理论、Maturana的multi–versus(拉丁语中为改变方向的意思)绝对比大多数现代文学和现代艺术都更为大胆，更具创造性。

一个人开始相信现有的参考模型已经很多，不可能再扩大它的数目，并且开始让步于这样的不安，这是一个达到极限时会出现的典型特征。这个时候他便开始参与建筑学的改革。

客观事实转为科学的学科间的融汇之后得出了结论，比如在客观事实和有机体的概念中出现的彻底的改变。客观事实不再属于全人类，也不再是来自活着的有机体。在物化了不同科学门类的综合过程中，这只是结果之一。这个古典的参考模型涉及的不同局部在输入–输出的联系基础上的逻辑关系现在看来已不再时兴。

自从有了这个意识，HOV开始将这个基本的概念运用于扩展研究，开始在不同学科圈所产生或想象的范例中研究生活空间。举例来说，这种关联到不同集体智慧的社会改革的可能性引发了Glossity项目的诞生，这导致了我们之前所定义的假想的社会模型以及空间的变化，并进一步导致定居行为的改变。

然而除了Glossity以外，对复杂社会的假想虚拟出它自身结构的外部混乱形态，这总是让HOV活跃在一个不具有导向性的，也没有任何先觉条件的观察点上。

这样的目的在于创造一系列包含了实验结果的假设性的基本概念。这种态度并不具有一个可以认知的顺序，它很接近那些惯用抽象概念的人的情感状态，但是仍然很难被定义。在最好的情况下，感官的联系建立在发源于思想的图像上，这是一个连续的创作体验，同样也试图对一些功能性问题有所解决——特别是那些文脉性很强的项目——坚持一个信念：在所有的动物中，人类无疑是适应性最强的。

这些实验性的作品都是源自一个自由的思想，我承认这不是能被所有人在所有时候都能理解的思想。但是，即使一个新的想法被发现是错误的，正因为我们以前不能构想出这样的想法，这就证明了有可能存在这样一个未来，一个和我们所预期的完全不一样的未来。

思想可以从场景或参照中分离开来。一个苦心经营的项目可以从竞赛和委托人手中挣脱出来，这种机会有时出现在感知到它的周围环境和最初的要素之后。

所以，项目来自于它的文脉和有机体的关系，这就和Maturana所说的那句话具有同样的意味“行走是来自于双腿和地面的关系之中的运动。”

After a short reflection and a long talk with David Raponi, I decided to write a piece detached from the architectural over-exhausted close examination aiming to the construction of a critical cage that is often capable to confine the author.
Therefore I preferred to limit myself to the transcription of my sensations flown from the visual tasting of an architect who loves conceptual fields so little explored so far.
In an author like HOV the fundamental role of the computer in the process which transforms an idea into a visual shape is evident.
It is superfluous and maybe impossible to ask oneself whether within this cybernetic fusion it could be possible to find distinct roles and merits belonging to the man or to the machine.
Instead I find it interesting to verify the fact that this fusion has succeeded in respecting one of the maybe few bonds of creativity, that is the capacity of interpreting the reality of contemporary men.
In order to do that, HOV used a simple and maybe inevitable process: he almost chemically united to this big constructor of human reality which the computer is at present, and within this new shape HOV started thinking to Architecture.
When I think of some of rationalist architects' works and visions at the beginning of the 20th century, I realise that the present society has just started to accept their message nowadays.
In fact more and more "griffed" and minimalist defined houses recall the avant-garde edifices of the 30's in an clear way.
The question comes out spontaneously: will a similar fate happen to cybernetic Architecture?
To understand that, I think we should start from the premise that an aesthetic expression is commonly accepted only when it is possible to perceive it in the multiple languages of society.
Moreover these languages should have a certain media power in order to be first assimilated and then adapted to the requests, or better, to the desires of the community.
I would like to make some considerations about the architectonic current - which I like to call cybernetic - within which I put HOV, to get to a final evaluation.
Cybernetic Architecture derives from the unique skeleton of contemporary society, that is computerization.
Starting from this simple but extended matrix, filtered through the net of sciences before (especially of Biology and Cosmology) and then of contemporary Philosophy, the result is a powerful architectonic language which is remarkably distant from what was born before the computer era.
In the case of HOV, a strong element detaching it from the ordinary is the fact that its architectures are often thought for social aggregative forms which are completely unrelated to the west contemporary society.
The social bonds are rightly transformed by the author into formal weights, capable of influencing the project in a determinant way. Therefore I tend to suppose that the more the society will get closer to HOV's visions, the more it will possible to see HOV's architectonic typologies accepted and realised.
Another point which I find very interesting about HOV and the current it represents, is the necessity of conceiving the architectures in the cyber-space, that is outside human physical existence.
The rules of Physics in the cyber-space are very different from those of the natural environment where the human body is collocated.
Just think of the fact that we can change or eliminate the force of gravity.
Another interesting phenomenon is the possibility of manipulating the consistency of matter so that we can equalize the full and the void, redistributing or even inverting the figure of the subject.
In the cyber-space the physical context is no more in God's hands or in the laws of science, but simply in those belonging to the individual, the one who enters the cyber-space and decides to mould it according to his will.
In the cyber-space, matter has become a mere concept.
Moulding a shape in a space where it is possible to release oneself from almost all natural bonds is certainly a further separation from this kind of Architecture and the previous ones.
Nevertheless HOV, differently from other architects of the same current, does not bring the composing process to the limit, since the desire of taking its creations into the universe of human physical existence is always present.
HOV investigates the constructive possibilities in the passage of its models from the computer space to the physical one of man, making hypothesis about the techniques and the materials needed.
During the process of concretisation HOV often proposes unusual construction materials which are instead common for other activities.
For HOV the desire of testing itself in the human physical existence respecting the principles of its

own architecture is so present that it is constantly invited to think about new materials in addition to the new shapes.
This author's desire seems to be that of bringing his own ideas to the limit of feasibility in the attempt – almost unconscious – of pressingly moving the cyber-space near to he physical space of man.
Another interesting aspect of the formal projecting through the computer is the tendency to abandon the instrumental filters represented by plans and sections. The work is made directly on a model, perceived in its complex, which is deformed and assembled within time.
During the modelling process the points of view vary continuously, we sail around and inside the shape, assimilating it in order to go on moulding it. I would say that the idea is perceived through the movement, so that time becomes an unavoidable component together with dimensionality. A consequence of this kind of modelling process is probably the fluidity of shape which tends to be infinite but limited. Every portion of the surface is immediately linked to the adjacent ones, there is no break in continuity. Another consequence of this technique is the tendency to create enveloping surfaces more than full masses.
A common valence in conceptual works is the necessity of finding a dialogue or, simply, establishing relations with the existing world.
In the Architecture field the shape, even being born by the stylistic features shared by the designers, is defined through its relationship with the physical context where it is collocated. With HOV this dialectical relation with the surrounding space is almost lacking and this happens since HOV – the architectonic context – is no more the physical space or, let me say, the genius loci, but the man himself.
The cyber-space, where the matter is a non physical but conceptual entity and senses become almost an appendix of the perceiving process, is the ideal place to project an architecture more addressed to the individual than to the social mass. Even if HOV's works are so sensuous, they would like to exist beyond sensorial reality in the attempt of engraving the pure ideas. Sensuousness is a necessary ingredient to transform this architecture into an emotional primer. It is like tasting volumes as if they were an agreeable natural event destined to being savoured not through our senses but, absurdly, through our emotional rationality. In other words, in order to know HOV's architectures and get an emotional beat from them, they should be read after understanding that what support them is not physical matter but reasoning complexity.

Andrea Carloni

HOV

在与大卫·拉伯尼交谈后，我思索了一下决定写一些东西。它有别于建筑学上为了严谨的结构而进行过分精密的检查，这种思想往往会禁锢作者。

因此，我更加喜欢用我的感觉限定自己。这些感觉来自于对这样一个建筑师的视觉品味——热爱探索鲜人涉足的概念领域的建筑师。

在像HOV这样一个设计工作室中，电脑在进程中所起到的基础作用是十分明显的。它将一个概念转化为一个视觉实体。

在这个控制论融合过程中，让人们区分人与机械的角色和价值是多余的，或许是不可能实现的。

然而，这种融合是否已经能够不妨碍人们诠释现代人现实的能力（创造力禁锢中的一个），我认为这是一个值得核实的有趣话题。

为了能够进行核实，HOV经历了一个简单而又必然的过程：他将电脑和人类现实的巨大结构有机地结合在一起，并通过这个新的形式开始对建筑的思考。

当我想起20世纪初一些理性建筑师的工作和创作，我明白了现今社会正开始逐渐接受他们的信息。

事实上，越来越多的“griffed”和极少主义者定义的房子用一种清晰的方式令人回想起了20世纪30年代的前卫建筑。

一个问题自然而然出现了：控制论建筑学是不是会发生相同的命运？

为了理解这个问题，我认为我们应该从一个前提开始：一种美学的表达，只有当在社会的多种语言中都有可能感知到它时，它才能被广泛地接受。

此外，这些语言应该有某一种媒体的力量，使得其能够先被吸收，再迎合各种要求，或者满足社会的需求。

我喜欢称呼这股建筑潮流为电脑控制论，希望能对它进行考量，并由此对HOV进行最终的评价。

控制论建筑学是从现代社会的独特骨架中衍生出来的，那就是计算机化。

从这个简单但范围有所扩大的基质开始，穿透了以往的科学（尤其是生物学和宇宙学）和现代哲学的格局，得出的结果是一种强大的建筑语言——显然远离了电脑纪元之前诞生的建筑语言。

在HOV的情况中，一个强大的要素使其与普通情况区别开——他的建筑往往是针对了社会的集合形式，这与当代西方社会完全不相关。

设计者将社会的束缚转化为正式砝码，这能够以决定性的方式影响方案。因此，我趋向于这样一个假设：如果社会离HOV的理想越近，HOV的建筑类型学就会更多地被接受和理解。

我发现HOV和他所代表的潮流有另一个有趣的方面，那就是在电脑空间中构思建筑的需要，而这是在人类的物理存在之外的。

电脑空间的物理规则与人类生活的自然环境大不相同。

想象一下我们能够改变或者消除万有引力。另一个有趣的现象是操作物质密度的可能性，这样我们就能够平衡物质的实与虚，重新分布甚至完全颠倒物体的形状。

在电脑空间中，物理学内容不再是“上帝之手”或者是自然界的法则，而是简单的属于个人——个人进入电脑空间根据自己的意愿决定如何铸造物理规则。在电脑空间中，物质已经仅仅变成一个概念。

在这样的空间中塑造形象，能够从几乎所有自然界的束缚中解放自己，这当然是这种形式的建筑与以往建筑更深层次的不同。

然而HOV与相同潮流中其他建筑师不同的是，他没把创作过程局限起来。因为他一直希望自己的创作能够进入人们生活的物理世界领域。

HOV在技术和材料方面做出假设，在它的模型从电脑空间到人类生存的真实空间的转换中探讨建造的可能性。

在将想法具体化的过程中，HOV经常提议用与众不同的建筑材料来代替普通材料。

对于HOV来说，他们渴望在人类存在的物理世界中测试它们的成果，这与它们自己的建筑理论相关，于是就需要经常思考引入新的材料以及新的外形。

这种设计者的心愿似乎在尝试中局限了自己，几乎是在无意识中，迫切地将电脑空间接近人类的物理空间。

通过电脑创作正式的方案有另一个有趣的方面是放弃以平面剖面为代表的传统手段。这种工作直接在模型上进行，直接感知到它的复杂性，而模型可以在一定时间内变形再组装。

在模拟的过程中，观点在不断地变化，我们游历在形状的周围和内部，吸收消化并继续模拟模型。

我认为，这个概念是在运作的过程中逐渐被察觉的，所以时间与维度一样变成了不可或缺的组成部分。这种模拟过程的结果可能是形态的流动性，这可以趋向无穷但却是有一定限制的。表面的每一个部分直接与临近的部分连接，在连续性上没有空隙。这项技术的另一个结果是趋向于创造封套式的表面而不是整个物体。

思维活动中的一个常见的要素是寻找对话的需求，简单来说，就是建立与现实世界的关联。

在建筑学领域，即使是来自于设计者们的风格特色，外形也是由建筑与场地文脉之间的关系而定义的。在HOV的设计方法中，这种与环境空间的辩证关系几乎失去，这是由于HOV的建筑的文脉已经不再是物理空间或者一个地区的特色，而是人类自身。

电脑空间里，物质不是物理学上的实体，而是概念上的实体。感官几乎变成了感知过程的附属品。电脑空间是理想的设计建筑的地方，这更多是对于个人而不是对于整个社会。

即使HOV的工作是如此地依靠感觉，在挖掘完美的理想的尝试过程中，他们希望能超越感觉现实而存在。知觉是将建筑转换为情感的表达的必要成分。就好像我们不是通过感官，而是有些荒谬地通过情感理性来品味这些建筑，就像它们是自然界中和谐的一部分一样。换而言之，为了了解HOV的建筑，并感受到它们情感的节拍，我们应该在理解它们之后再进行解读，支持他们的不是物理学的物质而是推理的复杂性。

安德里亚·卡罗尼

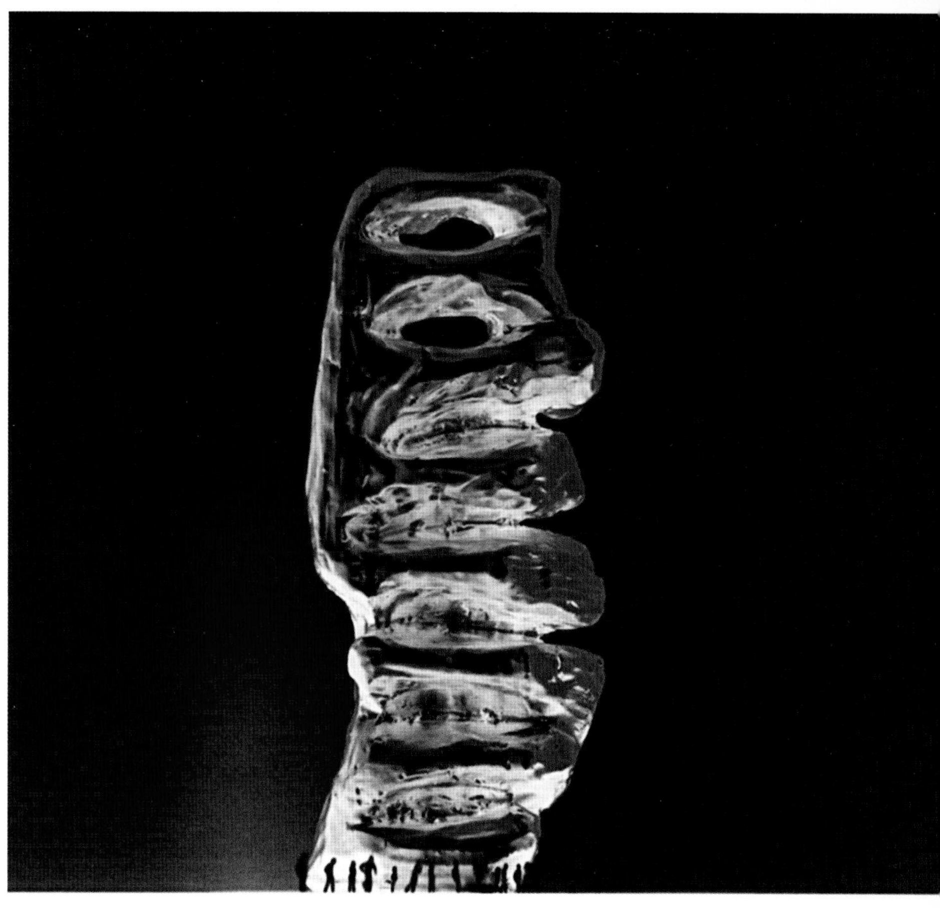

HE WILL EVENTUALLY BE A "SENATOR"

Writing a few comments on the work of David Raponi provides an excellent opportunity to consider (or rather reconsider) more closely the creative work of talented young architects in the age in which we live: at the beginning of a new millennium.

There are not many people in the world, as is only right and has always been the way in the past, who stand out among their colleagues for the boldness with which they fearlessly taken on new challenges, inventing stylistic idioms which are very often close to pure experimentation to the detriment of professional profitability, as we know it.

Nowadays, the leading exponents of architecture, highly acclaimed, widely published, acknowledged and famous the world over (to a greater or lesser extent), all on the verge of turning sixty, have made their mark as great masters by learning to combine new building methods and materials with their own exceptional ability to gradually let go of their conventional compositional know-how ready to set out on new stylistic-aesthetic adventures, decidedly in antithesis to the historical-rational canons.

This task is now made easier by the latest computer tools, which all design firms now possess and which allow creative mental concepts to be easily transferred to executive graphics or hyper-real digitalised images.

Despite this progress in computer technology for representing designs, all architects from the generation prior to David Raponi, bearing in mind they come from more or less traditional education backgrounds when thoughts used to be set down on paper by hand, using the usual millenary instruments like a ruler and set-square, still think up their ideas subconsciously following their own personal aesthetics, all of which inevitably constrains and confines any great leaps of thought or imagination.

To really understand how David Raponi sets about representing and formulating his projects, bearing in mind how we may visualise them two-dimensionally as experimental hypotheses not really supposed to be built, we need at least a rudimentary knowledge of computers, so that we can understand how one of his mentally constructed thoughts of an idea initially starts to take shape on a virtual basis, ready to adapt to the preconceived demands of design, before eventually materialising on the computer with no limits on its form, colour or structure.

Something parallel happens to the poet when he tries to give voice to a feeling or mental intuition making free use of the language at his disposal, regardless of grammatical or lexical rules.

This freedom of representation, free from constraints and formal-constructive canons, in which school cultural education and personal professional experience only work together marginally, at least in the field of architecture, lets him face up to nature and the environment on an even standing, without shying away or making up stories about existing structures that still need to be remembered.

Competing ambitiously (and with no inhibitions in terms of merits or ethics) with the natural environment or constructions built by man is the kind of ambition associated with great innovative architects. David is certainly a member of that club of privileged young people, and it is only a question of time until we see the fruits of his talent. Due to the natural progression in architecture, I am certain that, in a few decades, he too will become a "senator" and look at the next generations with an air of curiosity and just a little envy.

Cesare Maria Casati

14/5/2006

他最终会成为一位“评议员”

撰写一些关于大卫·拉伯尼工作的评论为我们提供了一个很好的机会，可以来思考（或者是重新思考）生活在新千年开始之际有天赋的年轻建筑师的创造性工作。

世界上像这样的人并不多：现在和过去都是正确的，在同行中以勇敢而突出，他们面对挑战毫不畏缩，发明了风格上的术语。我们都知道，这些用语十分接近于损害专业收益的纯粹实验。

现在，在世界上受到高度赞扬、广泛关注与认同的建筑学的领军人物（在或大或小的范围内）都接近六十岁。他们通过学习结合新的建造方法、建筑材料与他们自己特殊的能力，都已经成名成大师。他们能够敢于自己传统的技术知识，敢于冒险尝试新的风格美学，果断挑战拥有悠久历史的教条。

现在这个目标能够通过最新的电脑工具较为轻易的完成，所有设计公司都掌握这些技术，它能帮助允许创造性的精神概念更加容易得转换为可执行的图象或者超现实数字化影像。

尽管表达设计的电脑技术越来越进步，所有的建筑师——从先辈到大卫·拉伯尼——都牢记着他们或多或少都是从传统教育背景出来的。想法原来是用手记录在纸上，并使用沿用了千年的工具像尺子、三角板。他们仍然下意识地运用个人的审美理论构想出想法，所有的这些都不可避免地限制拘束了思维想象的任何重大进步。

为了确切理解大卫·拉伯尼如何着手描绘和明确叙述他自己的方案，我们必须记住在二维空间内将它们形象化，就像那些不会建成的假想方案一样。另外，我们还需要一些基础计算机知识。这样我们能够理解他精神上构建的一个想法最初是如何在虚无的基础上开始形成的，并是如何满足设计的预想要求的。而这些在最终电脑将它们形象化之前没有形式、颜色和结构的限制。

相似的情形也发生在诗人身上——当他试图传达一种感觉或是精神上的想法时，他会自由地支配使用语言，而不管语法或词汇规则。

在传统的教条中，学校文化教育和个人专业经验很少共同作用。而这种表达的自由性则远离了这些约束和教条，至少在建筑学领域，可以让设计者勇敢地用一种平和的身份面对自然和环境，而不是回避或者编造有关需要铭记的现有建筑物的故事。

与自然环境、人类建造建筑的竞争（没有在价值或伦理方面的约束）是与伟大的创新建筑师相联系的雄心。大卫是有这样的特权的年轻人中的一员，我们将会看到他天才的成果，那只是时间问题。

根据建筑的自然级数，我确信在几十年内，他也将成为“评议员”，并且带着好奇心和仅仅一点点嫉妒看着下一代成长。

Cesare Maria Casati
2006年5月14日

"I knew the extra-dimensional trip was a hard one, but I did not expect to be catapulted into a world where emotions and sensations were so strong to thoroughly wrap up my body that pulsated rhythmically at every single point. I finally was in Glossity. I had the impression of having been there already, I was living a déjà vu, but at the same time, everything seemed completely new to me. I was living in a state of well being and satisfaction: energetic flows fed me and I was in love... The matter surrounding me was soft and, at mere contact, it transported me into a sort of estranging trance..."

The sense of amazement and bewilderment one feels when observing HOV architectures for the first time – sinuous and fluctuant plaits, soft and fluid bodies in estranging landscapes – is a striking one and it certainly pushes the observer to deepen the knowledge of them, within the consciousness that such productions are exceptions in Italian architecture.
David Raponi, starting from personal passions and feelings, created with HOV a study that, conjugating the love for sculpture, quantum physics, mathematics and cognitive biology, carries out an activity of research oriented towards the change of relationship with reality: more specifically with the multiplication of the reference plans. If in traditional logic the opposition is settled down between two poles, the one of the reality and the one of the imaginary, we can perceive that this polarization is attenuated in the logic of the flow. Thus the appearance of a temporality flow marks a deep transformation of the space that was dominated by the obsession of considering the reality free from any imaginary remainder, be it emotional or symbolic.
Therefore Hov resumes "some conclusions produced by the cross-disciplinary convergence into the scientific field: the radical change of the notion of reality and organism and, in the attempt of turning over the most ordinary points of view, the less obvious aspects of experience". The ideas are born, following the thought of the epistemological anarchist P.K. Feyerabend , by occasional events dictated by the emotion of a moment or by a particular contingency...
By the way, I like to remember one of David Raponi's thoughts: "magical or right moments to face a u-turn in life do not exist, maybe they will just appear as such to us only afterwards." And he still asks this question to himself: "Why cannot we expect anything else? Why cannot we tell an adventure of the mind with the images of an architecture plan?" And finally "much of our creativity, ideation, fantasy is elsewhere. And necessarily, in the spirit of my personal research – a re-foundation of the reference models and an overcoming of the disciplinary limits - the references cannot be 'architectonically correct' ".
"We spend our time and our life in contemplating what we have already contemplated: that is the most insidious conclusion and our habitat is built on redundancies. We erect the analogous and the similar, it is our architecture, and those who have a different or a distant perception are our enemies."

P. Virilio, The Negative Horizon

Hov fully expresses the tendency of the new world that moves from the solid state to the liquid one and, just as it happened during the passage from the Middle Ages to the Modern Age, also the psyche moves from the liquid state to the solid one - to the heavy thoughts.
The visual polarization created during the Renaissance by the schooling, then supported by the introduction of the press, generated the long lasting illusion that space was empty since it was impossible to observe something in the void between objects.
In the virtual reality the touch, the sensory perception of the physical space is no more outside the show but within the show itself, it is the turning over of the perspective, of the spectacular images that perspective once expressed through the trompe-l'oeil. The interval is being filled up, we have lost the neutral space that, in the western conception, was well placed between the spectator and the image.
Starting from his own imagination the individual delineates projects and conceives plans that he can then decide to put into practice within the real world. The imaginary takes shape and it is organized through "possible worlds" to live in or to go to, simultaneously or subsequently. Besides, Raponi defines Glossity as a "set of episodes without a context, which are also partly indifferent to one another even belonging to a homogenous group, with a relatively uniform distribution and without privileged positions".

"We tend to live in a world of certainty, of perceptive solidity devoid of doubts where our

convictions lead us to believe that all things are just the way we see them, and what we believe in cannot have any alternative. That is the situation in which we live daily, it is our cultural condition, our way to be men."
Humber to Maturana and Francisco Varala

One must agree when David Raponi asserts that "even if a new idea reveals itself to be a wrong one, the fact that we were not able to conceive it before shows that the future can prove extremely different from what we expect". On the contrary, borrowing the holographic theory by David Bohm, what if we realised the existence of an implicit order in the universe - an order we do not see - and of an explicit one that is what we really see? The reality would not be more than a hologram of real "objects" placed in other places or times. If this is true we obviously are "self-deceptions", very similar to all the things that exist "outside us". Holograms reading holograms. Is it possible for us to understand rationally where, when and what is the true reality of which we can only express the shape?

Luigi Affuso

MULTIVERSUM

“我知道在附加的空间中旅行是十分艰难的，但我没有期盼被带入这样一个世界，在那里情绪与感觉如此强大地包裹住了我的身体，使身体在每个拍点有节奏的跳动。终于我来到了Glossity。我有印象曾经去过那里，我来到一个似曾相识的地方，但同时，所有事物对我来说都完全像新的一样。我生活在安宁满足的状态下：充满活力的花朵孕育了我，我坠入了爱河……围绕我的东西都很柔软，仅仅碰触一下便令我着迷……”

人们第一次看到HOV的建筑之后会感到惊异和困惑，因为远远看来它们是充满了蜿蜒和起伏的褶皱、柔软流动的物体。HOV的建筑是一种冲击，它的确会推动观察者加深对其的认识，并给人留下这样的印象：这些是意大利建筑中特立独行的作品。

大卫·拉伯尼从个人的热情和感觉出发，与HOV一起创造了一种学说。将爱变化为雕塑、量子物理学、数学和认知生物学。他开展了一项研究活动，是针对与现实关系的变化，更加明确得说，则是建筑参照图系的增加。如果用传统的逻辑来说，这分为两派对立，一派是现实派，另一派是假想派，我们可以觉察到逻辑会削弱这两派的对立。因此短暂的思考的出现标志着空间深层次的变化，无论就情感上还是就象征意义而言，这种空间都受到现实的控制，没有任何想象的余地。

因此，HOV继续了“在科学领域跨学科产生的结论：现实、有机体概念的根本改变，并尝试推翻最平凡的观点和经历体验中不够显著的部分”。

这种观念的诞生得益于P.K . Feyerabend（认识论无政府主义者）的思想，并且被来自片刻情感或者特殊意外的偶然事件所激发。

顺便说一下，我希望能记住大卫·拉伯尼这一个观点：“面对生活中的转折点时，不可思议的或者合适的时刻是不存在的，可能它们仅仅在事后才会出现在我们面前。”

他仍然在问他自己这个问题：“为什么我们不能够期盼其他的东西？为什么我们不能一起在建筑设计上进行大胆的冒险？”最终“我们大量的创造力、构思能力、幻想去了别的地方。我个人研究的精神在于参考模型的重建和规则限制的克服，那是十分必要的。而这些参考不能是‘建筑学上正确的’”。

“我们花费了时间甚至毕生来思索我们已经思索过的东西：那是最阴险的论断，我们的居所是建造在冗余之上的，我们竖立起相似的东西作为我们的建筑，而那些有不同理解的人就是我们的敌人。”

引用：P. Virilio, The Negative Horizon

HOV充分地展现了新世界的趋向——新世界正从固态变为液态，正像世界从中世纪向近现代转变所发生的事情一样。灵魂也从液态变成固态——转化为沉重的思想。

文艺复兴时期的学校教育创造了视觉的两极分化，经过出版物的传播支持，产生了长久不衰的幻想——空间是虚无的，因为在物体之间的空洞中不可能观察到任何东西。

在虚拟现实中，触摸和物理空间的感官知觉已不在物体之外而在物体自身中。这颠覆了以往的透视图画法，打破了曾经通过错视画派表达的壮观画面。空隙得以被填补，我们失去了在西方的概念中的观众和影像之间的不确定空间。

个人从自身的想象出发，描绘了方案，构思了计划，然后他就可以决定在现实世界中实行这个方案。想象得以成形，并通过所居住或者所到达的“可能的世界”而组织起来的，这个过程可以同时进行也可以有先后次序。此外，拉伯尼将Glossity定义为“一系列没有上下文的情节，即使属于同一组群各部分之间也没什么关系，有相对统一的分布但没有特别的位置”。

“我们趋向于居住在一个确定的世界，有理解的、可靠的、没有疑问的世界。在这里，我们相信所有事情就是以我们所看见的方式进行，我们信仰的不会有任何改变。那就是我们每天生活的情形，是我们的文化状态，我们为人处世的方法。”

引用：Humber to Maturana and Francisco Varala

人们必须承认，当大卫·拉伯尼断言：“即使一个新的想法被发现是错误的，正因为我们以前不能构想出这样的想法，这就证明了未来有可能和我们期待的完全不一样”。相反，借用David Bohm的全息理论，是否可能我们能意识到世界中存在一种隐含的规则——一种看不见的规则，同时还存在一种我们能看到的清晰的规则？现实不过是真实“物体”在不同空间、时间的全息投影。如果这是真的，我们显然是“自欺的”，就如同存在于“我们外部”的所有事物一样。

全息图阅读全息图，我们能否理性地理解，我们仅仅能够表达外形的事物，它们的真相是究竟何地、何时，又是什么呢？

Luigi Affuso

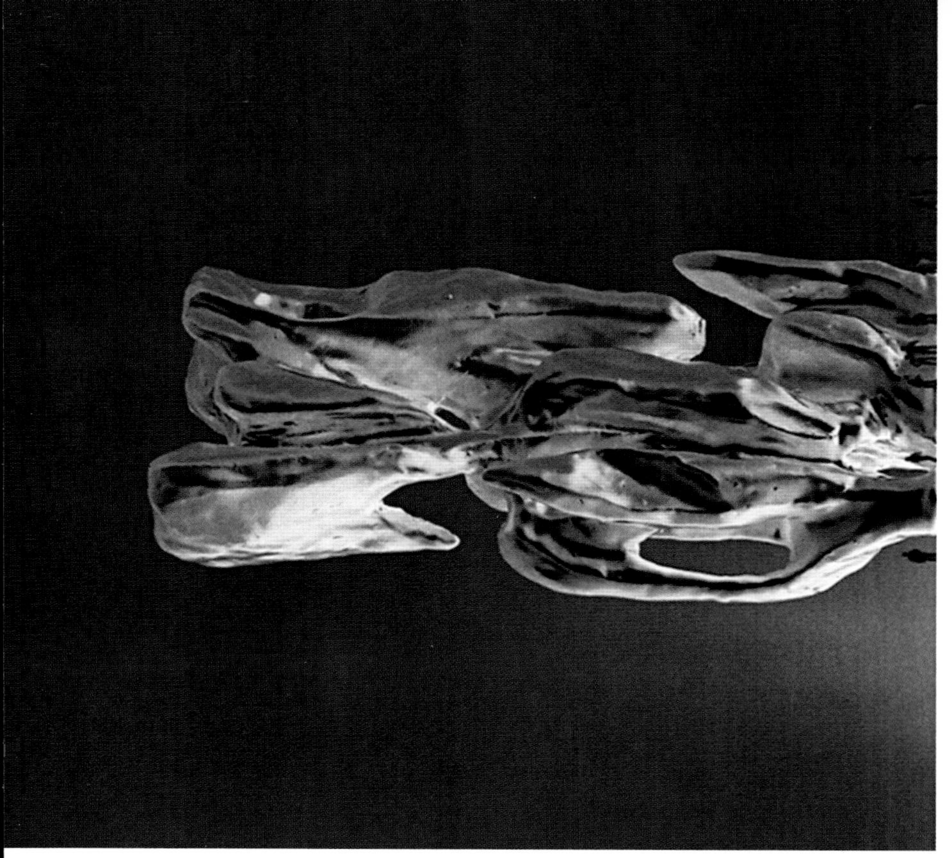

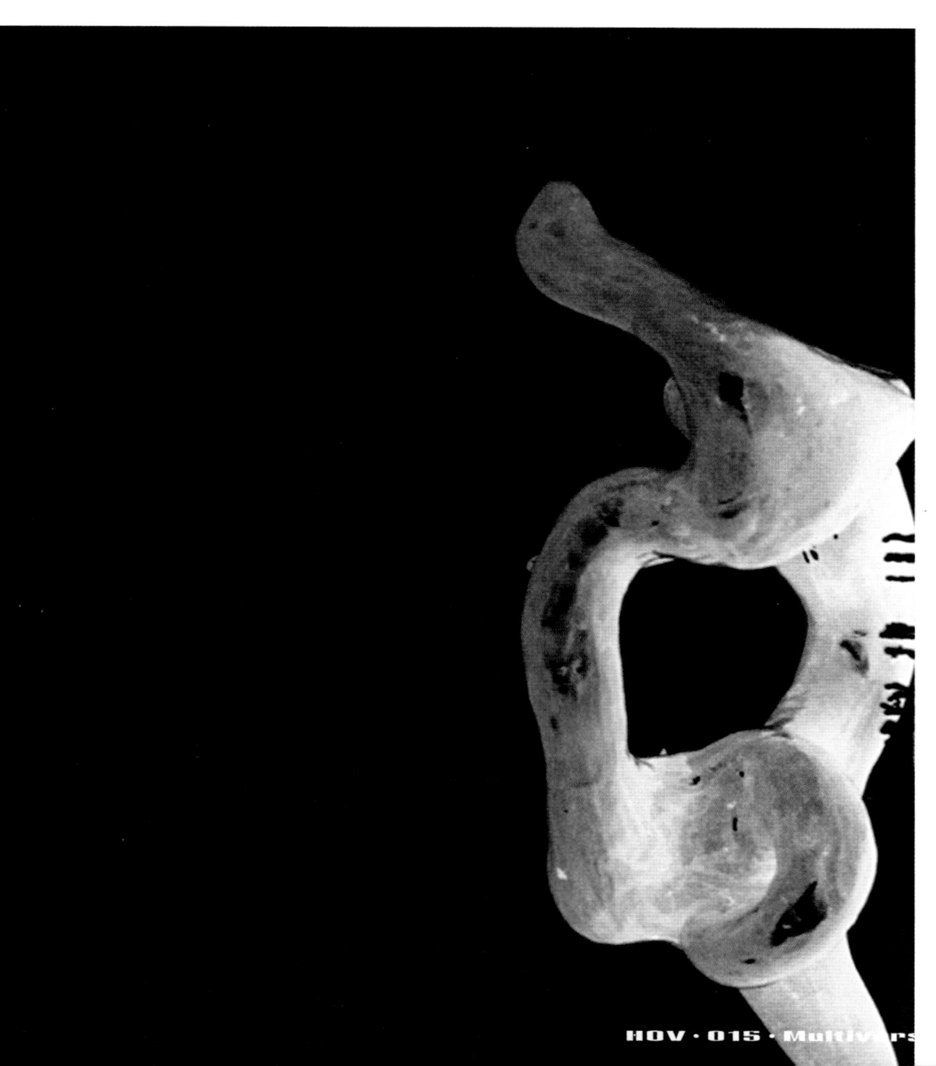

HOV: S-CULPTORS OF SCIENCE

What is the deepest motivation for researchers? The twin desire to give meaning or express a desire, a reasonable desire contrasting with pure, absolute, radical desire. In architecture, radical applies to those people working outside functional needs and, at the same time, beyond their own personal expression, all those who give up architecture to move towards Architecture free from the constraints of knowledge.

There are two possible ways of innovating: from the outside and from the inside.

Some believe that architecture moves forward drawing on extraneous disciplines and fields of learning to gain new strategies and ways of thinking, others adopt the opposite approach selecting principles internally to produce transformation; take, for instance, how the combined use of a steel skeleton and lift has internally revolutionised typologies, forms and spatial relations making it possible to develop skyscrapers.

External innovators receive input from a world in which scientists often turn out to be more creative and radical than artists, a world in which mathematics, geometry, physics, chemistry and biology set some of the boundaries within whose realms the input is found for investigating new possibilities.

Can HOV's work be read along these two divergent lines?

A variety of projects calls for an approach combining the attainment of pure desire and innovation from the outside and an innate passion for sculpture. Two themes sum up the key research issues and most intricate lines of experimentation undertaken by David Raponi: the city and the tower. A third theme of great topicality, the museum, draws on all the input from a series of international competitions.

Glossity is an experiment for an ideal settlement. It takes on great importance at a moment in time when cities designed for hosting millions of inhabitants need to be rebuilt from scratch.

"Glossit's living systems maintain themselves by producing their own sub-systems, which, in turn, produce the global structural organisation required to keep them alive and let them reproduce. They are autonomous structures whose system is totally self-referential, thinking only about keeping itself going, and all the actions it seems to carry out towards the outside are in actual fact aimed at keeping itself intact in face of environmental distrurbances.

In other words Glossity is precise. This society possesses an organised structure capable of holding onto and regenerating its own unity and independence in relation to constant variations in the surrounding environment by creating its own constituent parts, which, in turn, help generate the entire system".

After making some general descriptions, David Raponi showed what happened inside Glossity.

Two projects exemplify certain interesting features that fit in with the readings just mentioned: "The intensive reproduction centre is a meeting place inside whose oneiric spatial layout random love stories unfold for reproduction purposes. Space itself and sensorial involvement, diffused by matter itself, lead to a state of well-being and satisfaction. No structural component is hard and enduring, just as nothing can be connected to a notion of furnishing".

The centre does not have any specific stylistic stages, just a series of likely configurations. The first structural plan is a made of an inorganic synthetic material, it then develops through self-generating elements rather like coral. The cladding is made of overlapping neural networks protected by inert materials of the same consistency as silicon resin.

"The reflective field of isolation is a meeting place outside which every living organism can open up its own ego beyond the intellectual abilities and general awareness it has acquired. As in the case of the reproduction centre, the first structural layout is provided by people, but here there is no synthetic support. Its entire interior is full of life. Matter is organised around self-generating units - emitter molecules - custom-made in the laboratory. Stimulated by body heat through their receptors, they use chemical emanations to induce an estranged state. To begin with, everything is one single carefully arranged mass, the building/organism then transforms and re-directs itself according to the mass's density levels and directions".

The field cannot be penetrated, there is no interior space. Introspection and spirituality come to the fore, and we are freed from any conventional notion of function and space.

Indispensable experiments on individual Glossity settlements create expectations for a full analysis. It is only natural to think of a preliminary idea of an overall design intended to be a revolutionary model of sustainability, a master plan capable of

structurally altering thinking about the creation of new cities.
A less extreme approach than an isolated field, but nonetheless free from constraints governing the use of interior space, can be found in experiments on a set of towers, some liquefid in form, others like cutting blades. The homage to the Swiss artist Giger is a modern rendition of Egyptian tombs, a tower inside which there are only a few square metres serving living purposes, less than 1% of the built volume.
Even in the design for the sea tower and New York tower, functional requirements do not figure among the features affecting formal decisions, even though more inhabitable space is used. Even the project for a museum in the ancient town of Pentedattilo, an intriguing abandoned old rocky settlement in Calabria, works along the lines of suggestion and emotion, as well as slavish re-use of rubble.
HOV's strategy does not involve functionally recovering small houses to use them for exhibition, reception, laboratory, catering and trading purposes, as the tender specified, but rather the occupation of strategic places for contemplating the harsh natural surroundings and indulging in solitary reflection on the site's state of abandonment.
The wall of reflection, spiritual centre, and laboratory of wind and earth are pre-selected places for study, observation and meditation. Carefully positioned on the outskirts of the settlement, they are only used by a few visitors. The crystallising of the ruins with no set functional programme turns into one of the project's strong points, a sort of romantic approach to Ruskin-style ruins integrated by a series of high-tech glass and steel artificial appendixes knitting into the natural setting.
HOV has set a target for its research for the competition to design a virtual museum organised by newitalianblood.com: the museum of emotions, a provocatively real space hosting virtual works. Despite carrying out complex modelling to achieve the desired form, the key figures in the exhibition are still people, the various stages in their feelings and emotions: surprise, fear, displeasure, anger, joy, satisfaction, happiness, carefreeness and peace. This Kind of museum hosts them as works and outlines how they constantly develop and transform. An art model representing everybody proposing a substantial change in relations between observer and object. The observer turns into a subject and interactive participant.
"At them time of the first works made of clay and plaster in '94, I already had the felling that the very structure incorporating the reference models for the architecture was outmoded and strained. These attempts, close to sculpture, confirmed by own belief about the dissolving of boundaries between different disciplines in the name of gradual integration. A study of the surprising similarities in sciences produced last century, which I have slowly been examining, has result in my abandoning any reductionist approach and triggered off more carefully aware investigations defined as projects, however bizarre they might seem at times. Indeed, examining the data emerging from these interdisciplinary convergences, we arrive at a gradual change in our notion of reality and organism as the idea of a universe is replaced by the concept of a multi-side. Here how reality shows itself cannot be represented in an objective field and, as a matter of fact, we can only take one aspect of reality and order it in our experience. Reality, which is no longer one and the same for all human beings, is also accompanied by a change in our notion of space, which is no longer exclusive and determined but composed of a series of evolutions taking place on many simultaneous, compresent but different levels. Space linked to becoming in all its continuous interactions dynamically guiding, maintaining or changing how it is perceived".
Inspired, on a purely emotional level by topological studies such as Klein's bottle, the Etruscan Venus and non-directable sufaces, David Raponi has now abandoned conventional materials to express himself through sophisticated software for three-dimensional modelling. Right from the very preliminary stages, viz, the sarch for forms and materials for making them, ha is still determined to experiment: organic materials like bird tissues just tested to create super-fast chips, semi-conductor polymers (also of an organic nature) and regenerable composite materials deriving from the shipbuilding and aeronautical industries.
In those cases un which the necessary materials have not yet been experimented on, extreme technological ideas are being considered.
There is no conclusion, ad HOV love to emphasise at the end of all their writings. And there is no attempt at labelling into critical categories by the writer of this article, just the simple desire to help spread greater awareness of the research under way and a hope: to soon see the creation of those works capable of keeping up promising levels of theoretical experimention.

Luigi Centola

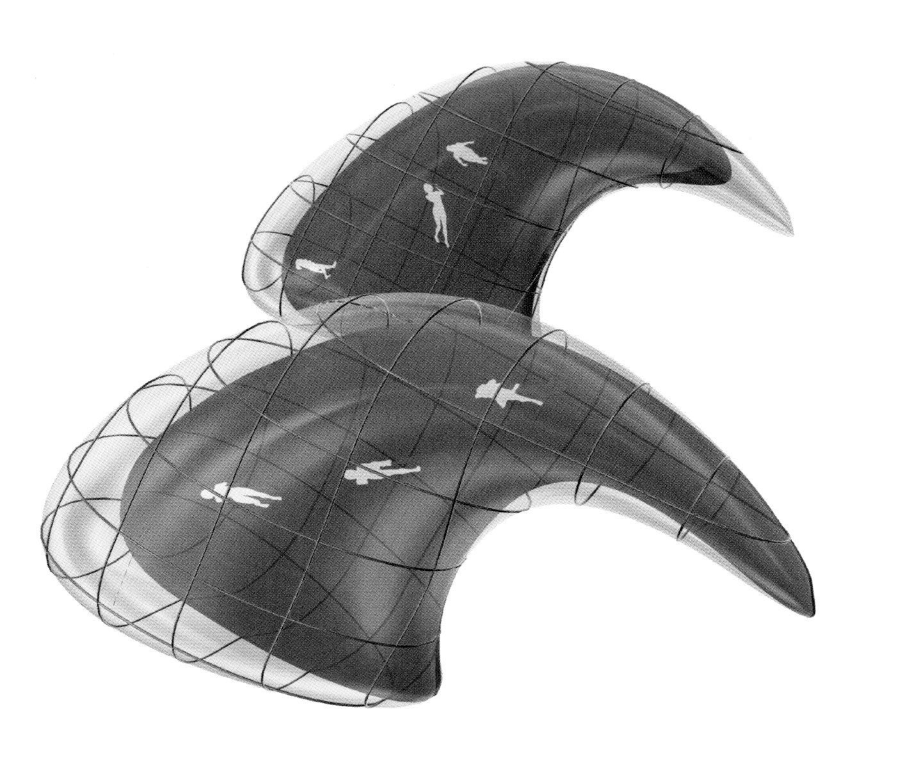

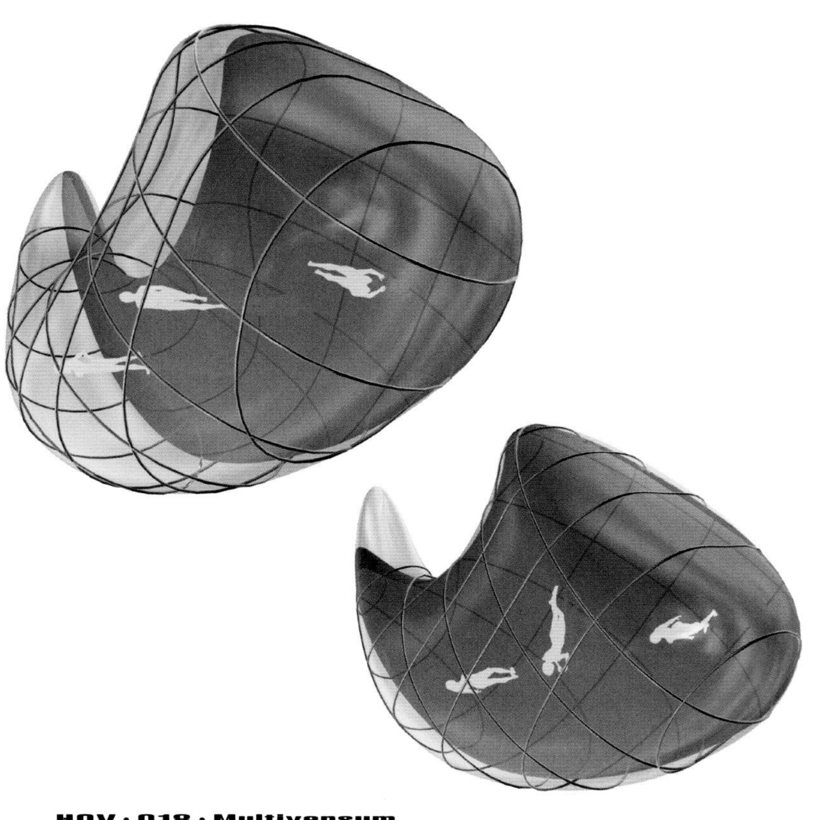

HOV：科学的雕刻家

研究者最深动机是什么？是给愿望一个意义或是表达愿望，是与纯洁、完全、根本的心愿相对应的合理的心愿。在建筑学中，这些根本的心愿适用于超越了功能需求进行工作的人们，同时超越了他们个人所表达的意愿，也适用于所有放弃建筑学的人走向了没有知识束缚的“建筑学”的人们。

进行革新有两条可能的途径：从外部开始和从内部开始。

有些人相信建筑学正逐渐吸收外来学科，并获取新策略的学习领域和新的思考方式。其他人采用了相反的方式，选择了在中心产生变革的原理。举例来说，钢结构骨架和起重机的结合彻底地改变了类型学、形式和空间关系，从而可以使摩天楼成为现实。

外部改革者从外界接收信息，在那里，科学家比艺术家更加有创造力，更加激进；在那里，数学、几何学、物理学、化学和生物学都设立了一些分界线。在这些领域中，信息的接收都是为了研究出新的可能性。

HOV的工作能够通过这两种具有分歧的线路进行解读吗？

大量的方案都要求将外部纯粹的心愿、改革与对雕塑品天生的热情相结合。这两种主题概括了研究的关键论点和大部分大卫·拉伯尼试验的复杂线路：城市和塔。第三个主题是关于伟大的时事性话题——博物馆，它吸收了一系列国际竞赛的信息。

Glossity是对一个理想居所的试验。为容纳数百万居民而设计的城市需要从零开始重建的时候，这个试验有着重大意义。

“Glossity的生存空间系统通过产生子系统维持自身，这样，它们就能够轮流产生全局的结构组织，使得母系统存活、繁殖。它们是自治的机构。它们的系统是完全自我指示的，只考虑维持自己的运作。系统执行的所有对外的动作，事实上都是为了其自身不受到环境扰乱。

换句话说，Glossity是精确的。这个群落拥有组织完善的结构，能够创造自身的组成部分，轮流帮助产生整个系统，在不断变化的周围环境中维持、革新自身的统一和独立。

在进行了一些概括性的描述之后，大卫·拉伯尼展示了Glossity内部所发生的事情。

两个方案例证了某些有趣的特征，这些特征符合刚才提到的要点：“强化繁殖中心是内部的汇集点，在这里梦空间随意设计的爱情故事是为了繁殖而展现的。空间自身和情感参与，由物质本身散布开，通向一个安宁、满足的状态。没有什么结构成分是坚硬而不朽的，就好像没有东西可以和装饰的概念相联系一样。”

繁殖中心没有任何特殊的形式上的层次，只是一系列漂亮的结构外形。第一层建筑平面是采用无机合成材料，接着通过自我繁殖元素发展起来，就像珊瑚虫一样。覆层是采用重叠的神经系统网而构建的，这些网络由像硅树脂一样坚固的惰性材料保护。

“隔离的反射区域是在外部汇集的中心，在这里，任何一个活着的有机体可以在超越智力和普通清醒需要的情况下展开自我。就像在繁殖中心的情况一样，第一层建筑平面是由人类提供，但是在这儿没有合成材料的支持。它的整个内部都充实了生命体。自生单元周围有很多实验室定做的发射器分子。通过接收器来靠生物热激发能量，它们采用化学散发诱导进入一个远离的激发状态。本来，万物都是自我设计谨慎的单个物体，那么生物体建筑就可以依照物质密度等级和方向改变它自己。”

因为没有室内空间，所以场地不能够被渗透。内省和灵性涌现出来，我们脱离了传统功能、空间观念的束缚。

对于单个Glossity居所需要进行必要的实验，这创造了对于完整分析的期望结果。

很自然我们会想到需要一个对于总设计的初步想法，它是一个有关维持能力的革命性模型。至于考虑到新城市的创造，那就是从结构上改变总体规划。

和隔离区这个手段相比，有一个相对不是十分极端的方法，但是它通过使用内部空间而摆脱了束缚。这种方法能够在塔的建立、液化形式的试验中看到，还有其他的诸如切削刀。瑞士艺术家Giger的作品是一种埃及墓葬的现代表现，一个塔内只有小部分面积是用来生活起居的，少于建筑面积的1%。

在海之塔和纽约塔的设计方案中，更多的居住空间功能得以使用，即使如此，功能需求也并不影响方案的整体决定。即使在Pentedattilo的古老城镇建立博物馆的方案中（在卡拉布里亚的一个废弃的迷人的多石地带），方案也是跟随着人们提议和情感，同时也谦卑地重新使用了碎石。

HOV的策略并不包括小房子的功能型恢复，不是用于展示、接待、试验、餐饮等分类目的，而是为了能在被遗弃的场地中，占据一片战略上的场所，让人们可以凝视粗野的自然环境。

反射墙、精神中心、风和地球实验室是用以研究、观察、沉思的预选场所。

仔细划定的居所边界只供一些游客使用。没有设立功能性程序的使废墟成形变成了方案的一个强大的特点，一种浪漫的罗斯金风格的废墟被一系列在自然景色中编织的高科技玻璃和人造钢附属物整合了起来。

在newitalianblood.com网站上，HOV为一个虚拟博物馆的竞赛研究项目设立了一个目标：情感博物馆，一个具有煽动力的实空间容纳了虚拟的作品。不管完成这个心愿需要实现多少复杂的模拟，展览会的关键特点仍然在于人类、人类感觉与情绪的多种层次：惊奇、害怕、不愉快、生气、高兴、满足、快乐、无忧无虑和安宁。

这种博物馆容纳了它们，作为不断发展、改变的作品、外形。它是一个艺术模型，它代表了每个人都经历了观察者和物体之间所计划的真实的改变。观察者变成了一个物品和一个交互式的参与者。

“1994年，在他们的第一个用粘土和石膏做成的模型中，我已经感到，这种由结构和参考模型拼合的建筑物有些过时和牵强。这些接近雕刻的尝试，以逐渐融合的名义，被消除不同学科界线的信念所证实。上个世纪科学界里曾出现过令人惊奇的有关相似性的研究，我曾慢慢地检验过这项研究，这导致了我沉溺于探究还原主义的门径，并引发了许多被定义为项目的谨慎明了的调查，尽管它们有时可能看上去会有多么奇异。事实上，通过检查各个学科间融合的数据，我们得到了一个关于现实的观念逐渐改变的过程，有机体作为万物观念的想法被多边的概念代替。这里现实是如何展现它自己的，在客观领域中还不能表现出来，事实上，我们仅仅能从现实的一个方面着手，在经验中指挥它。现实不再是只有唯一的一个，对于所有人类也不再相同，现实也随着我们对空间观念的改变而改变。空间的概念不再是唯一确定的，而是包含了一系列同时发生、共同表现但又在不同等级的进化。空间在动力学导向的联系下成为连续的相互作用，保持或者改变了它被感知的过程。”

令人很有启发的是，通过拓扑学的研究（比如克莱因瓶、伊特鲁里亚的维纳斯和非直接接触的表面），在一个纯粹的情绪级别上，大卫·拉伯尼现在已经抛弃了传统的材料而改用精密的三维模拟软件来表达自己的想法。正是从这个初级阶段开始——为制作模型而寻找形式和材料的阶段——他依然决定进行试验：像鸟类组织这样的有机材料用来测试制造超高速芯片、半导聚合体（也是一种有机物）以及来自造船、航空工业的合成再生材料。

在这些例子中必要的材料还没有被试验，极端科技的概念已经开始被考虑。

HOV乐于在他们所有的文章中进行强调，没有结论被得出。这篇文章的作者并没有尝试把它归为评论类文章。作者只有一个简单的心愿，希望这对更加明确地宣传这个研究有一些帮助，并期盼不久就能看到这些工作的创造，到达可以继续理论试验的水平。

Luigi Centola

GLOSSITY

"[...] There are about 12.000 species of ants, and some live in very small nests of a few hundred ants, and some are members of very big nests, counting millions of ants. Now it's interesting to see the difference of behaviour. In small nests every ant behaves independently, but in the large nests, there are collective motions, the intelligence is in the collectivity. And what is corious and somewhat frightening is that in the large ant nests, many of the species are blind. What will be the result of the information society? Will this lead to a collective form of life, or will it make the life of the average citizen more rich, more varied, and lead to an increased quality of life?"

Ilya Prigogine

We are aware of taking part at a deep change in the field of architecture. We feel there is no other possibility to enlarge the model (or the models) so far regarded as a reference. It is as if the maximum limit had been attained, beyond which the structure can not stand. Not just an expansion of the theoric bases that support architecture, but also a process of integration among the different sciences caused by the downfall of the different disciplines boundaries. Therefore the central point is not introducing a change to solve a problem, but modifying the basic concepts. Through an interdisciplinary perspective you realize a radical change of the ideas of "reality" and "organism", and subsequently you also get to a change of the relation observer-observed, the former being a fundamental part of the latter. Reality is neither only nor external to living beings. Its essence can not be attained. This means that knowledge mirrors the structure of the organism it is exploring much more than the structures of the external reality.

This implies:
a) In such a perspective all the points of view are used together and can not be subordinate each other. In other words, every observation / operation is neither external nor neutral. The multi-verse of H. Maturana (1990) - not the Uni-verse - is the way reality reveals itself. We can attain just one of the aspects of reality and read it through our experience.
b) In a perspective of self- organization the living being transforms the environmental external pressure in an inner order. "Experience" means that external pressures, or casual environmental forces, may be important for the organism because they shape its world (meanings, perceptions, time) which did not exist previously.

Since 1999 HOV has been exploring the experimental aspects in the life spaces within the paradigms of the different disciplinary areas. From chemistry to biology, the possibilities of social transformations depending on forms of collective intelligences, led to a wide project - [glossity] - where, once a model of imaginary society has been defined, consequential spaces and settlements have been associated. Society, in glossity, is organized in a well defined way, in which a structure of its own is self determined in relation to outer perturbations.

In this perspective the living beings transform, in a unitary and synchronized way, the environmental outer pressures in an inner order. Each group of activity has its own perception of time, but the latter is best used depending on the structures of the organisms and on the tasks they have been given. That is why you find yourself right there where you are supposed to be. There are no alternatives. The total lack of casual elements in everyday life does not prevent the satisfaction of all the biological needs isolated by the community itself.

[glossity] is an imaginary installation, an extreme world. Episodes without a context, detached one from the other, are parts of a homogeneous whole. A group of elements without time. The limits of the morphology are no longer as they user to be, the installations find a proper place at the utmost depth as well as on the highest top. Concentrations will be only apparent, but the distribution will actually be comparatively uniform. Variations of densities even if considerable, in a vital space inter-connected in a continuum, are no more than trivial fluctuations. The result is a homogeneous system projected is such a way that any observer, from whatever point of view, cannot assume a privileged position.
[glossity] clearly conveys an abstract reflection , the projects do not represent real objects.

They are mental experiments in spite of the physical, chemical or biological objections that may be raised.

David Raponi

[GLOSSITY]

“世界上有大约12000种蚂蚁，有的数百只生活在很小的巢穴，也有的数以万计生活在很大的巢穴里。现在观察它们行为的差异是很有趣的一件事。在小巢穴里的蚂蚁，每只都独立行动，但在大巢穴里，有很多集体行为，而集体行为是更加高等的智力行为。有趣同时又有一些可怕的是，在蚂蚁大巢穴中的，很多种群是瞎的。信息社会的结果会是什么呢？它会导致集体化的生活形式吗？会使普通市民的生活更加富有、更加多样化吗？会提高生活质量吗？”

Ilya Prigogine

我们知道我们正参与建筑学领域的深层次改变。我们觉得目前为止没有其他的可能性可以扩大模型。好像最大的极限已经达到，超越这个极限的话建筑就不能立足。不仅是支持建筑学的理论基础正不断扩充，更因为学科间的界限模糊导致不同科学相互结合。因此，重要的并不是为了解决问题而寻找改变，而是更改基本的观念。通过深入了解各学科间的关系，你能够认识到关于“现实”和“有机体”概念的根本性改变。随后，你也能够了解到观察者和观测物的关系改变，前者变成后者的基本部分。现实对于生物体来说不是唯一也不是外部的。我们不能够得知它的本质。这意味着知识反映出了有机体的建筑，它比外部现实的建筑所探索的要多得多。

这意味着：

a）在这样的看法下，所有的观点都是共同被使用，互相之间没有从属关系。换句话说，每一个观察/运作都不是外部的或者中立的。H. Maturana(1990)所提及的是多元宇宙而不是单元宇宙，就是现实展现自己的方式。我们只能获得了现实的一个方面，并且通过我们的经验来理解它。

b）在自组织的观念中，生物体将环境的外部压力转化为内部秩序。“经历”意味着外部压力或者偶然的环境力，可能对生物体很重要，因为它们塑造了自己的世界（含义、理解、时间），而这些以前并不存在。

自1999年以来，HOV已经在不同学科范畴内进行了探索生命空间的试验。从化学到生物学，社会转变的可能性依赖于集体智慧的形式，这种可能性会导致更广阔的方案。Glossity中，一旦想象社会模型被定义，相因而生的空间和居所就联系在了一起。在glossity中的社会是组织完善的，它的建筑相比外面的混乱是依据自身状态决定的。

以这个观点来看，生物体采用整体的和同步的方式，将环境外部压力转化为内部秩序。每个活动组群都有自己关于时间的理解，不过，对后者最好的使用，是依赖生物体建筑和赋予它们的目标。这就是为什么你就在应该在的那里，没有选择。日常生活中偶然元素的缺失的全部，不会妨碍满足所有被团体孤立的生物学需求。

Glossity是一个想象的装置，是一个极端的世界。互相分离的没有上下文的情节，是统一整体的部分，是时间之外的同组元素。它们没有了以往的形态学限制，这些装置能够在极限深度和最高顶峰找到合适的位置。

集中是很显然的，但分布事实上也会相对地均衡。即使是可观的密度变化，在内部相互连接为一个整体的生命空间中，也不过只是琐细波动。设计结果是一个均匀的系统，从任何观点出发，任何观测者都不能够采取有特权的位置。

Glossity明显传达的是抽象的概念，不能代表真实的物体。它们是精神的试验，不管是否存在物理、化学、生物方面的异议。

David Raponi

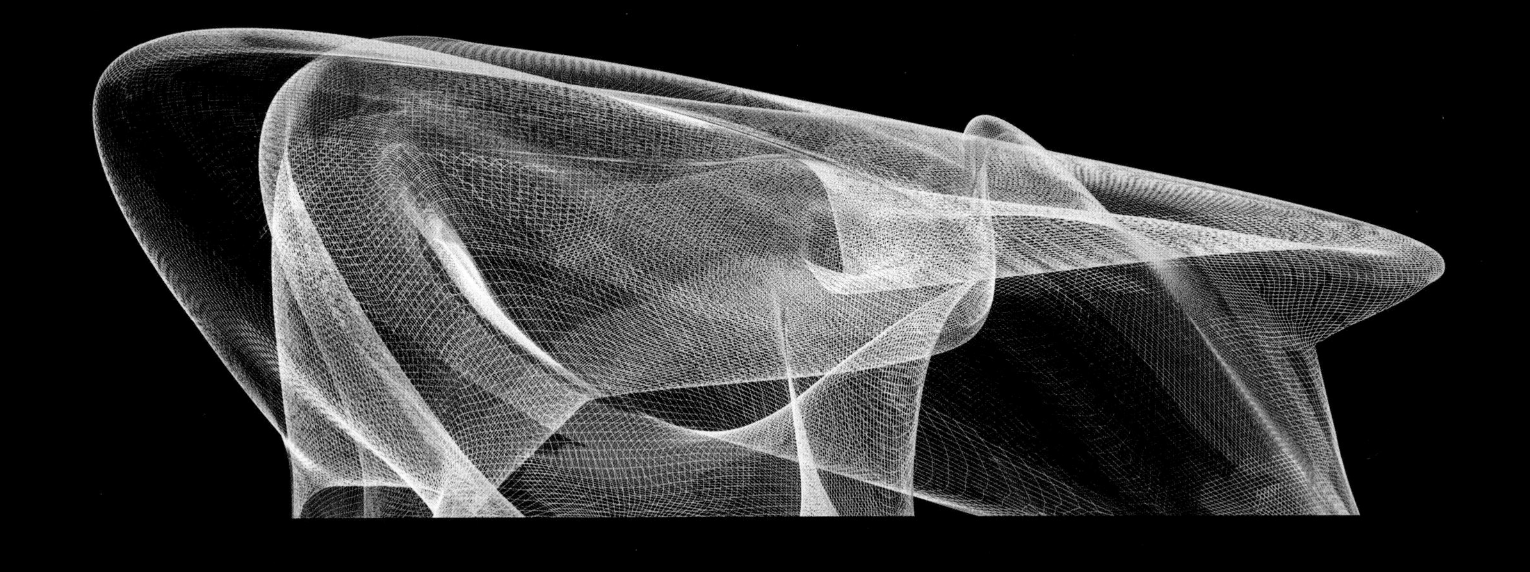

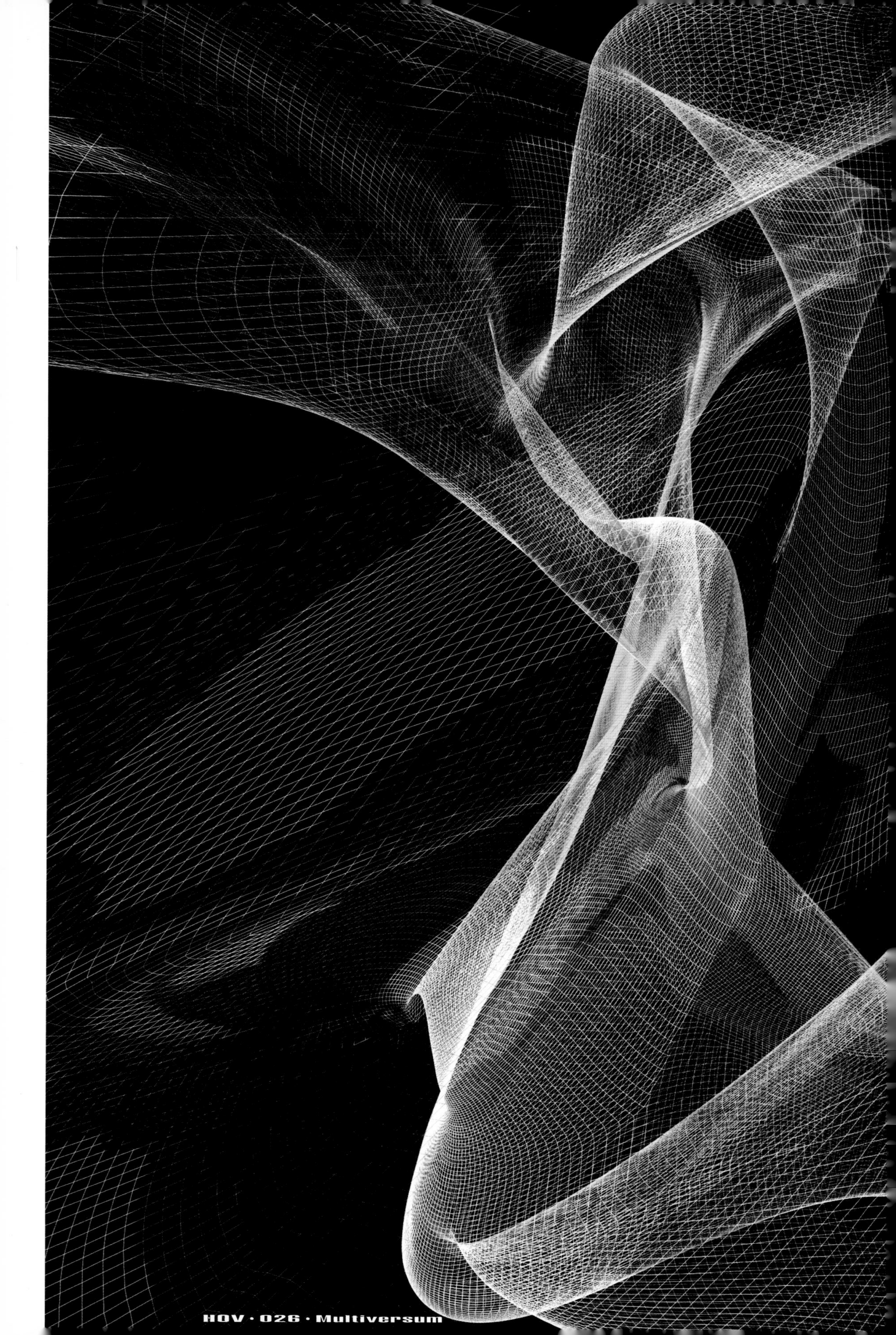
HOV · 026 · Multiversum

[colonization] is a projecting programme for objects that can indifferently find their location in spatial ambits for their own nature located.

They stand for a new principle of organization and do not mix up with the other visible objects.

The net that links them together included aspects that appear obscure to the author himself but that certainly convey a vision leading out of the architecture and inside of it at the same time.

The inspiring subject comes from the contemporary physics: the idea according to which each element is able to include all the other ones cannot be imagined in the ordinary space and time; it describes a different reality with its own rules. A definite mathematical meaning can be associated to this concept, but it is impossible to visualize it; it is a specifically relativistic aspect and we do not have any direct experience of a multi-dimensional world.

殖民化是对于这样一种目标设计的方案，它们能冷静地在空间范围内寻找到自己自然的位置。

它们代表了组织的新原理，不会和其他可视物体混淆。

将这些联系在一起的网包括了连作者自己也不知道的一些方面，但是它的确传达了一种同时通向建筑学外部和内部的景象。

令人鼓舞的主题是从现代物理中来的：每个元素会包括所有其他元素，这个观念是不能够在普通空间和时间中想象的。它用自己的规则描述了一个不同的现实。明确的数学意义可以与这个概念结合，但是不可能使其形象化。这是一个狭义相对论观点，我们对于多维空间没有任何直接的经验。

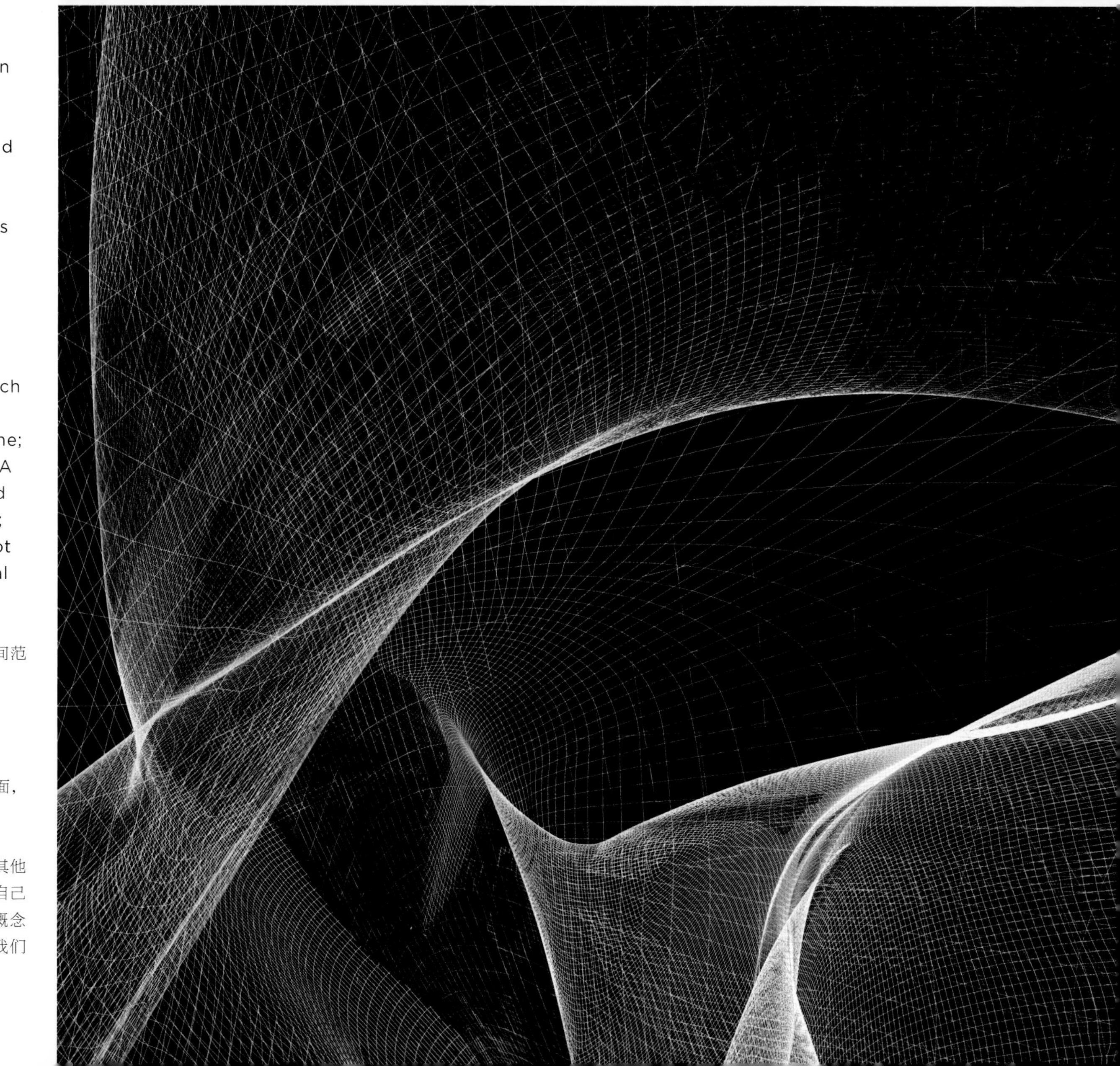

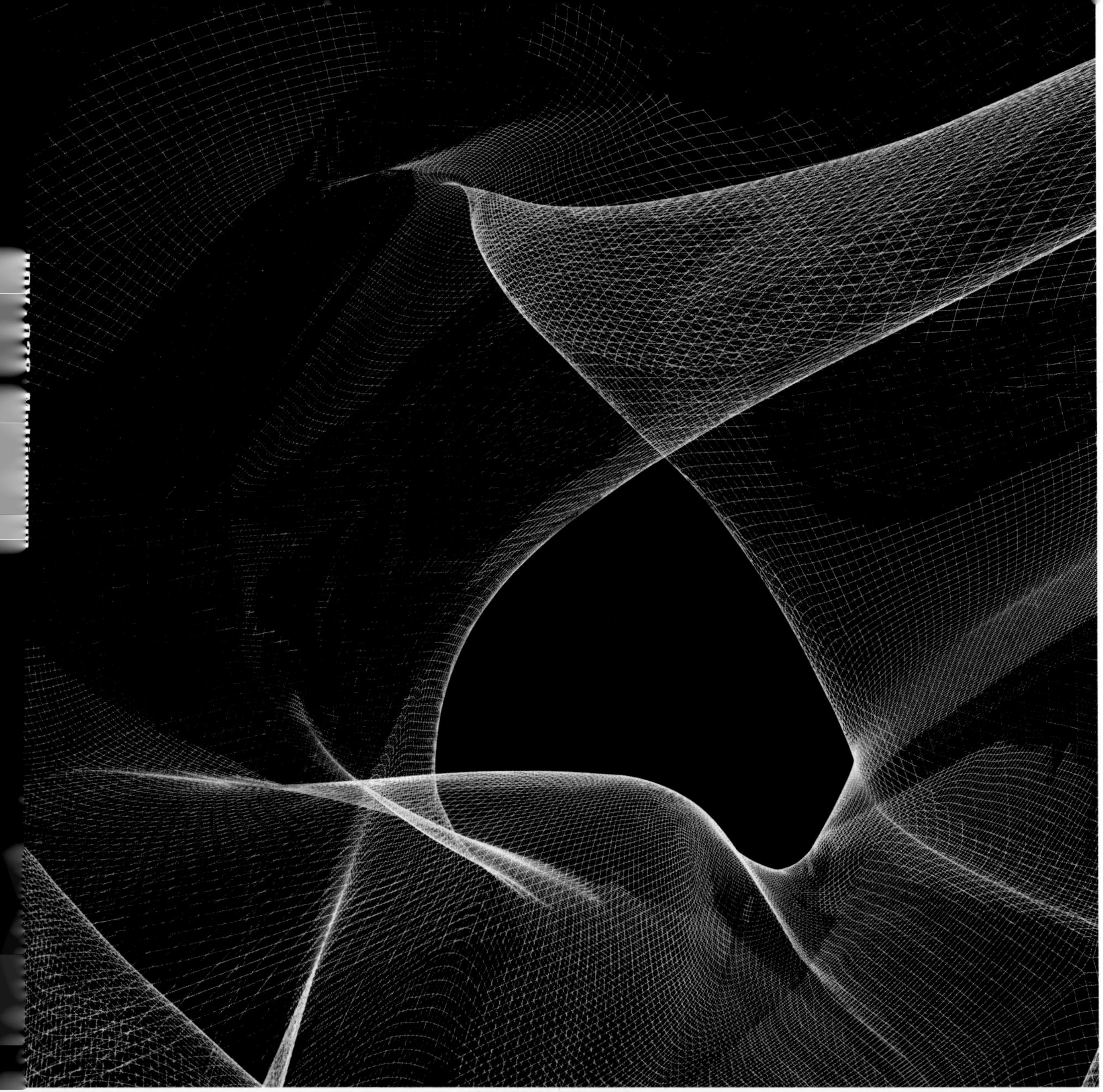

Glossity as a new-born embryo, a vital breath
revealed within walls of no material.
Neither solid nor liquid aeriform but indefinable
substances recorded in their passages of state, in
their thorough becoming...
sublimated substances bereft of thickness, odour,
flavour.
Glossity as an abyss, revealed but impregnable.
Which does not flow and does not breathe.
Not human tainted, it changes in abstraction.
An invertebrate without spine and without skin, a
fictitious frame, maybe the mental one inscribing
sensations, emotions, feelings...
Maybe, in negative, the void circumnavigated which
assails us at dawn, when our daily anxiety shows
itself and cannot be masked anymore...

A CENTRE
The space zero, the global reset leading back to
light, to the beginning...
In order to meet, to blossom
Also - is tired of rolling around with no start and no
return
Without the hope which generates the absence of
arrival
Resuscitate the alternative...
Glossity, do not guard us, do not protect us,
dissolve our prudence
reveal us to ourselves
fling the doors of emotions open...

blossom us
transparent
and genuine like you are.
Then mislay us, propose us to the rest
And may it overflow us...
February 2002 Federica Bianconi

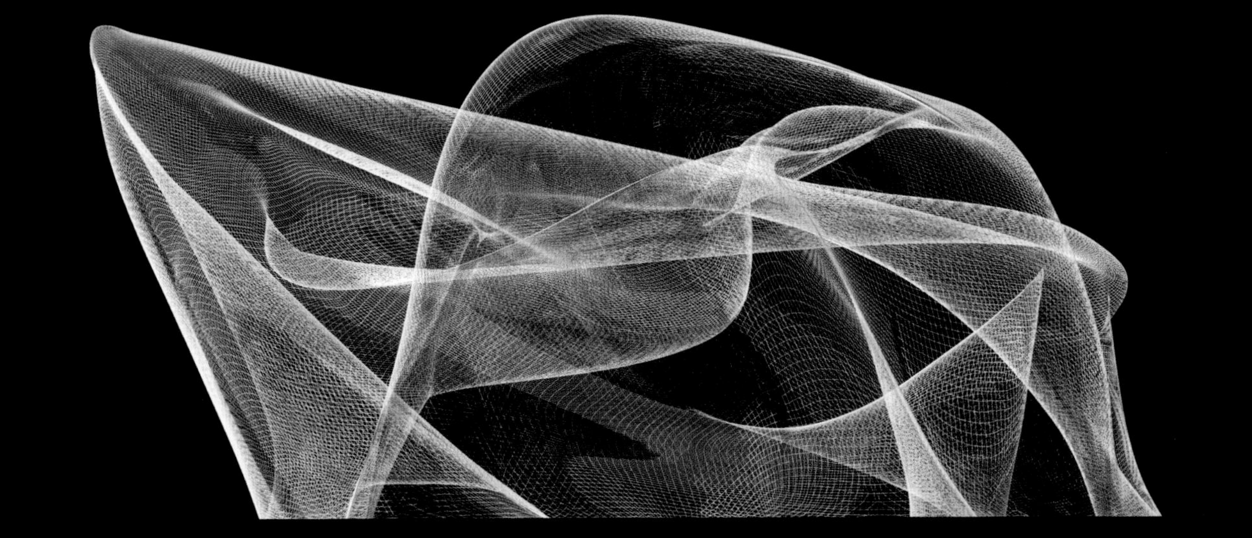

HOV · 029 · Multiversum

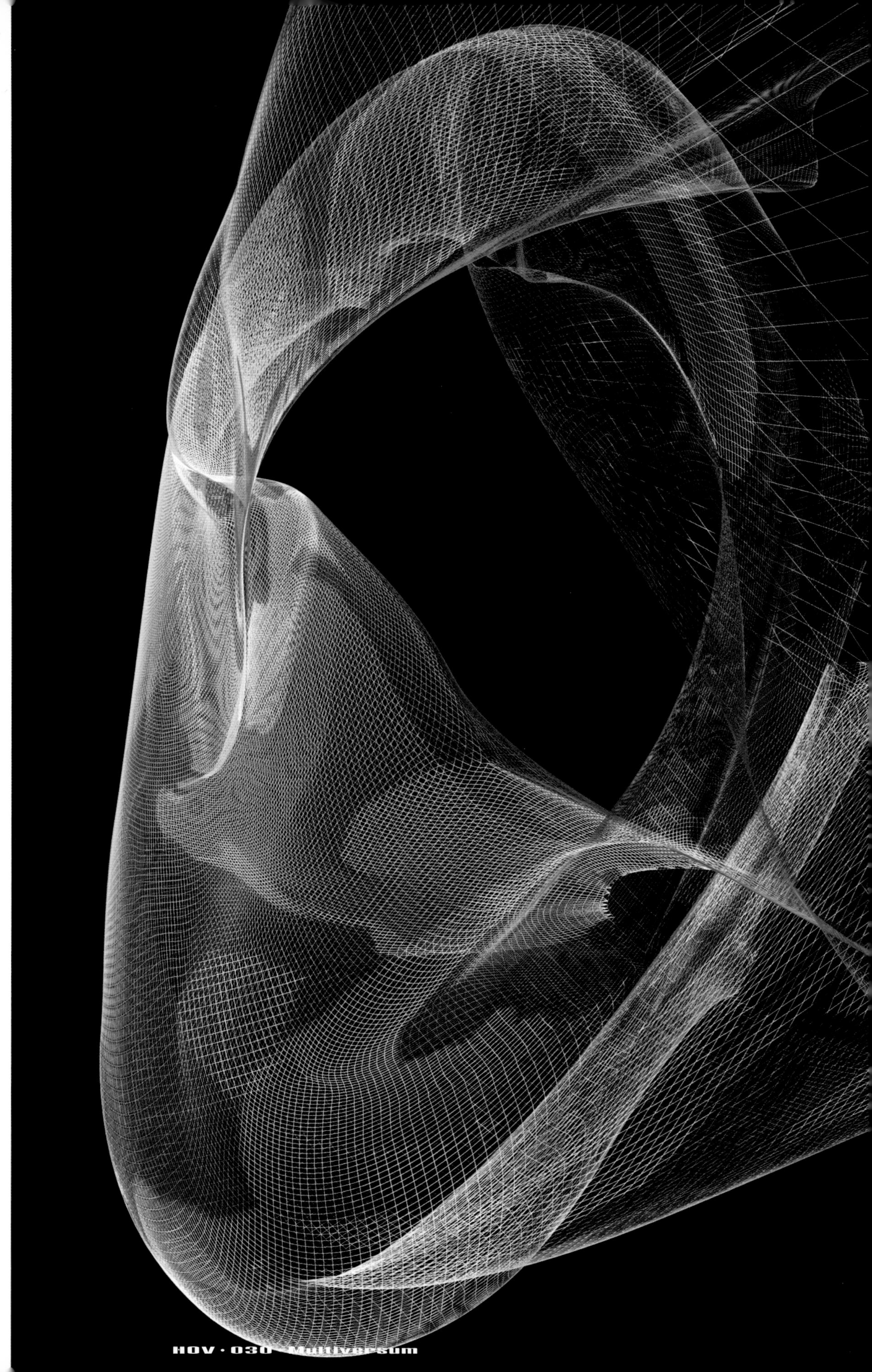
HOV · 030 · Multiversum

Glossity像一个新生的胚胎，在没有物质的情况下展现生命的气息。

不是固态、液态也不是气态，而是在它们一段段状态中记录下的不能定义的物质……

它完全升华除去了厚度、气味和滋味。

Glossity像一座深渊，显露在外却不受影响，没有流动和呼吸。不受人类感染，它在提取中改变。它没有脊椎、没有皮肤，是假想的结构，可能是描绘感觉、情绪和知觉之类的精神构架。

也许，消极地来讲，我们无法逃避虚空在拂晓时的攻击，当我们每日的焦虑显露出来，无法再继续伪装的时候……

一个中心

零度空间，全球的重置带回了光明，带回到开端……

为了相遇，也为了绽放，

厌烦了没有开始没有回归的流逝

没有产生无法到达的希望

选择的复兴……

Glossity不是在守卫我们，不是在保护我们，

溶解了我们的谨慎，

使我们展现自己，

撞开感情之门……

使我们发展成为透明、真实的，

就像你们一样

于是把我们放在错误的地方，

推荐我们去剩余的地方

祝愿它能使我们溢出……

Federica Bianconi

2002年2月

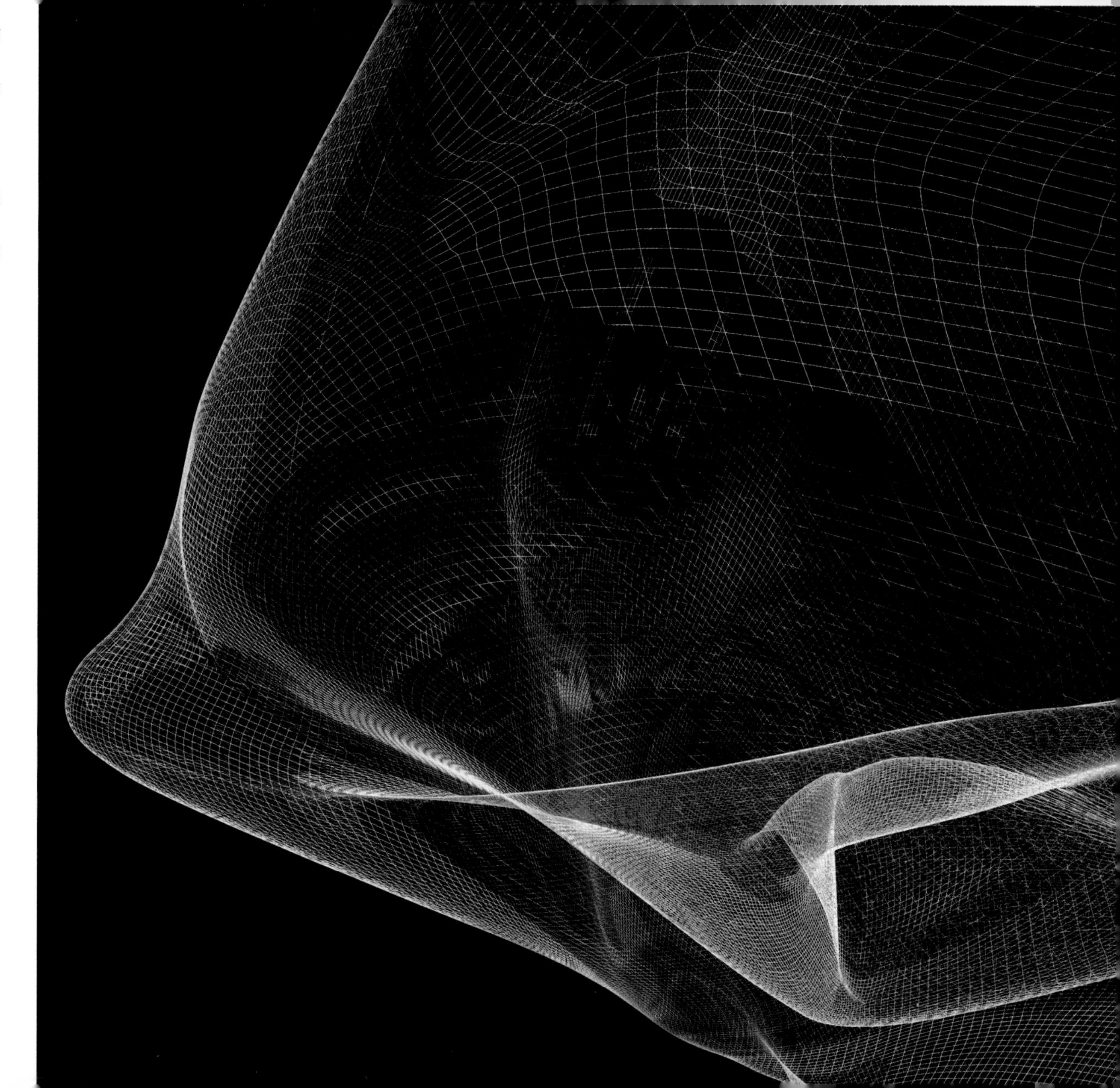

HOV · 032 · Multiversum

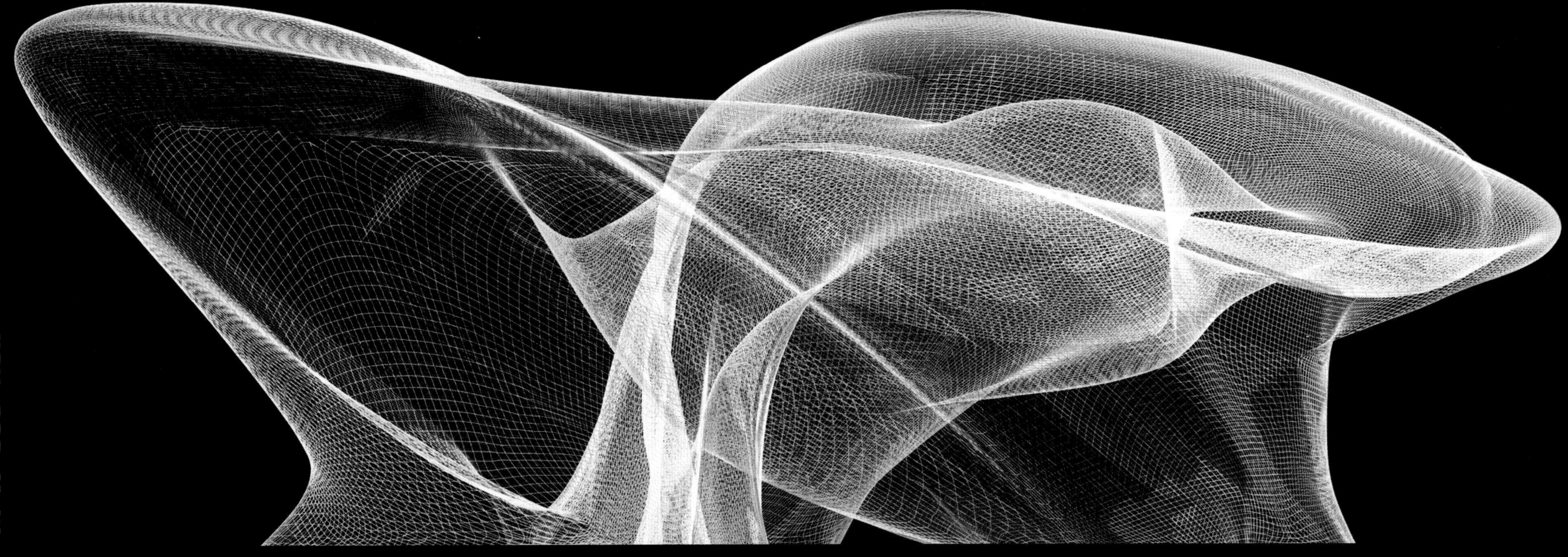

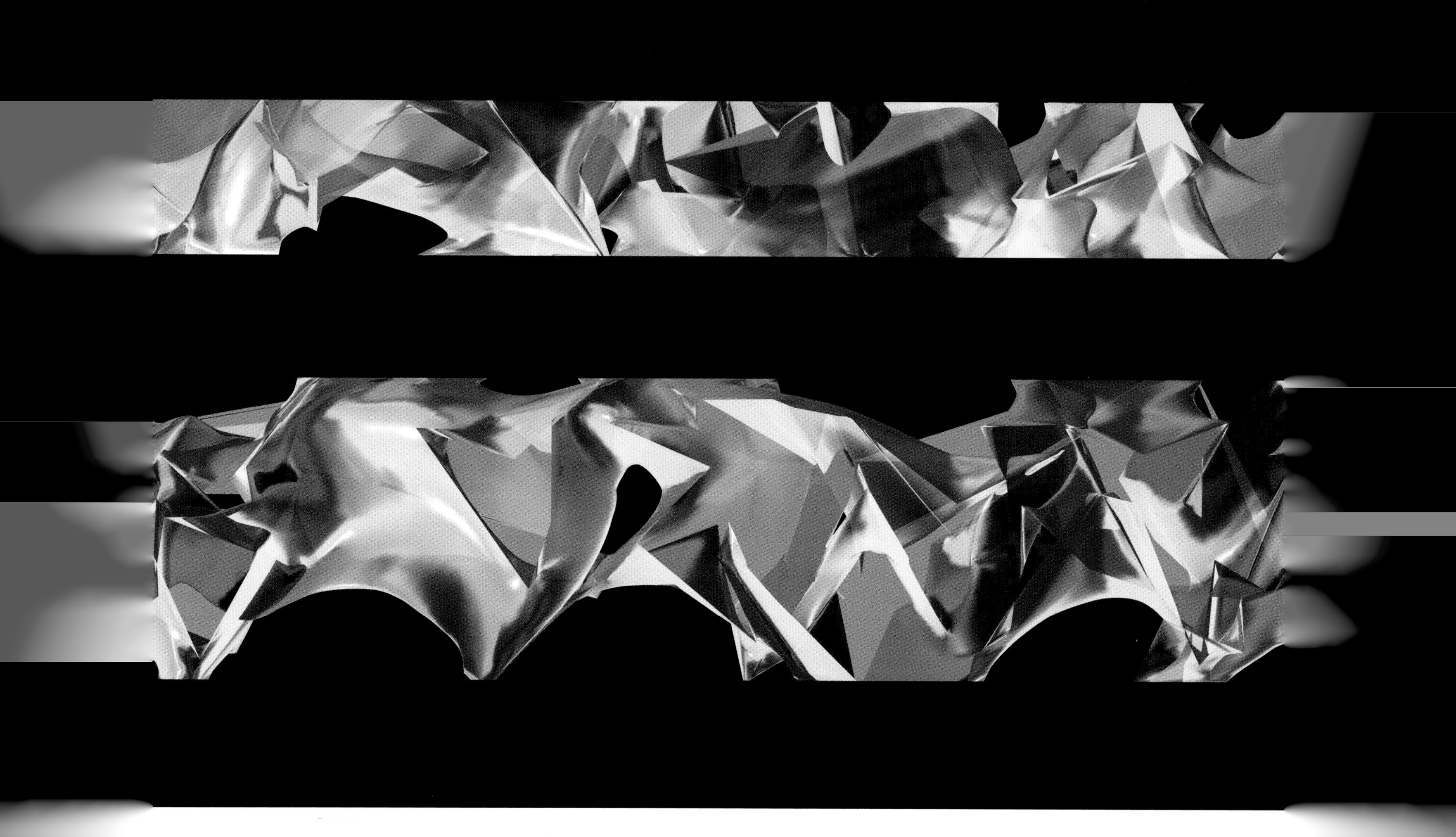

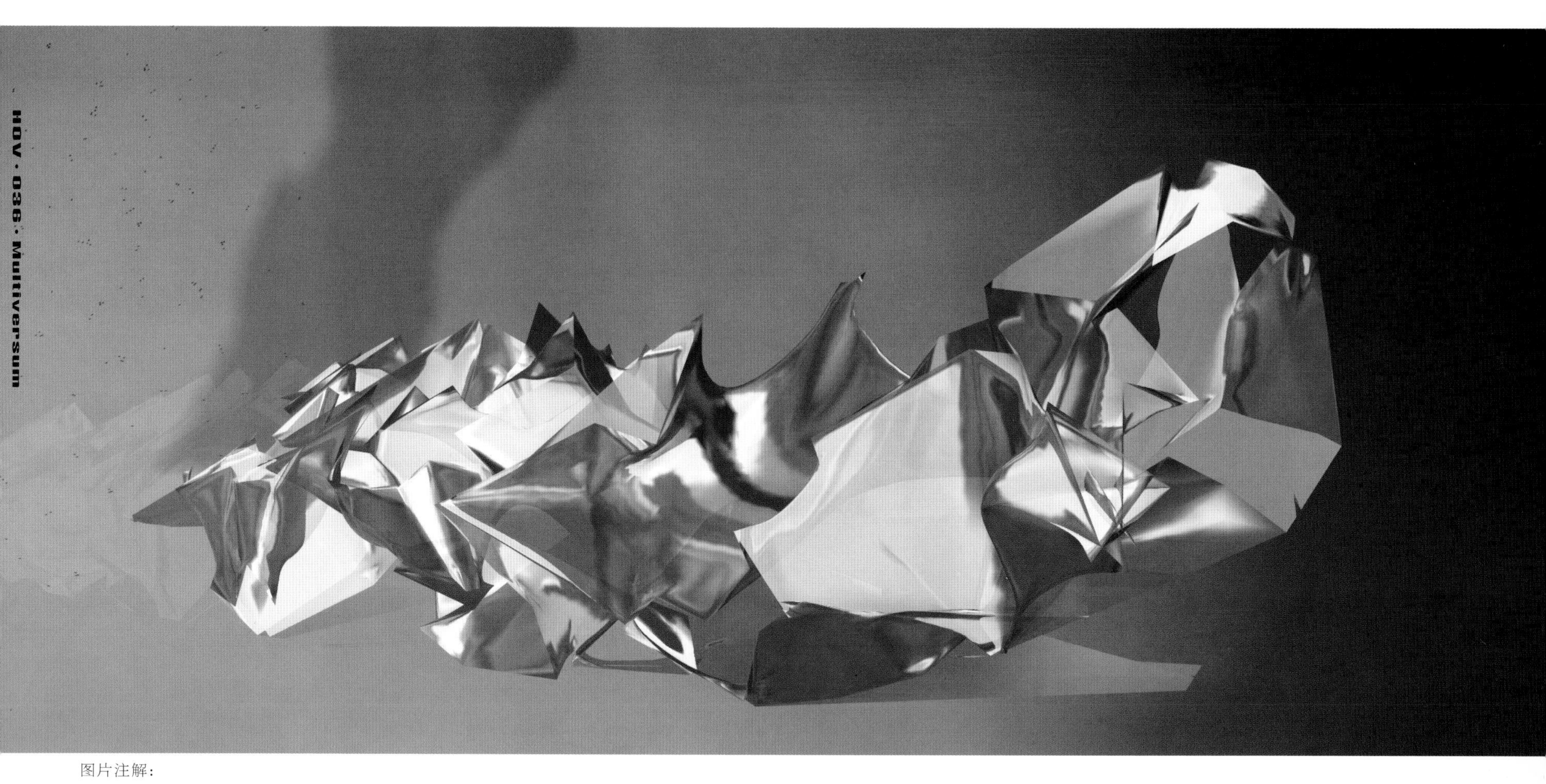

图片注解：

外视图和正面图

建筑的普通方针或其他参数在相对论发展下显然没有意义。建筑仅仅在其内部和人们生活的愿望中存在。强化繁殖中心经历克服了所有象征的需求和理解的内涵。我们知道什么在期盼我们，其他都不重要。

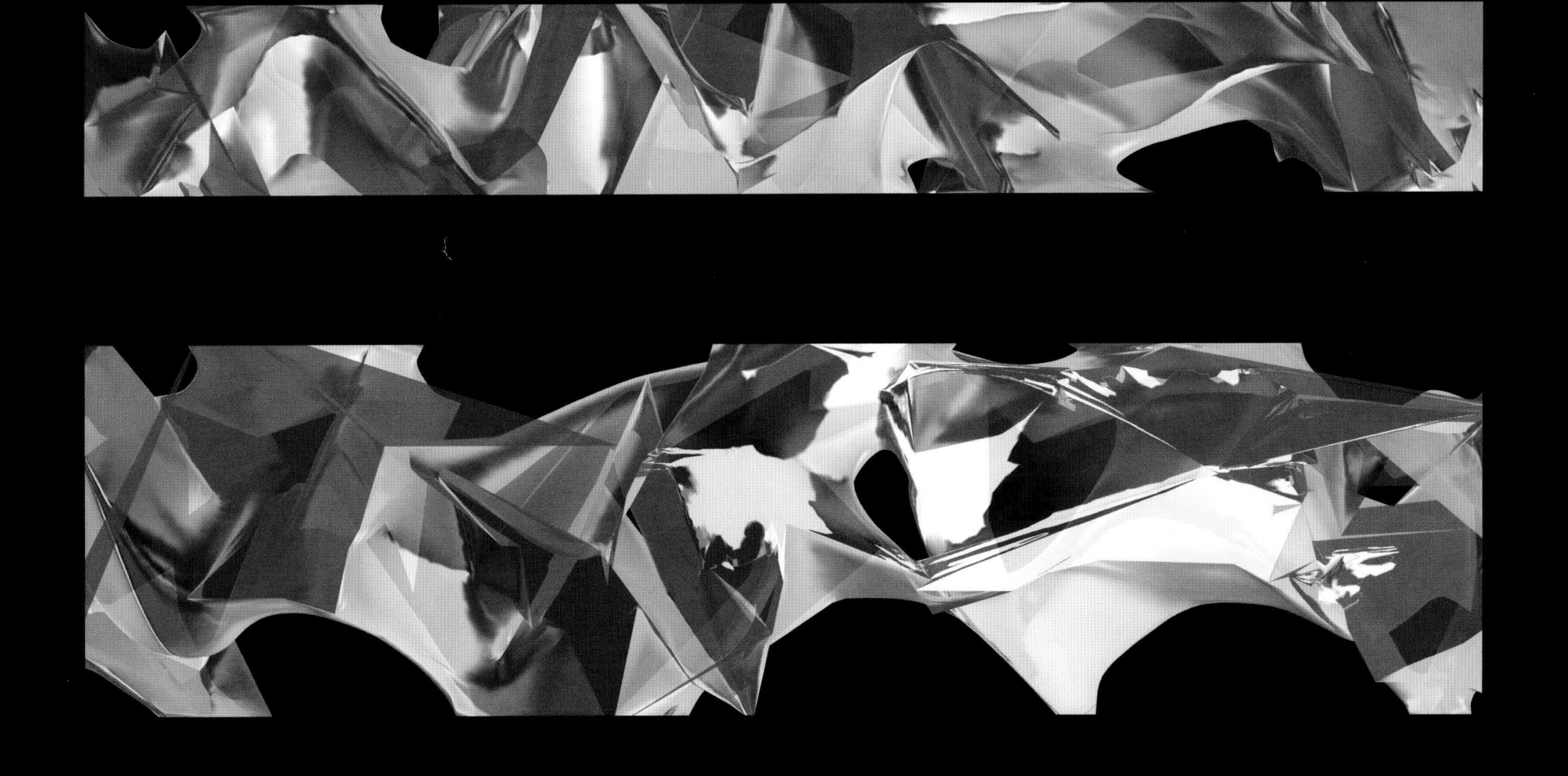

Picturess notes

external views and elevations

In such relativistic development the ordinary guideline or other parameters for the construction are evidently not significant. The building lives only and exclusively in its inside and the man and woman's desire of living the the intensive reproductive centre experience overcomes every necessity of symbolic or perceptive connotation. We know what expects us and all the rest has little importance.

The centre is a meeting place where, in an dreamy spatial values, big love stories are being lived as fortuitous meetings with reproductive purpose. In a very well structured and organized social framework, vital times are managed in a very precise way. The love experience is partially lived in such a virtual way that one can forget that woman and man in front of each other may have never seen before. Their relationship will be felt by both anyway, as the end of a love trail. The space and the sensory involvement widespread by the constituent material lead to a condition of well-being and satisfaction. Any structural component is hard and persistent and there is not any type of element that can be referred to the concept of furnishings (interior decoration). The constituent material, seat of diffuser neuronal nets, is soft and dynamic and includes the structure/skeleton.

繁殖中心是一个汇集的地方，在幻想的空间坐标中，宏大的爱情故事为了繁殖的目的偶然相遇。在一个结构紧凑组织完善的社会框架中，生命时间以非常精确的方式被设计。爱情的体验部分以一种虚拟的方式存在，以至于一个人也许会忘了面前的这个男人或女人是素未谋面的。无论如何两个人都会感受到这段关系，并成为了爱情轨迹的终点。空间和广泛传播的感官介入带来了安宁和满足的状态。任何建筑组成都是坚硬、持久的。没有任何种类的元素能够归属于内部装饰的概念。要素物质神经网的扩散体，它是柔软的、动态的，包含了建筑/骨架。

Picturess notes

structure

They represent four pictures of structural support form. They are not definite stages, but just different moments in the life of the building. In other words, the formation is probabilistic and the building will probably have that given image, but not necessarily. The initial structural plan is schematic and made by man out of an inorganic synthetic material, it is then developed by unitary self-generating elements with a bearing inner-skeleton, like coral for example, but with a quicker growth.

图片注解:

建筑

这四张图描绘了建筑的支撑形式。它们不是明确的阶段，只是建筑生命中不同的片刻。换句话说，这种结构是盖然论的，建筑将很可能会显现出这样的画面，但也不一定。最初的建筑平面是示意性的，由人类用无机合成材料材料建造而成。之后，由一元的自生元素和内部支撑骨架发展，像珊瑚虫一样，只是生长得快一些。

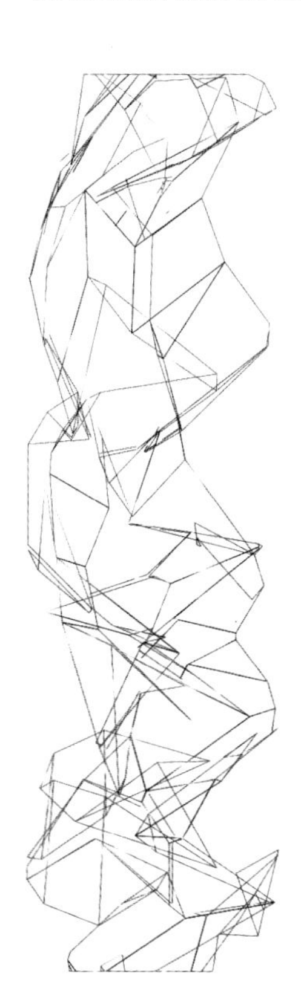

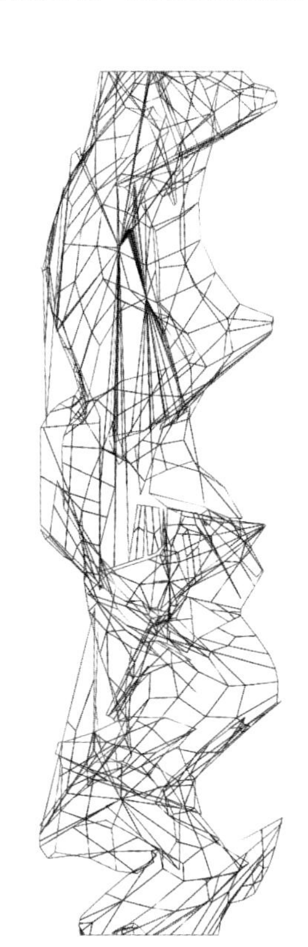

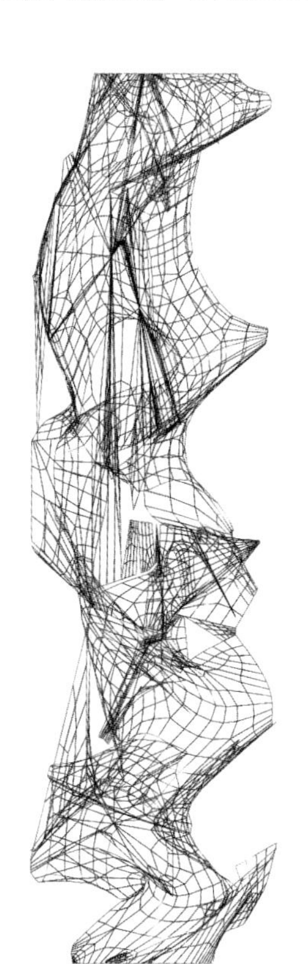

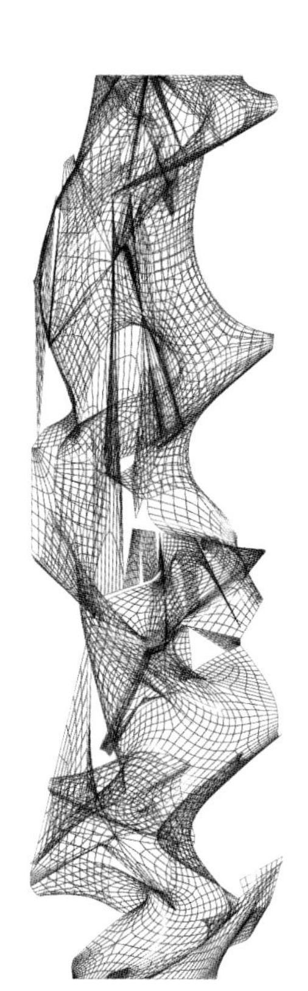

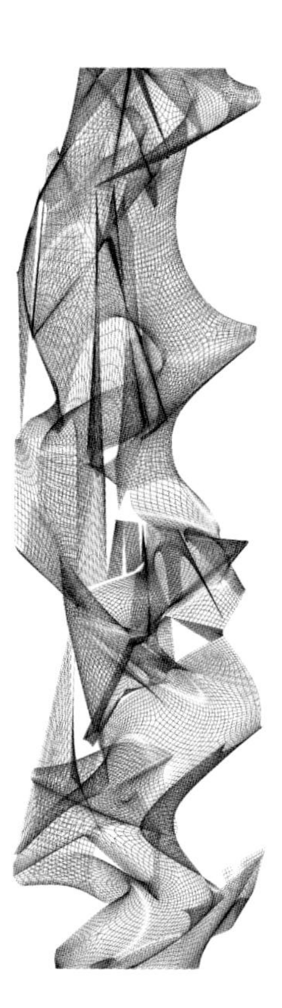

Picturess notes

inner spaces

The matter that covers the structure is made itself of auto-generating units of more complex nature if compared to the elements creating the support. They are described as a superimposition of neural nets protected by some material of the same consistency of a silicon resin. Such molecules, stressed by the pressure of bodies, by heat or noises, react to these perturbations with spreads and emissions - sensory and extrasensory - that induce the state of well-being and the illusion of the love relationship – which is not lived as such. For example among the extrasensory emissions, scenes of common life, happy moments shared, first dates, are sent to the minds like electrical and chemical impulses.

These aspects of life have never really happened.

图片注解：
内部空间
覆盖建筑的物质是由自生单元构成的，和支撑元素相比具有更复杂的天性。它们被描述为神经网的叠印，由硅树脂一样坚固的材料保护。这样的分子接受到来自人体、热和声音的压力，散发出去作为对外界扰乱的反应。这种反应是感觉上的和超感觉的，它引发了安宁的状态和与爱情相关的幻想，而这些幻想并不是真的这样存在的。举一个超感官发射的例子，普通生活的场景、和大家在一起的欢乐时光、第一次约会等都像电脉冲和化学脉冲一样进入人们的思想。而这些生活的场景从来没有真正发生过。

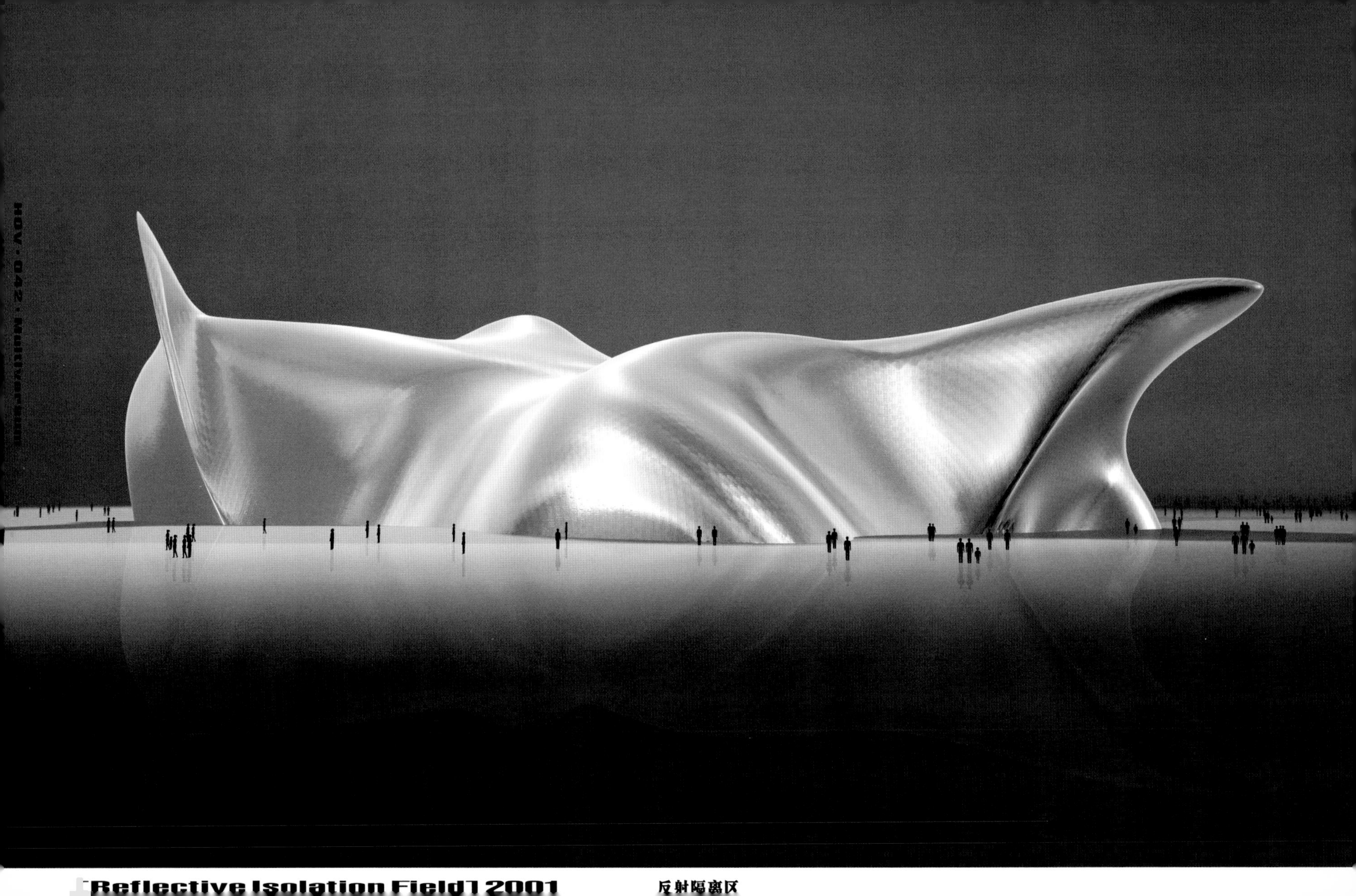

「Reflective Isolation Field」2001　反射隔离区

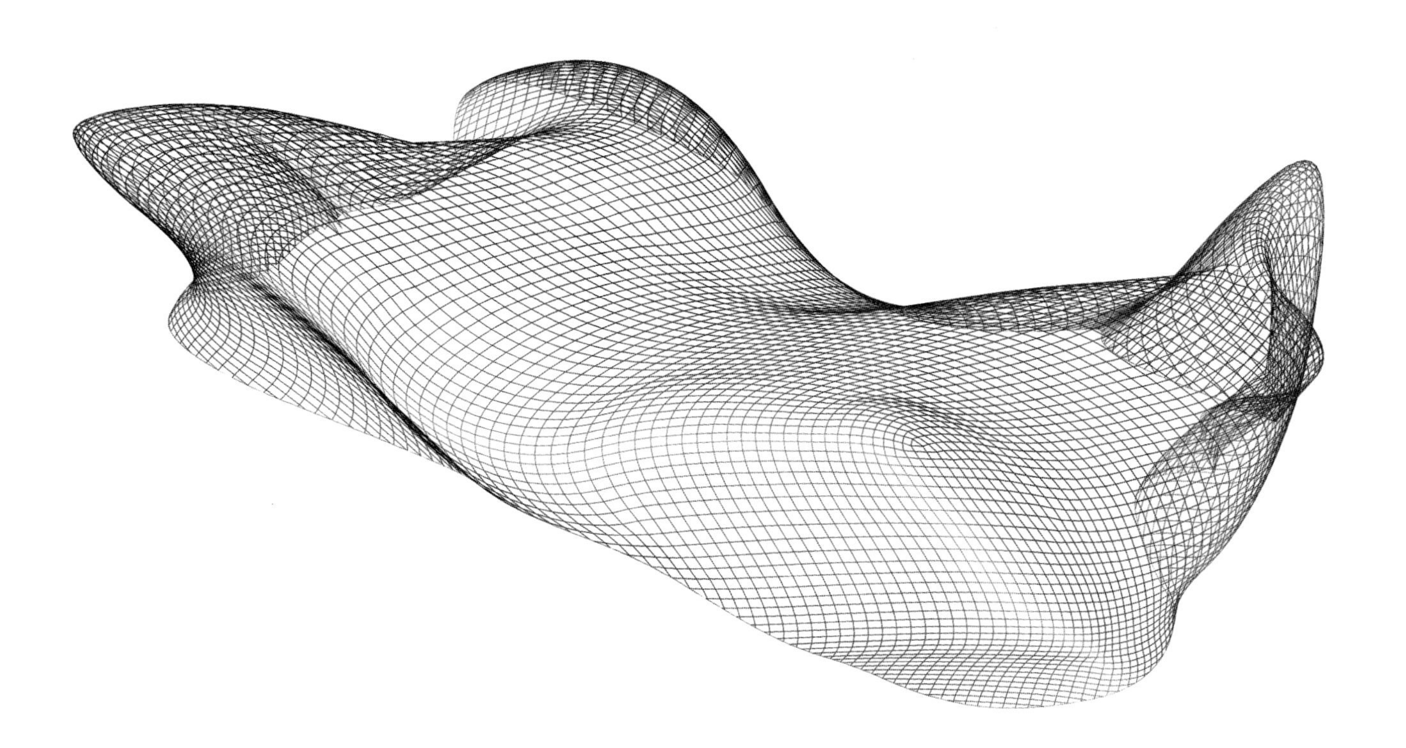

HOV · 043 · Multiversum

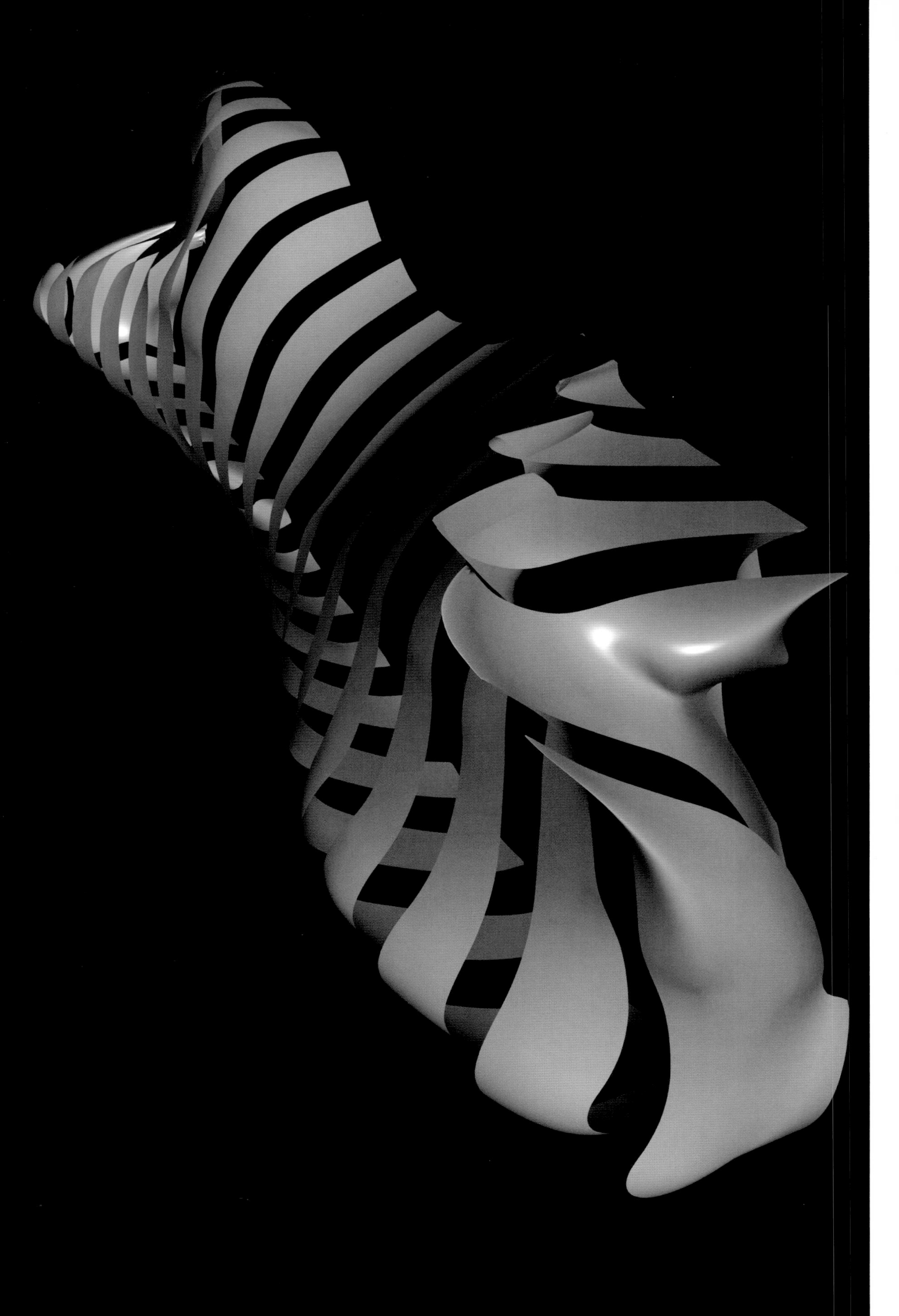

Spirituality, one of the basic aspects of this modern society of ours, is also attainable in Glossity. It is even enlarged, guaranteed and extended to all the activity groups in each different community.
Each living organism can show its ego and gets lost in it, beyond the intellectual or awareness abilities it has acquired. These latter have in fact no more reason to exist and they extinguish themselves as they are definitely not necessary to the preservation of the city, except for specific groups.
Similarly, the problem of religion or belief, is not dealt since it can find no space: the answers to it are just supposed for questions nobody is going to ask.
Once the skin of the structure is touched by the living organisms, it leads to an estranging "trance", priming a process of psychic revision that each one then undergoes in a physiological way.

灵性是我们这个现代社会的基本观念之一，在Glossity里也可得到。它甚至被放大、保证了，伸长到了每个不同群落的所有活动组群。
任何一个存活的生命体展示了自我，也迷失在其中，超越了所需求的智力或者意识能力。后者事实上没有理由存在。除了对于一些特殊群落，对于城市的保护它们也是完全没有必要的。
同样，宗教或者信仰的问题没有被处理，因为它们找不到余地：它的答案是假定针对没有人会提出的问题的。
一旦建筑的表面被存活的生物体接触，就导致一个疏远的“恍惚”，并准备好了精神修正的过程，然后每一个个体将以一种生物学的方式经历这个过程。

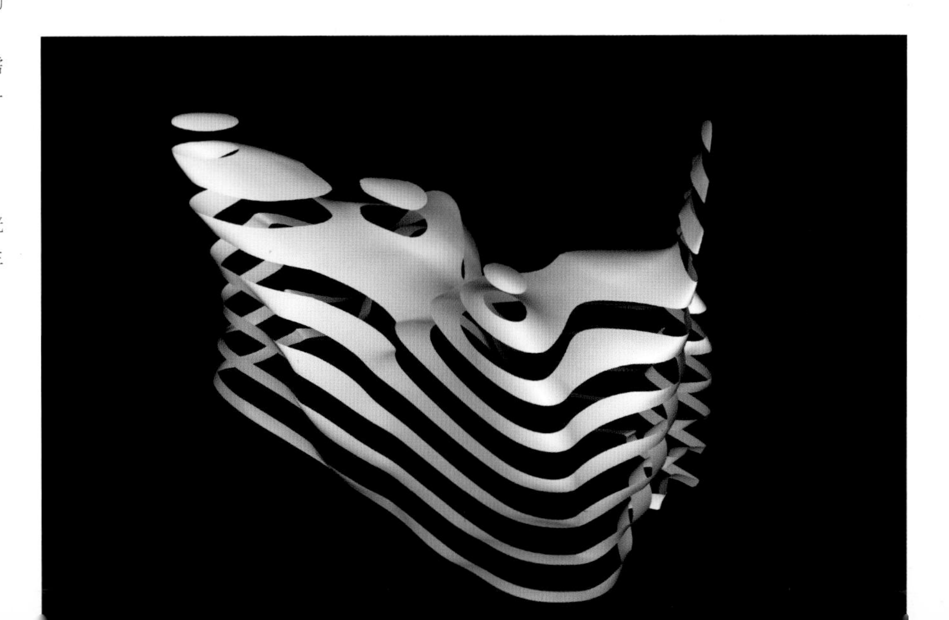

Pictures Notes
surface
The pictures describe an analysis of the surface of emitter organisms at a given moment
As in the reproduction centre the first structure is granted by the presence of man, but here the synthetic support is absent.

图片注解：
表面
这张图片描绘了某个给定时刻发射生命体的表面分析
就和在繁殖中心内一样，第一个建筑被人类的存在而接受，但是这里没有人造的支撑体系。

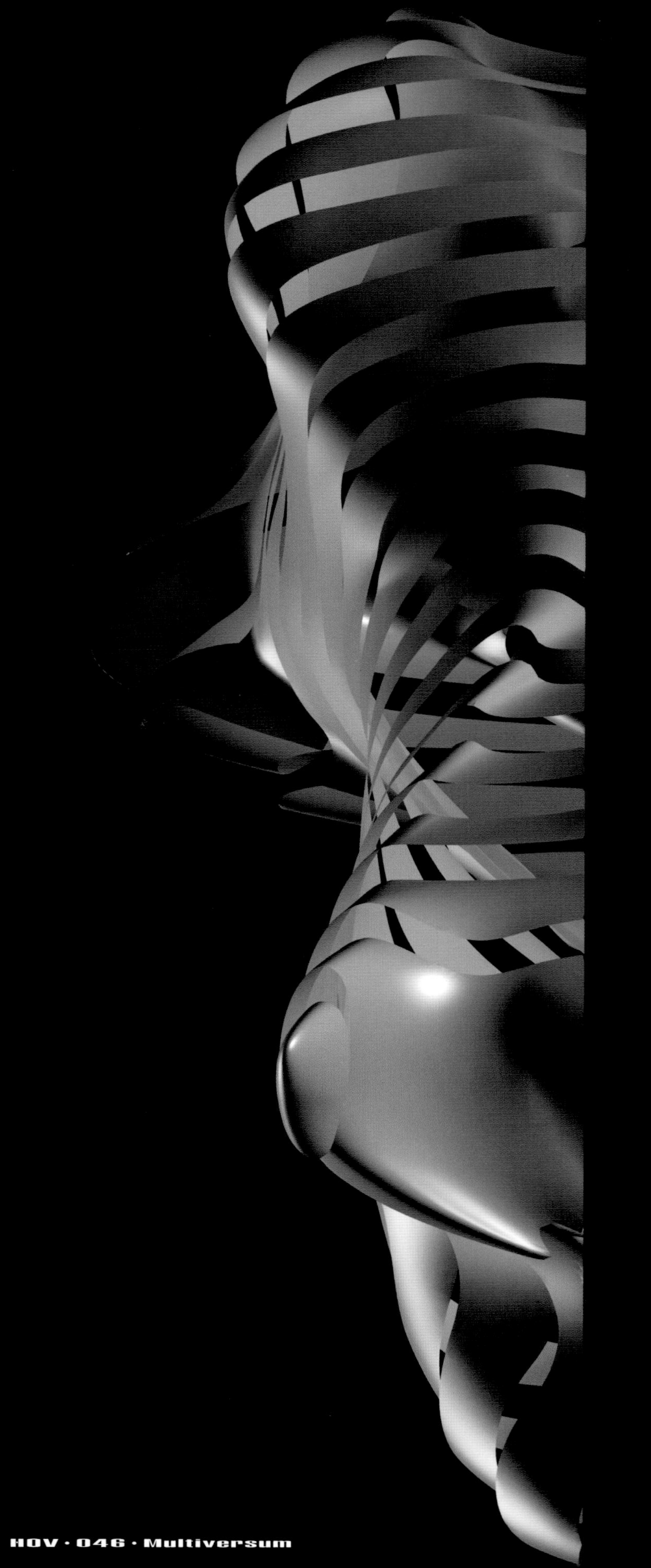

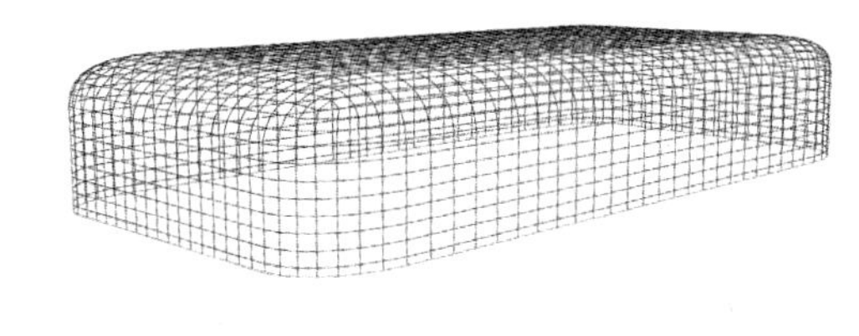

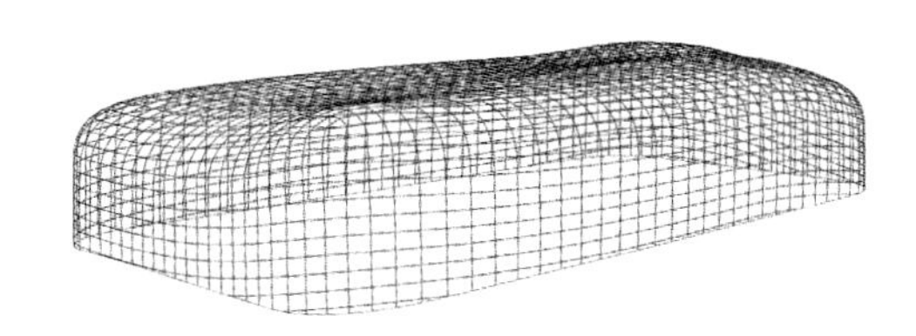

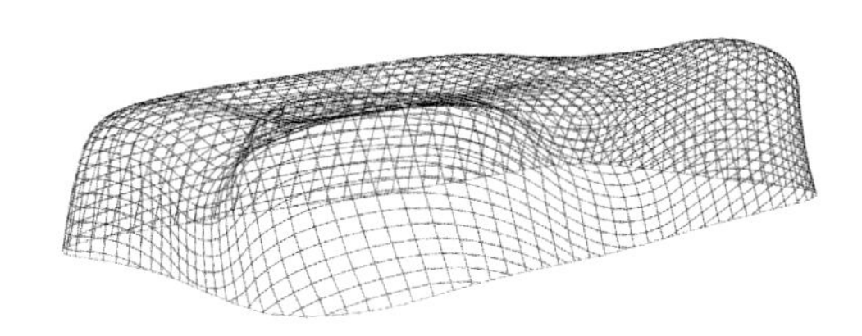

Pictures Notes
Matter is organised by self-generating units specially designed in the laboratory. Triggered off by body heat through special receptors, they act through chemical emissions inducing an estranged state.
To begin with, the building is just one single carefully arranged mass that gradually transforms and successively it is re-oriented according to the densities and the directions of the mass.

图片注解：
物质是由实验室特殊设计的自生单元组织的。由机体传热至特殊受体激发，它们通过化学发射作用产生诱导至疏远的状态。
首先，建筑只是一个被小心地设计过的集合体，它逐渐地转换，并相继根据块体的密度和方向进行重新定位。

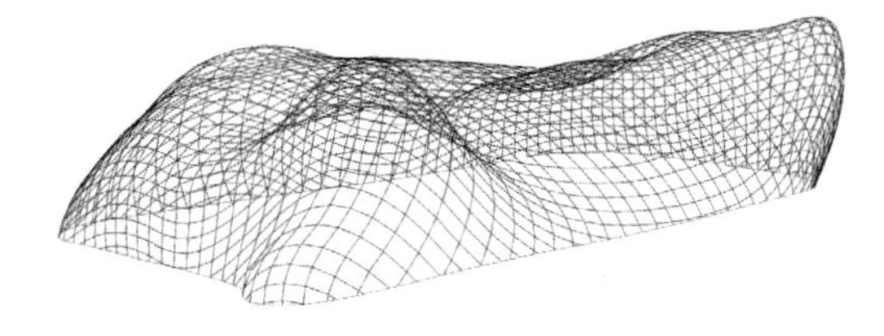

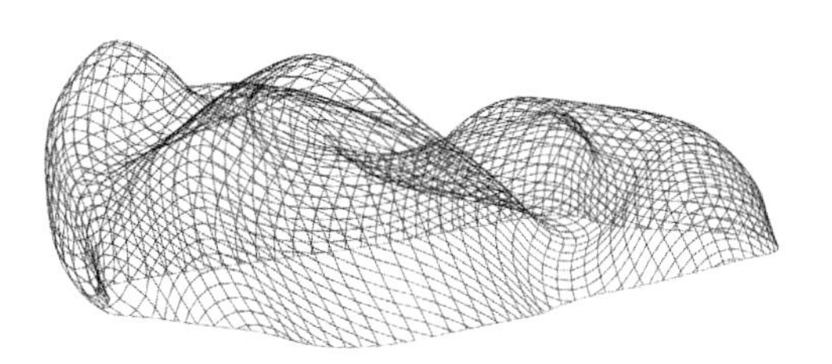

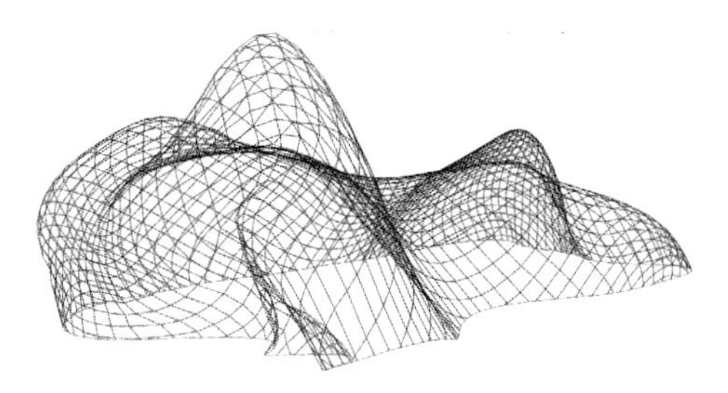

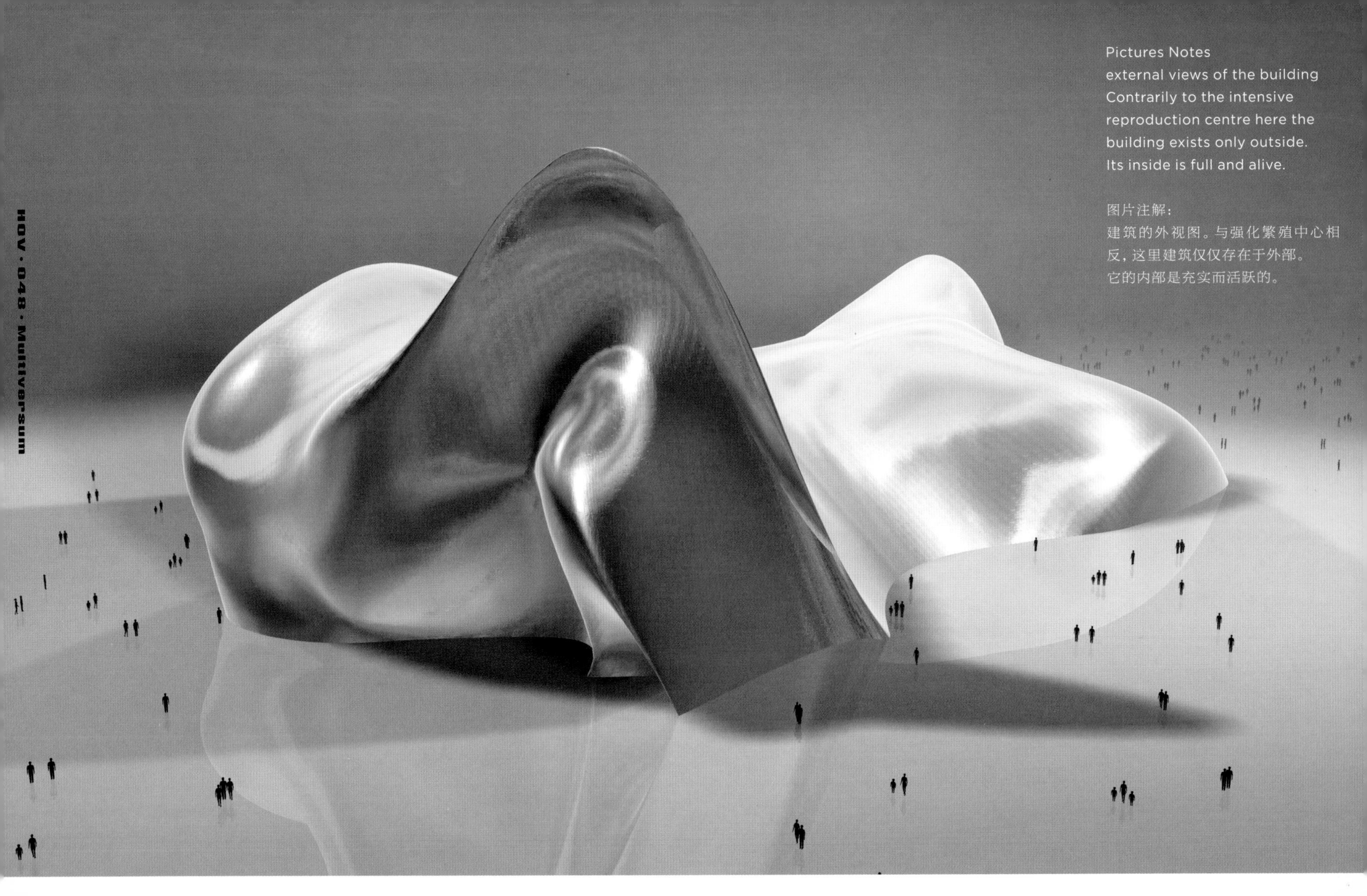

Pictures Notes
external views of the building
Contrarily to the intensive
reproduction centre here the
building exists only outside.
Its inside is full and alive.

图片注解：
建筑的外视图。与强化繁殖中心相
反，这里建筑仅仅存在于外部。
它的内部是充实而活跃的。

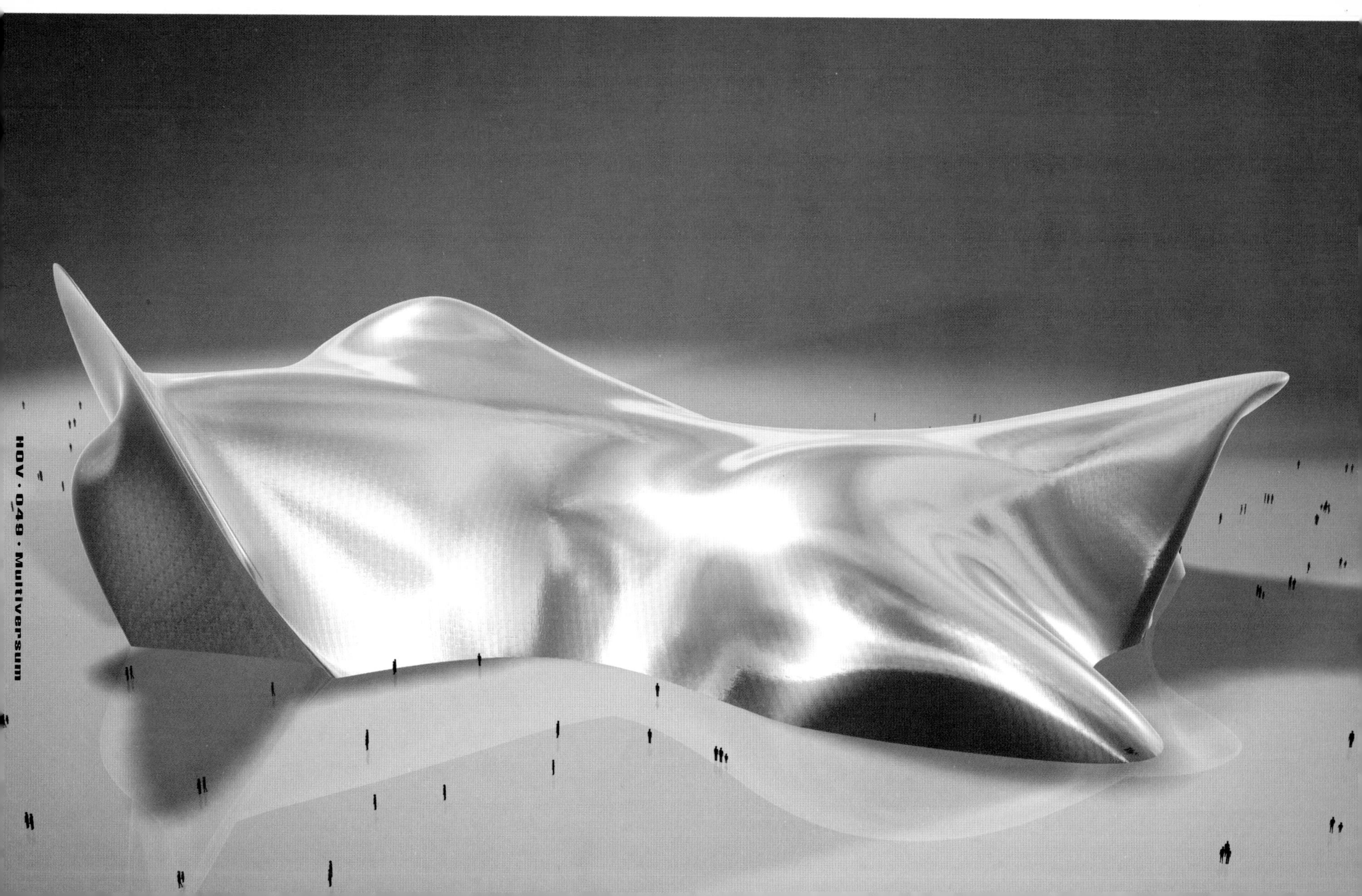

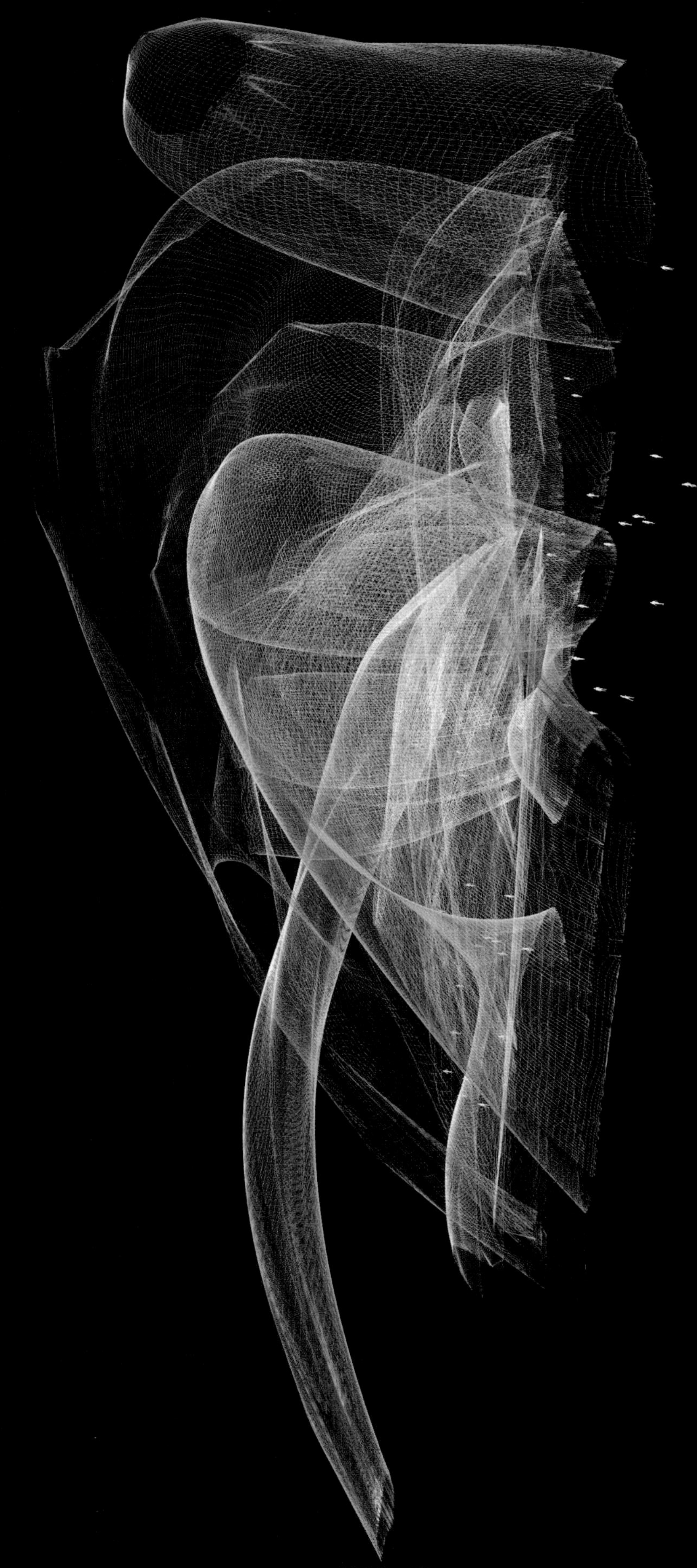

On the way of the glossity research a new episode is called Incubator. The centre is the place of control and reference for the generation of organisms in the fictitious society defined in other design experiences.

As a discretionary completion of the intensive reproduction centre, though well-balanced by the society itself, the Incubator takes part in the dynamics 'meeting/love/procreation' with the aim of freeing the procreating organisms from their physiological loads. It's a new dream being represented.

在glossity研究的过程中，有一种新的插件被称为孵卵器。在其他设计经历所定义的虚拟社会中，繁殖中心是用以对下一代生命体的控制与参考。

作为强化繁殖中心的一个自由决定的完成状态，虽然社会本身已经有了很好的平衡，但是，带着将繁殖生命体从生理学负荷中解放出来的目标，孵卵器参与了“相遇/恋爱/生殖”的动态过程。它展现出了一个新的梦想。

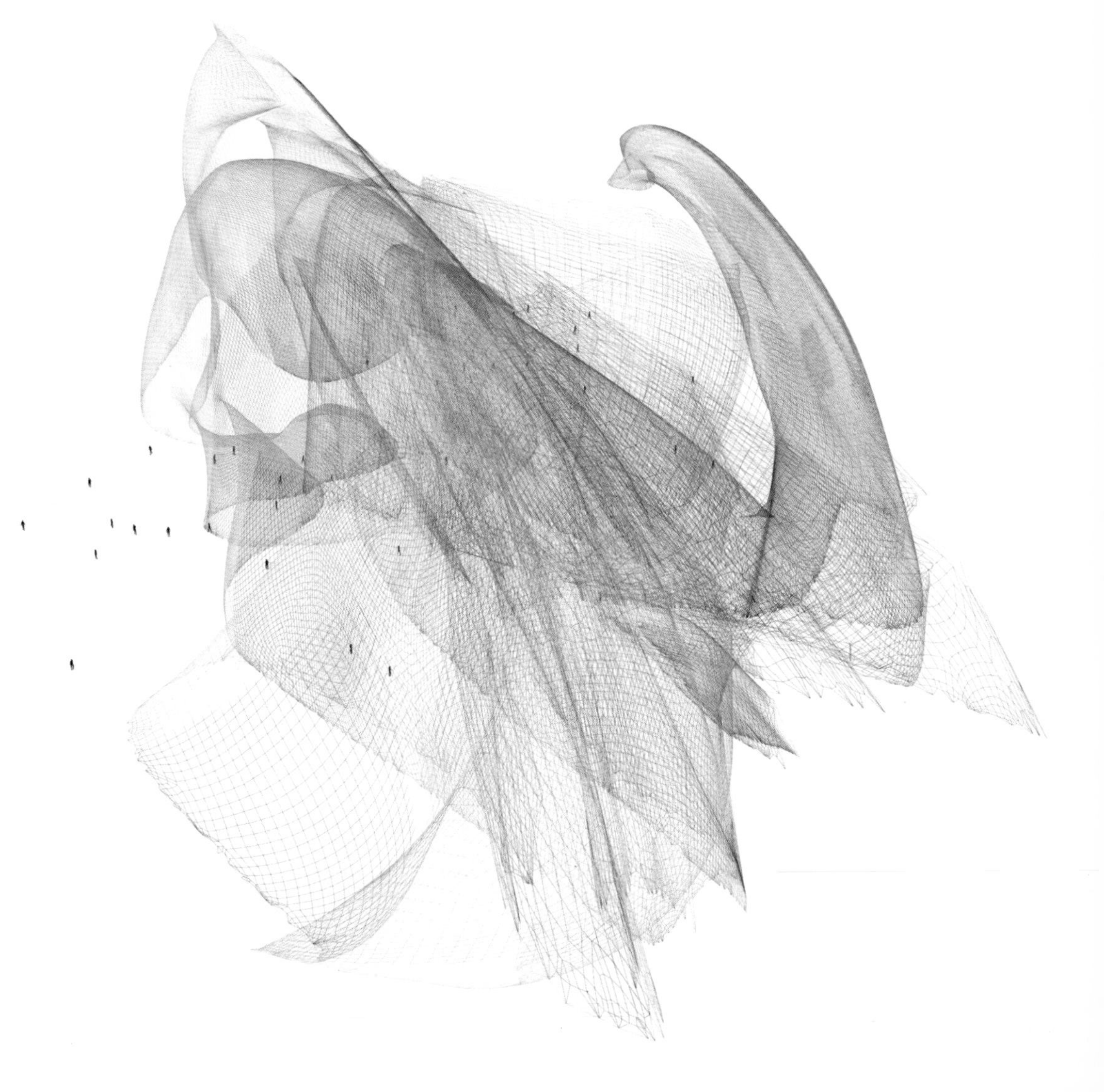

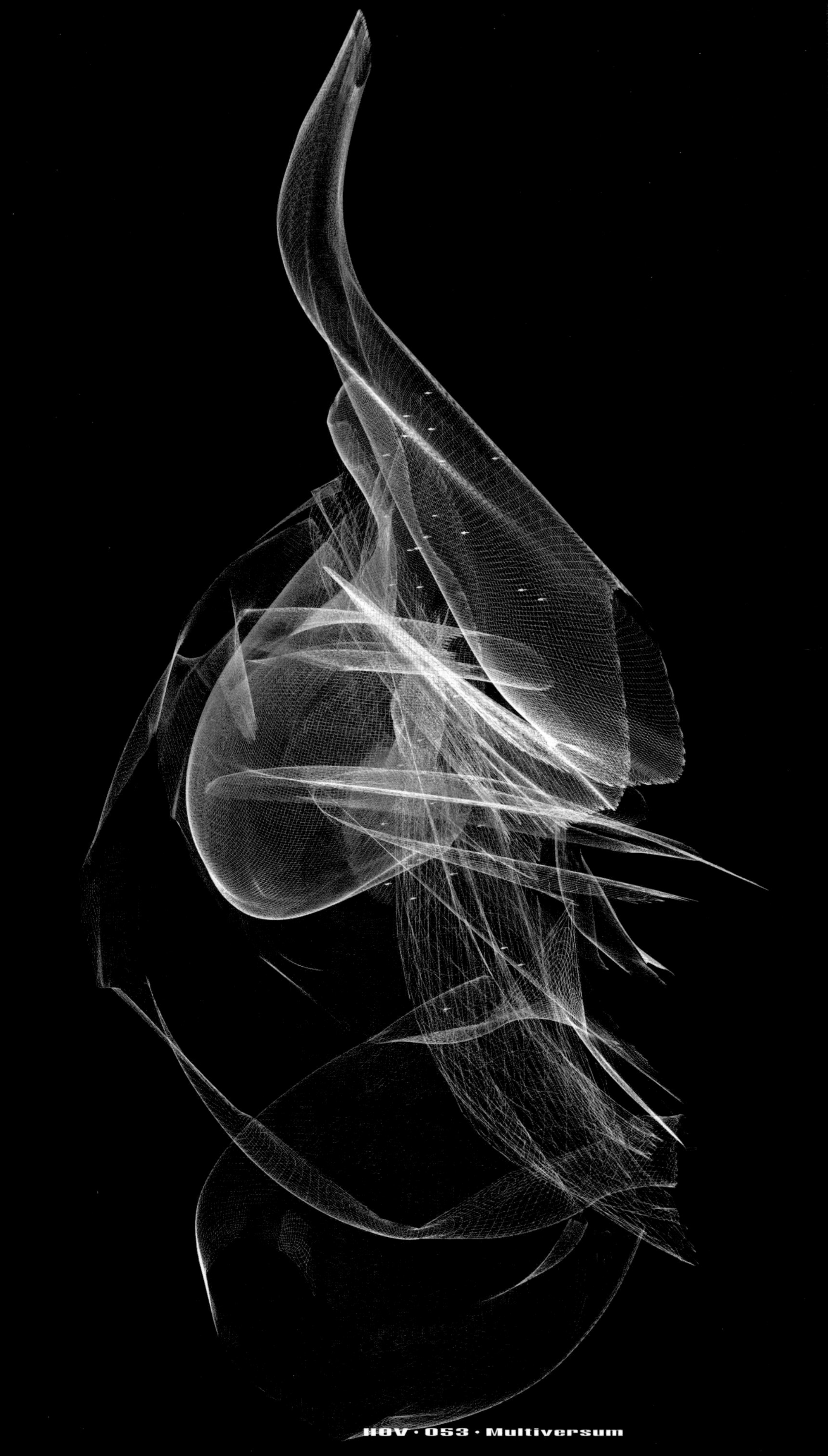

HOV · 054 · Multiversum

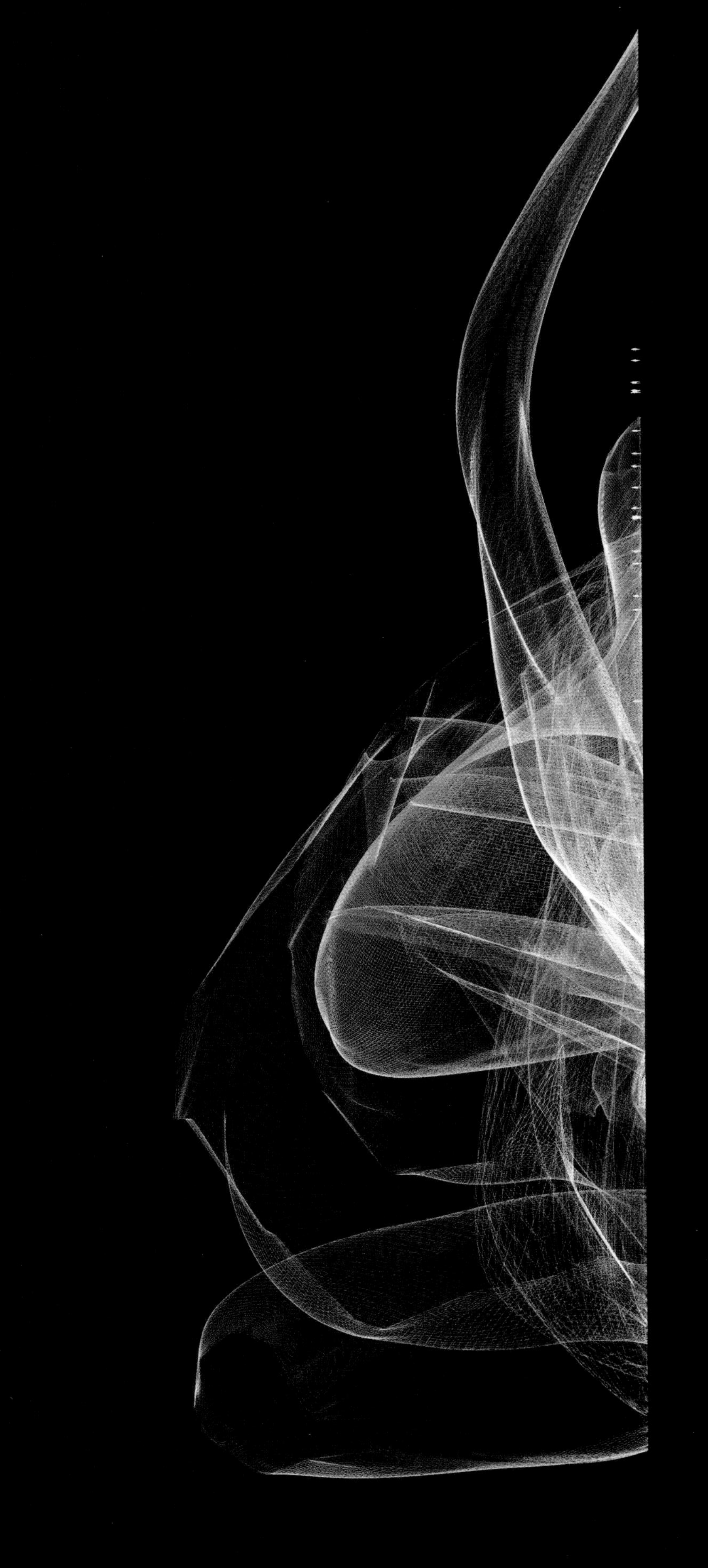

Light, star, you shine
You irradiate me with colours
I vibrate and expand within you
But the essence is in your drive
It is the way you hold the Sun
With no fear with no perplexity

To absorb it
And shed it onto me like a life powder
Onto my body
And with care,
My mind
estranged

You project onto every fold
To inundate me
Only me - always Transparent.

march 2002
Federica Bianconi

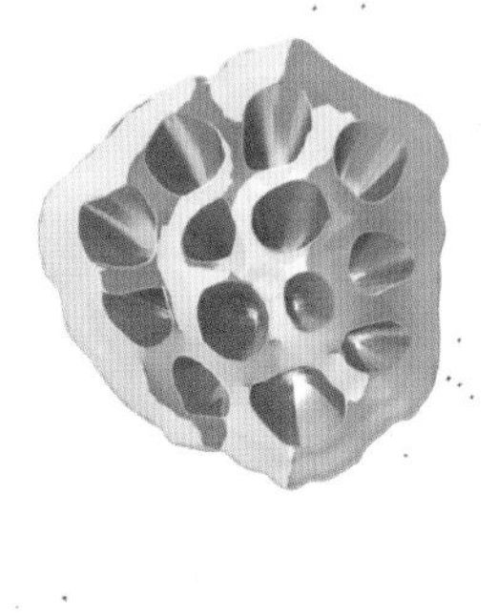

光，星星，你在闪耀
你用色彩照耀我
我在你之中摇荡扩张
但是本质在靠你驱动
这是你掌握太阳的方式
没有畏惧没有困惑

为了吸收它
像生命的尘土撒落在我身上
在我身体上
带着关爱
我的思想
疏远了

你射在了所有的折痕上
淹没了我
只有我——一直是透明的

2002年3月
Federica Bianconi

Superluoghi (Superplaces)

I am not surprised by the greater and greater presence of nuclei recognisable as homogeneous spatial ambits (specialised and auto-referential ones) where the superimposition and the interference of the activities is similar to a social micro-structure.

Even if limited to a few levels of interaction, and with a reduced outcome in terms of spatial articulation, if compared to a definite urban system, these systems potentially represent the first in a series of passages which, quite approximately, will lead to a progressive concentration into nuclei of special interest (buildings considered as "tools", structures as "instruments"), in the general setting of the social needs generated by collective motions.

The past human history showed that the advent of new resources (materials, processes, ideas) gave origin to bifurcations corresponding to new choices and consequent re-organisations. Up to the present time, the unexpected rapidity in the past and present evolution of information technology (the latest resource of all) has only partially permitted to evaluate all the positive and/or negative aspects of this model, leaving possible different paradigms open.

One of them is the emersion of collective motions, of "collective intelligences", especially in numerous social groups, with a progressive and not evident loss of the independent behaviours (not even evident for its same protagonists).

In this perspective, my personal need to have resort to abstract models on which I could experiment attitudes (or rejections) gradually produced a series of studies from which, on this special occasion, I drew "my flowers", a visual conclusion of my contribution.

"My flowers" is a high living concentration imaginary settlement developed on a phytomorphic geometry where every building, also in the overall association of the various elements, leads its own and autonomous life. A symbiotic relationship between the single human beings. The mother structure primes the unity of the colony.

An extreme vision of the above described possible paradigm.

Now, what will the future outcome be?

Will there be conformity to the collective thesis or will the system take a different way defined by diversified social nuclei with more levels of independence and autonomy?

David Raponi

Ancona, February 15th, 2007

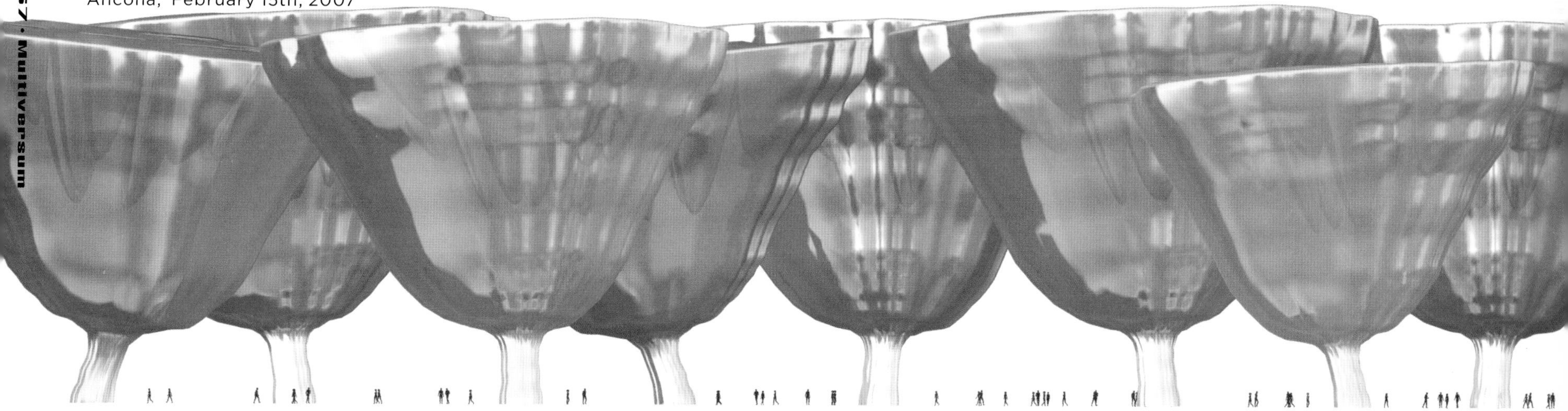

我的花朵

超级场所

我对于不断增长的核子并不感到惊讶。核子可被识别为均质的空间范围（被深入研究和自动提及的核子），这里活动的叠印和冲突与社会的微观结构非常相似。

即使被限制在一些交互作用的层面，结果的流失被看作是空间清晰度的提升，但是如果把这个系统比喻成一个确定的城市系统，那么它们就潜在地代表了一系列通道中的第一层级，大致类似的，在集体活动产生社会需求的一般环境中，它们会逐渐集中，进而成为特殊利益的核心（建筑物成为“工具”，结构成为“器具”）。

过往的人类历史告诉我们，新资源的出现（材料，方法，观念）总是起因于分歧，这些分歧有关新选择以及随后而至的重组。到现在为止，信息科技（最新的所有资源）以难以想象的速度发展，很难评价这个模式的积极和消极面，但它留下了有不同的范例的可能性。

其中之一便是集体运动和“集体智力”的出现，尤其是在众多社会组群中，独立行为有了进步的却并不明显的丧失（甚至是它同一个主角都没有很明显地丧失）。

在这个观点中，我希望对态度（或者拒绝）进行试验，我采用抽象模型的个人需求逐渐导致了一系列研究的产生。这样特殊的情况下，我画了“我的花朵”作为我贡献的一个可视的结论。

“我的花朵”是一个高度逼真虚拟的居所，由phytomorphic几何学发展得到。所有的建筑物也是多种元素的全部联合，引导了它自己和自治的生命。这是一种单个人类之间的共生关系。母结构建筑为群体的统一打下基础。

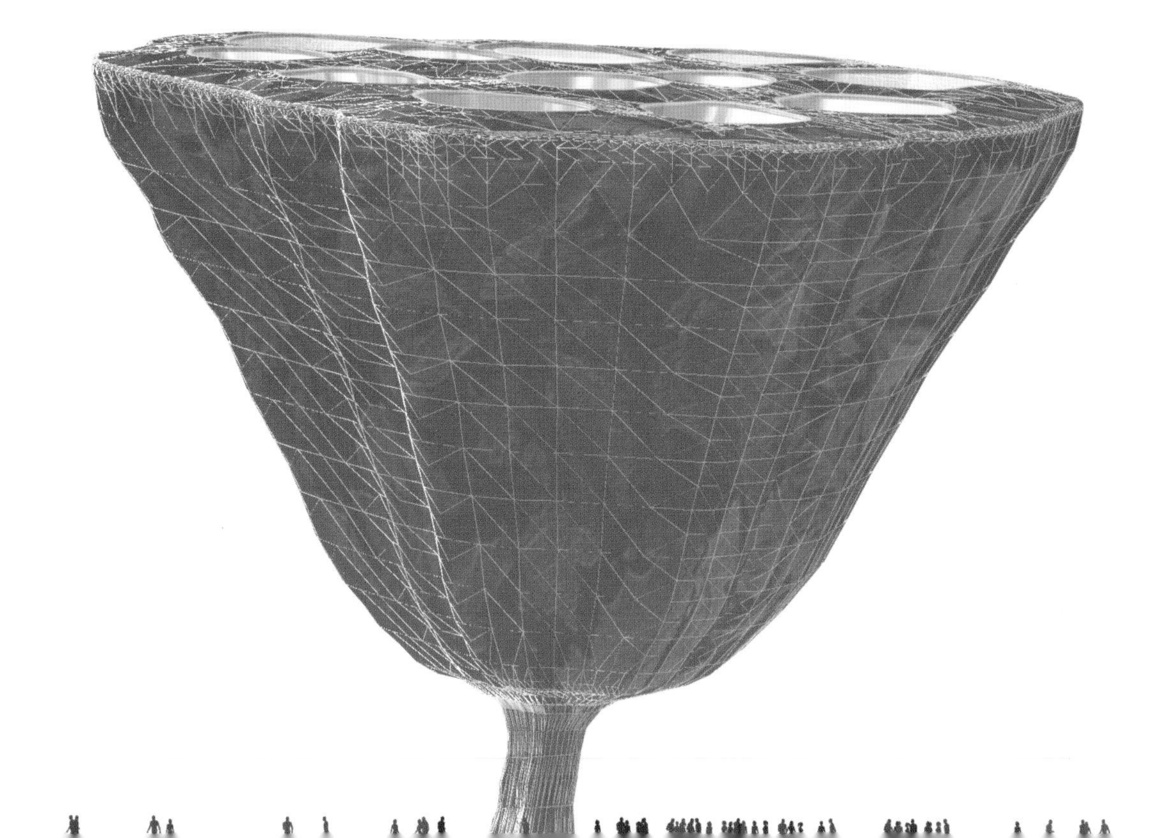

上面极端的景象描述了可能的范例。

未来的成果会是什么？

集体主题是否会一致？或者这个系统是否会有更多独立自治的等级，并由于多种变化的社会核子而走上一条不同的道路？

David Raponi

2007年2月15日

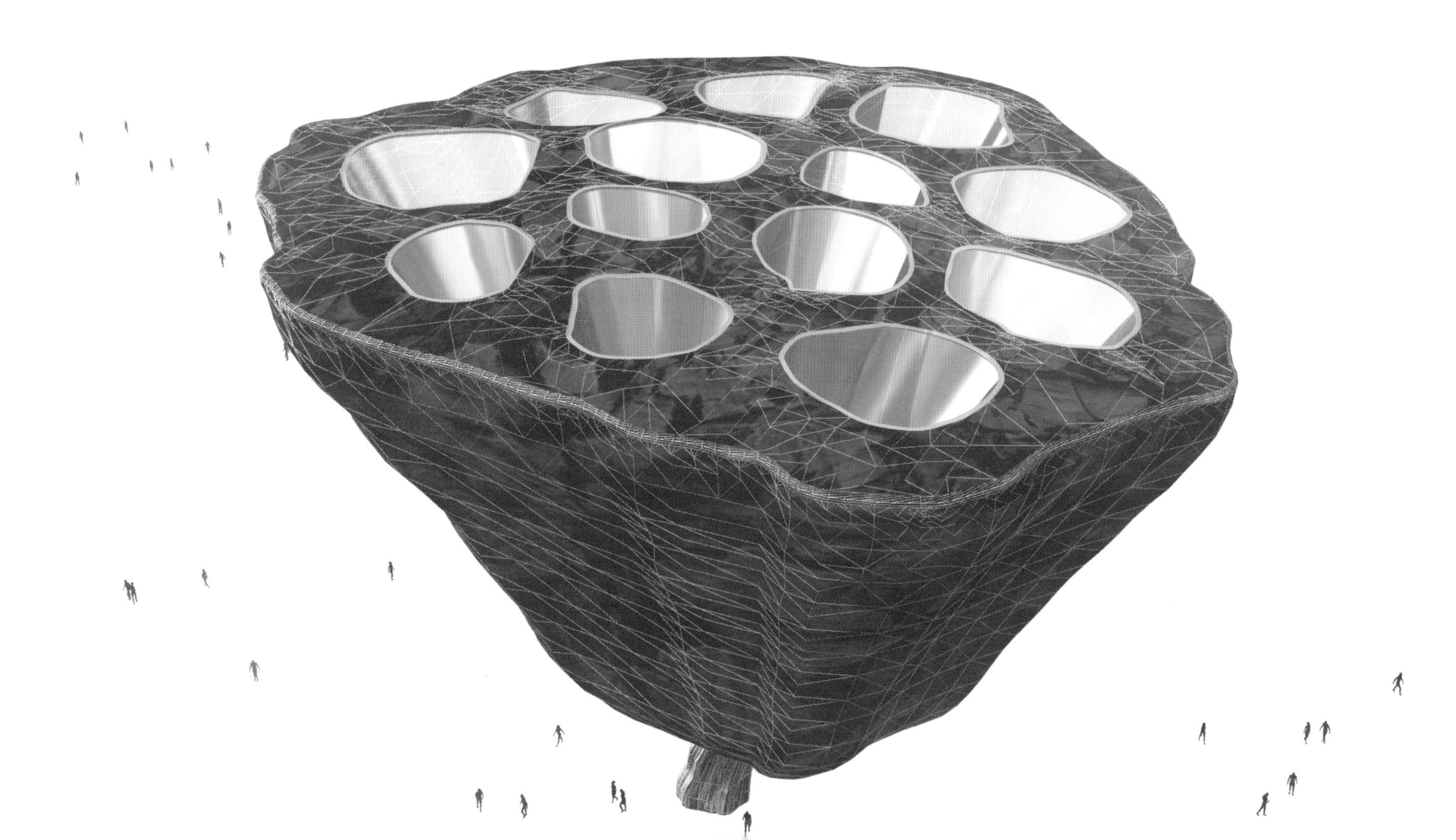

INTERVIEW WITH DAVID RAPONI

The interview with David Raponi is an excerpt from the work faq research by format-c Research Group, it was held at HOV office in Ancona in April 2004. It was then published in the volume faq 02.

<< The answers are in these projects... >>

(Filippo Forzato _format-c)
What does HOV mean?

(David Raponi_HOV)
HOV is the name of an ancient Egyptian god about which very little is known. The god was conjured up every time a decision had to be taken since it kept the emotions, the impending actuality of events and the condition of necessity away...
I liked the sound of that word and I thought it could be well whishing when I created my office. That was a bet, a courageous act. And when I started, in 1998, at the age of 33... yes - I said to myself - it's ok, the office is HOV!

HOV is in Ancona (note: central Italy, east coast - about 100,000 inhabitants), what are the main professional incentives in this city, which is a relatively small one?

In Ancona I love the contact with the sea, which just bestows a little of itself to the city, just because of the city's curious morphology. I love the algid character and the slight contrast of its light colours, I love Ancona's many secret rooms full of suggestions. The city collects intricate references in the history of the relationship between East and West, it's a border line on the sea. And moreover you can admire both dawn and sunset on the sea. There are steep cliffs, fascinating natural formations...
All this stretch of the coast represents an important part of my world.
Even if I love the word landscape, I've never made a slogan of it. I like the macroscopic elements of the environment, and the elements of the origin: water, earth, sky, big natural boundaries, and I can find them all here.

Theory and practice, the real and the virtual are based on architecture and mixed up in it, they contaminate each other and they resist to each other, they dissolve then regenerate themselves.
What are your personal considerations about your professional field?

Do you see all the tables with drawings and projects leaning on the walls of this room? The answers are in these projects...
They were born in a simple, natural way, without speculations.
One can like them or not. Many times I sat on the wrong side just because all the other seats had already been taken...
The timeless clothes, for example, were born after my sculptures - the "timeless objects" - and they were realised with mixed materials (clay, glue, resin, plaster, cement), then I called them "timeless" because I love the objects that cannot be immediately fitted in a precise time period, their collocation is uncertain, out of scale, out of place... they don't reveal their dimension.
They are clothes prepared for a remote future, thought as a sort of body armour with extended possibilities: I imagined that the cloth could establish a symbiotic relation with the body exchanging information on an organic base connection. The cloth as a personal assistant, as your confidential doctor, your adviser and your database, substituting every kind of imaginable tool.
One of these clothes has a complex geometrical matrix that is called Etruscan Venus, which is a mathematical surface thoroughly formalised only 20 years ago. Another one is a degeneration of a bottle of Klein (which is older, since it was defined in 1886), that is a non-rotary surface like Moebius' ring. And so on...
I like Geometry, Cognition Biology, Mathematics, Physics... and research spaces which, contrarily to expectations, are full of creativity and imagination. But the observer of my works is not compulsorily obliged to know the whole story...

There are people considering the phenomenon of virtualisation as a consequence of the architect's impossibility to be able to operate in a context which is hostile to the contemporary project. How do you comment on this statement?

Virtualisation is an artful issue.
I need to apply to an abstract model to experiment my attitudes (or rejections) on and this is a method shared by many disciplines.
One can observe the liberation of the strongest energies of creativity in the pureness of abstraction. Studies and researches need an experimental device pushed to the limit and that is

true for architecture as well.
The collocation of the critics, who consider me as a virtual architect, is casual. Anyway, even if all those considerations had never been made, I would have been - and I am - a pure architect.
Man thinks faster than he can create and his fast thought will bring him closer to many things that he will never be able to realize.
Those who enter the faculty of Physics can choose between a carrier in applied sciences or merely theoretical ones. Since that choice is not possible at the faculty of Architecture, I made everything by myself.

What is a critic of architecture according to HOV?

According to HOV, potentially, a good critic has got a great architecture culture, is a well-off person, who is full of interests and curiosity, who is brave and ready to recognise the talent, the hard work and the love for Architecture.
In any case, for me architecture is a less complicated thing than what critics say; I am sometimes surprised at the complexity of some abstract arguments, which are (maybe) far away from the minds of the creators whose architectures are being discussed.
Which Italian pieces of architecture do you consider as fundamental ones to visit? How would you suggest to visit and observe them?

All medieval towers that are accessible - going up till the top - preferably a little before the closing time. Abandoned and collapsing cities. The EUR district in Rome, at the beginning of a Sunday afternoon (in August), Viale Monza in Milan (on foot when it rains), Piazzale Michelangelo in Florence (for an aperitif at sunset), the second level of the lifts at Passetto in Ancona (during a windy day in winter when the sea is stormy).

Other artistic disciplines are always brought near to Architecture. Which films, books, photos do you suggest reading, seeing or watching attentively to deepen one's knowledge of architecture?

In the spirit of my personal and little aligned research, here you are some flashes.
Art: Bosch, Bacon, Giger, Giacometti.
Music: „Where there is music nothing bad can exist“ - Cervantes.
Cinema: all films with a strong creative and fantastic component (from Alien to Monsters & Co. ...)
Literature: Maturana and Varela, books about Mathematics, Physics and the History of Mathematics, the comics by Jim Meddik, Erasmus of Rotterdam, and so on...

An adjective to define the corpus of all your production...

Drastic.

Ancona - April 2004

与DAVID RAPON的访谈

与David Raponi的访谈是从format-c研究小组的FAQ研究工作中摘录下来的，2004年4月被保存在安科纳的HOV办公室内。之后以“FAQ第二辑”出版。

《答案在这些方案里面……》

(Filippo Forzato _format-c)
HOV意味着什么？

(David Raponi_ HOV)
HOV是古埃及的一个神的名字，关于他的了解很少。每次要做决定的时候，这个神就被魔法召唤出来，因为他能控制情感、事件即将发生的情况和之后必须的条件……我喜欢这个词的发音，我认为当我创造我的办公室时它会呼呼作声。这是一个打赌，是勇敢的行为。当我在1998年，33岁的时候，我告诉我自己，好的，我的办公室就是HOV。

HOV在安科纳（注：意大利中部，东海岸，居民数量大约为100,000），这个相对较小的城市中，主要激发你专业的是什么？

在安科纳，我热爱接触大海，由于城市有趣的形态学，大海能把自己给予这座城市。我热爱寒冷的特点和城市颜色轻微的对比，我热爱安科纳很多幽静的房间里充满了暗示。这座城市汇集了历史上有关东方西方关系的错综复杂的参考。它毗邻大海。此外，你可以赞美海上的日出和日落。这里有陡峭的悬崖，迷人的自然景观……海岸线的伸展描绘了我的世界中一个重要的部分。即使我热爱这个世界的景观，我永远不会为其设计一个标语。我喜欢环境的宏观元素和原始元素：水、土地、天空、巨大的自然边界，在这里我都能找到。

理论与实践，真实和虚拟都在建筑学的基础上，并且相互融合，它们相互浸染、相互抵触，它们溶解之后又再生。关于你的专业领域，你个人的考虑是什么？

你看见桌子上的图和墙上靠着的方案吗？答案在方案之中……它们从简单、自然的方式中来，没有做作。一个人可以喜欢它们也可以不喜欢它们。很多时候，我坐在了错误的一边，仅仅因为其他椅子都已经有人了……举例来说，永恒的服装是从我的雕塑中诞生的——“永恒的物体”，它们使用混合材料制作的（粘土、胶水、树脂、石膏、水泥），我将其称为“永恒”，因为我热爱不能够立即确定准确时间阶段的东西，它们的排列不确定，不合规定比例，不在适当位置……它们不展现自己的尺度。
它们是为遥远未来所准备的服装，被认为是一种有扩大用途的身体盔甲：我想象这些衣服通过与有机基质联系交换信息，与身体实现共生关系。衣服作为一个私人助理，作为你的秘密医生、你的顾问，是你的数据库，取代所有想象工具。
这些衣服有了非常复杂的几何学基质，叫做伊特鲁里亚的维纳斯，是在20年前已经彻底形式化的精确外表。另一个是克莱因瓶的降解（这个年代更加久远，在1886年就被定义），这是一个像莫比乌斯环一样不能旋转的外表。还有许多……
我喜欢几何学、宏观生物学、数学、物理以及探索那些与期望不同，充满了创造和想象的空间。但是我工作的观察者并没有被强迫了解整个故事……

有一些人认为虚拟化现象是一种建筑师不能根据文脉设计建筑而造成的结果，这是一种对当代设计方法的敌意。你怎么评论这种观点？

虚拟化是一种巧妙实现目的的方法。我需要构建一个抽象的模型检验我的看法（或是推翻我的想法），这是很多学科采用的方法。在纯粹的抽象中，一个人能够观察到创造力释放出最强大的能量。探索研究需要试验仪器推动到极限，对于建筑学也是一样的。这些批评家认为我是一个虚拟的建筑师，这是很随意地。不管怎样，即使没有这些批评，我也会是并且确实是一个纯粹的建筑师。人们的想象比创造速度快，快速的想象能够使他更接近很多事物，这个他永远不会意识到。物理学专业的人可以选择做实践家还是理论家。这种选择在建筑学中是不可能的，所以我自己做所有事情。

根据HOV的观点，建筑学的批评家应该是怎样的？
根据HOV的观点，一个好的批评家要有很广泛的建筑文化，是一个走运的人，充满了兴趣和好奇心，是勇敢的拥有天赋和勤奋，并对建筑学热爱的人。在任何情况下，对于我来说建筑学并不是一般批评家所说的那么复杂的事；我有时会惊讶于一些抽象辩论的复杂性，可能距离被讨论的建筑学创造很远。

你认为哪些意大利建筑是最值得游览的？你建议如何游览参观它们？

所有可以参观的中世纪塔，走到顶端，最适宜的时间是在塔关闭之前。还有就是被遗弃和损害的城市，罗马EUR区域，最佳时间是八月一个星期天下午的开始，米兰的Viale Monza（如果下雨最好步行），佛罗伦萨的米开朗基罗广场（作为日落的开胃酒），安科纳Passetto的第二级高地（冬天当大海有暴风时）。

其他艺术学科总是与建筑学十分接近。你建议留意阅读、观看哪些电影、书籍、照片，让人们加深建筑学知识？

根据我个人没有什么条理的研究而言，可以给你这些小建议。
艺术：希罗尼穆斯·博斯，培根，Giger，贾柯梅蒂。
音乐：……只要有音乐就不会存在不好的东西……赛凡提斯。
电影院：所有具有强大创造力和幻想成分的电影（从《异形》到《怪物公司》.……）
文学：马图拉纳和巴雷拉，关于数学、物理、数学历史的书，Jim Meddik的戏剧，鹿特丹的伊拉兹马斯等等……
用一个形容词定义所有你作品的集合……
猛烈的。

Ancona – 2004年4月

HOUSE

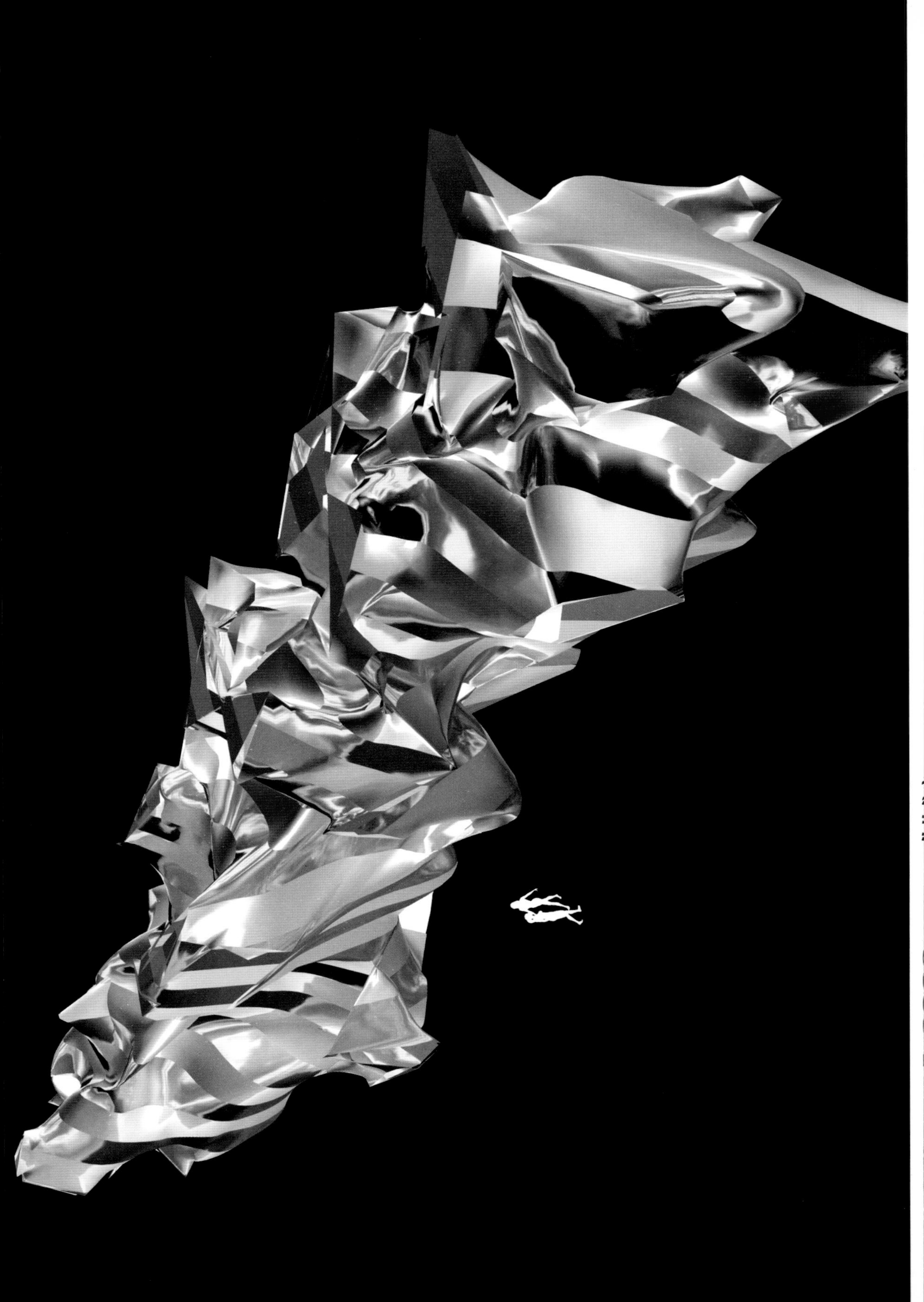

Block house is the product of one of the several studies in progress aiming at a possible living out of usual models. This house/refuge receives light from above through un-occluded folds. From outside it seems a metallic film for food conservation, hence its name.

Topologically it takes its origin, around the life spaces in sequence, from a degeneration and a disturb of a compact prismatic geometry. Technically the covering allows a thermal balance and an exact control of all the parameters of the house.

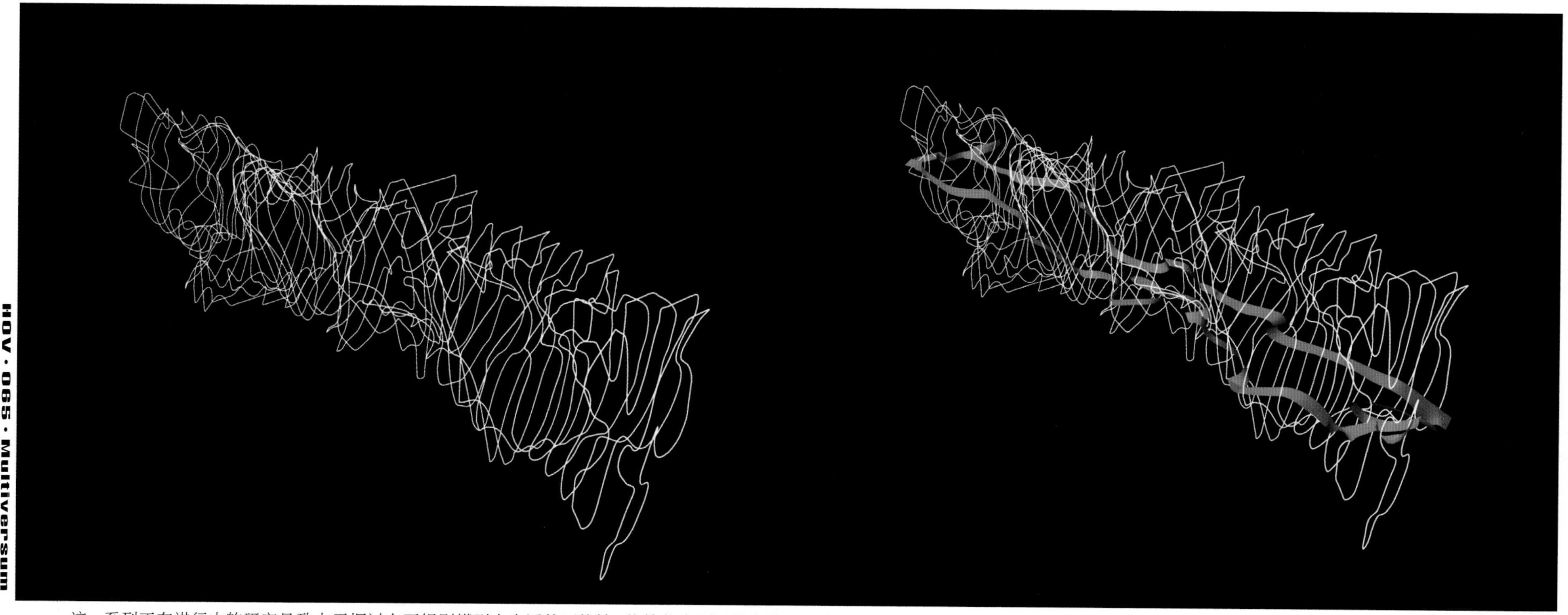

这一系列正在进行中的研究是致力于探讨在不规则模型中生活的可能性，体块住宅则是其中的一项成果。这个房屋/庇护所通过上面的无遮蔽的围栏采光。它外观看上去像储存食物的金属薄膜，由此得名。

它的原型来自拓扑学，在生活空间周围，依次打破一个紧密的棱镜几何体。技术方面，这层表皮使得房屋的热量达到平衡，并可以给房屋的所有参数进行精确的控制。

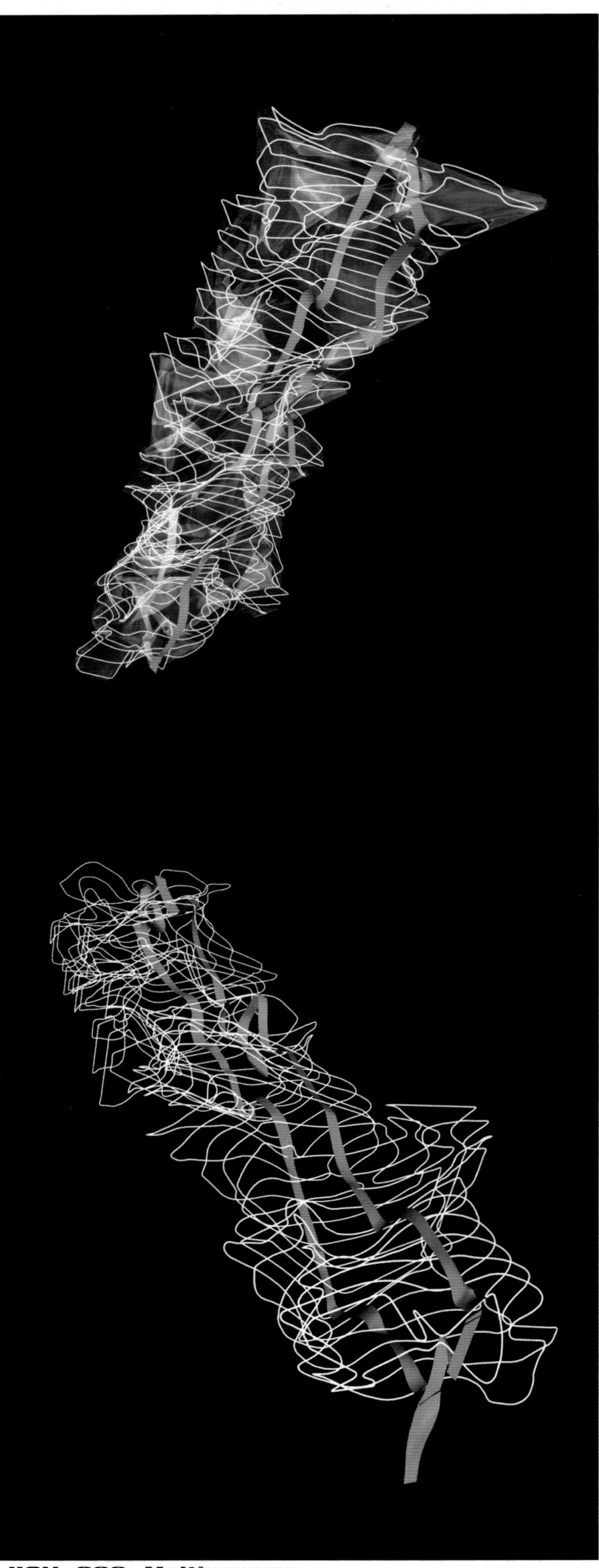

studio
entry
utility
wc
stairs
living room
library
dining room
kitchen
master bedroom
bedroom
bath room
wc

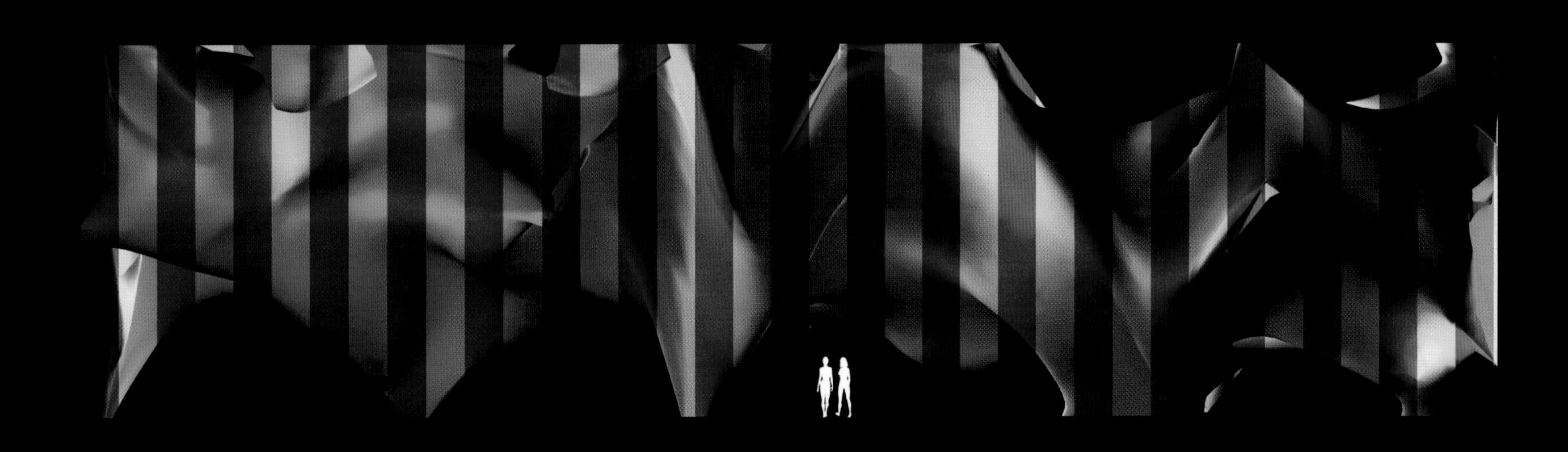

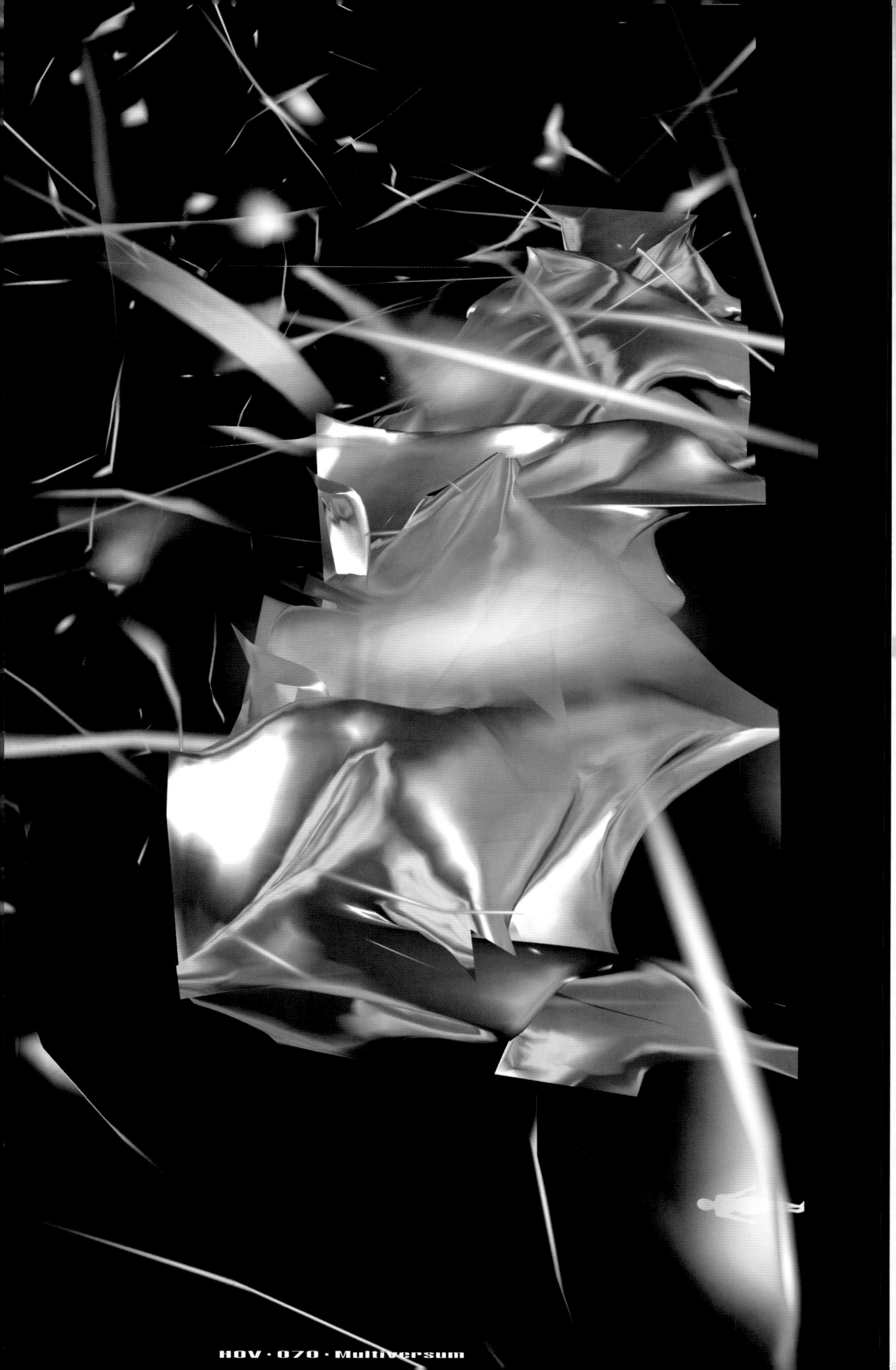

HOV · 072 · Multiversum

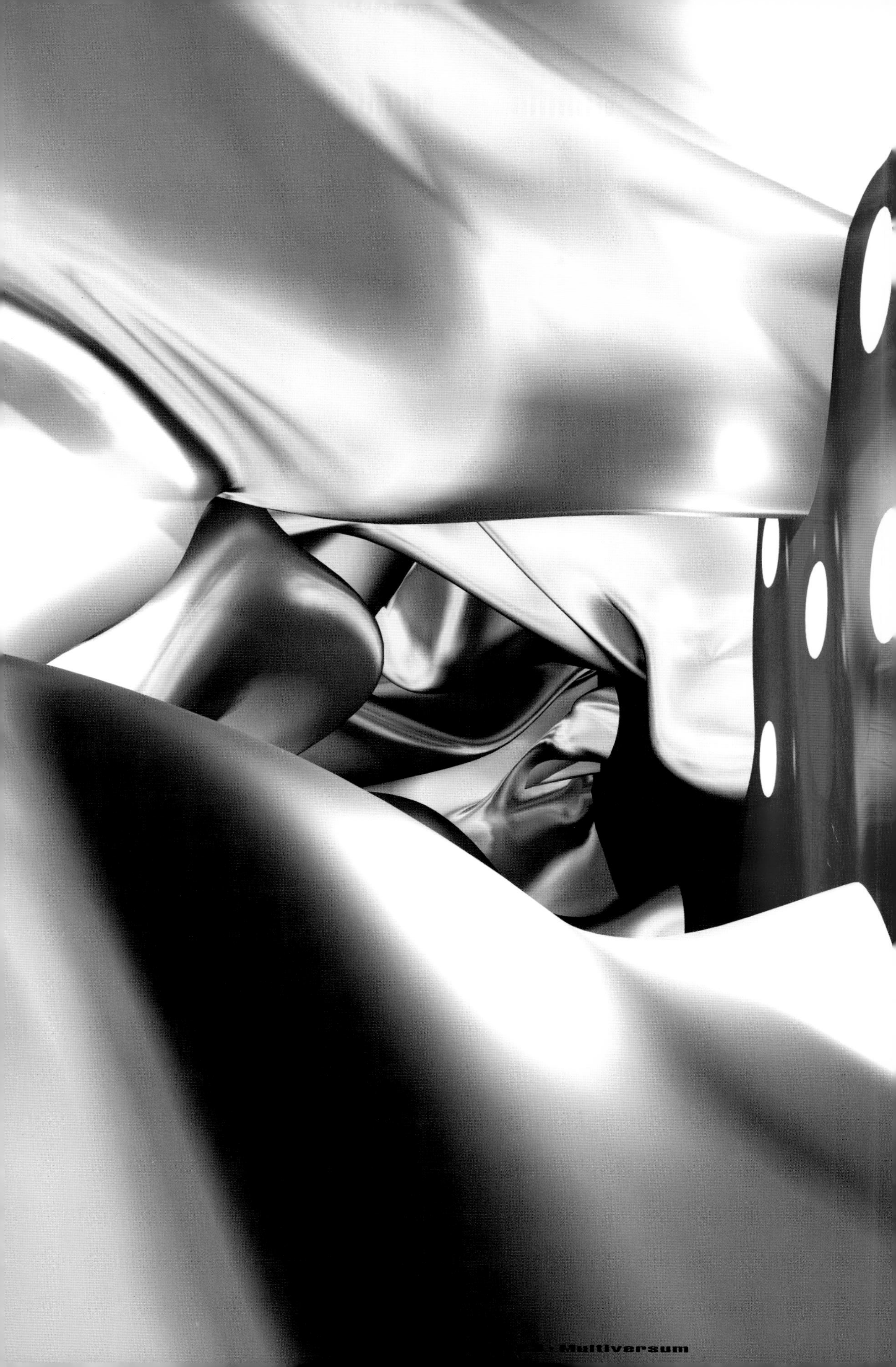

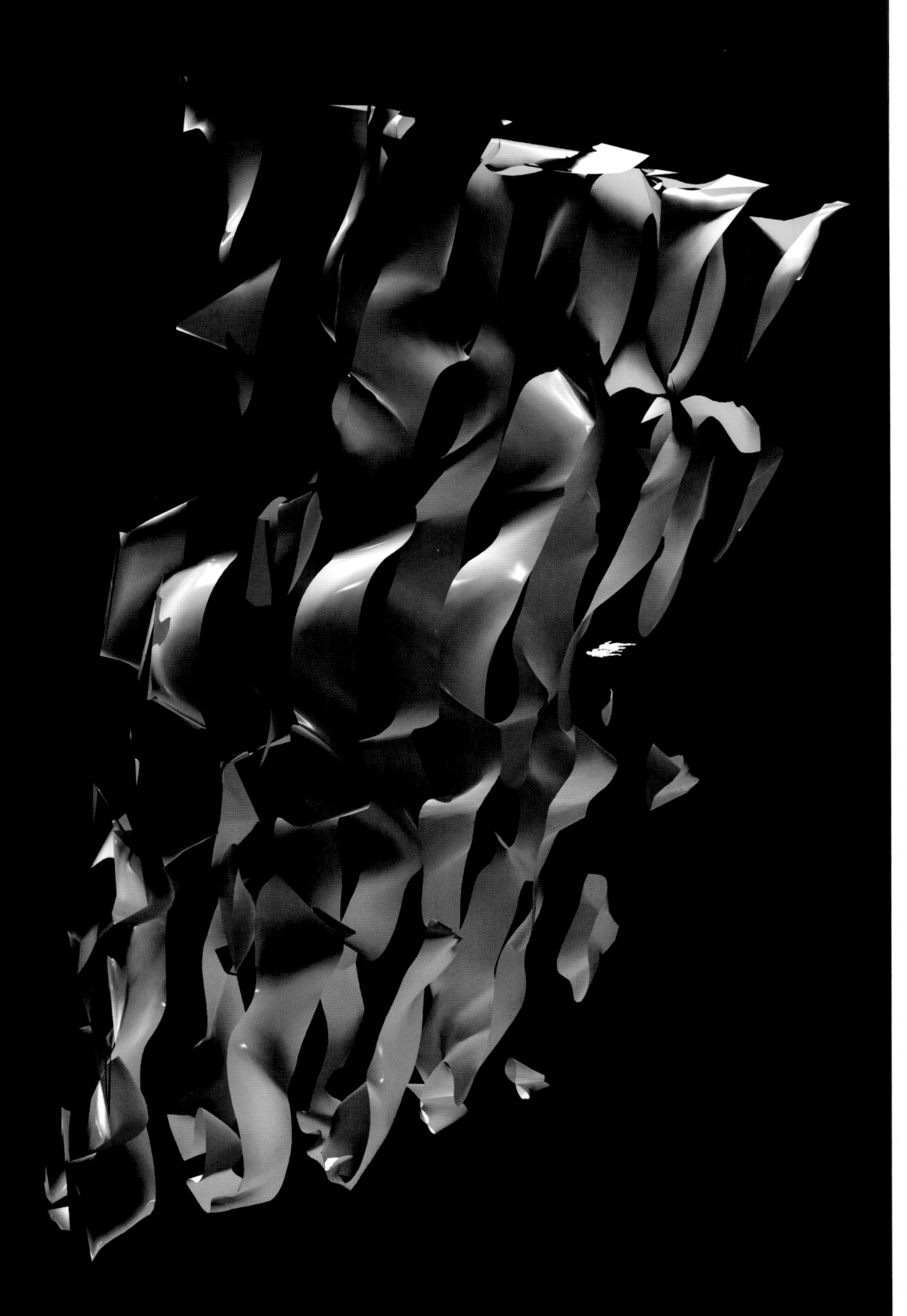

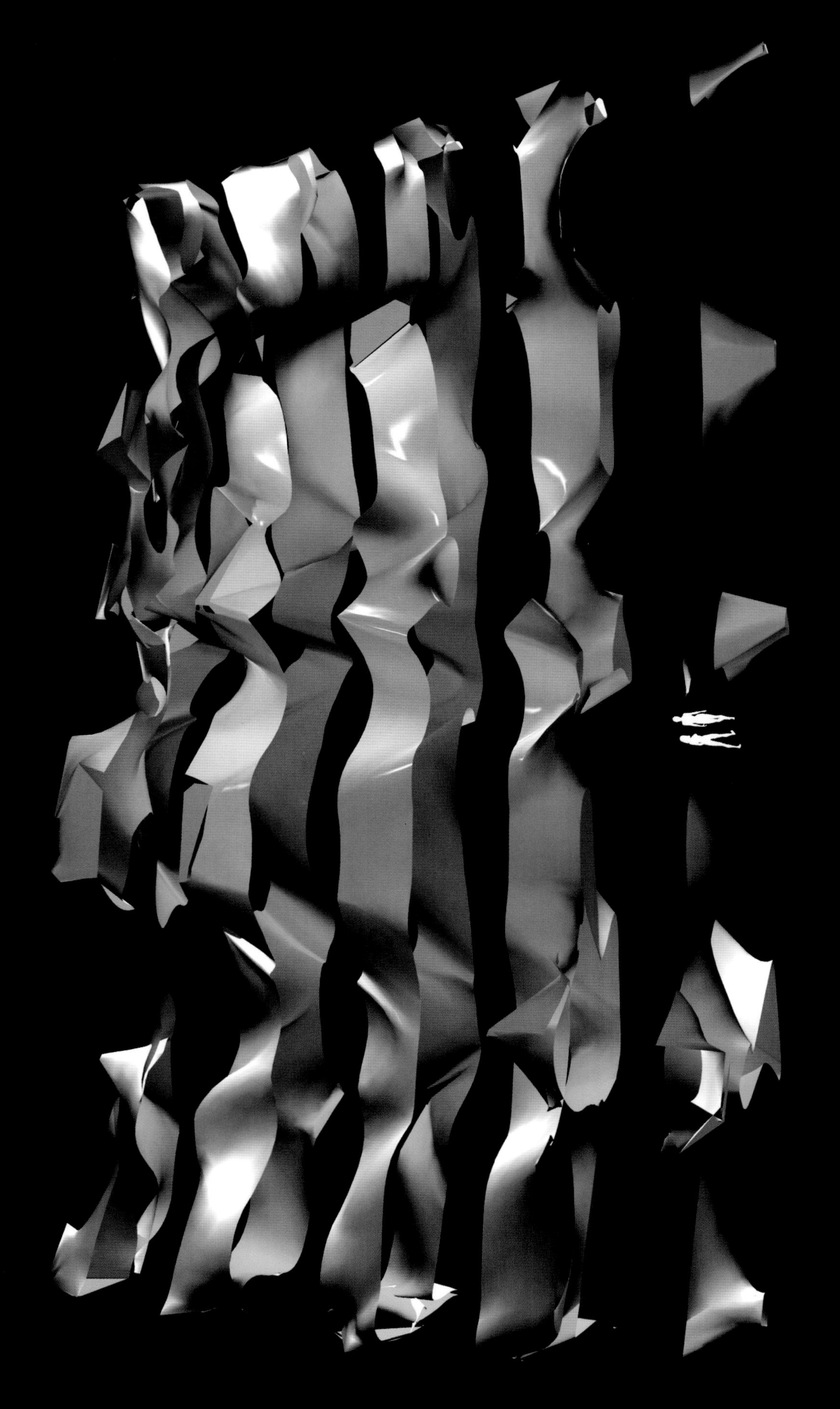

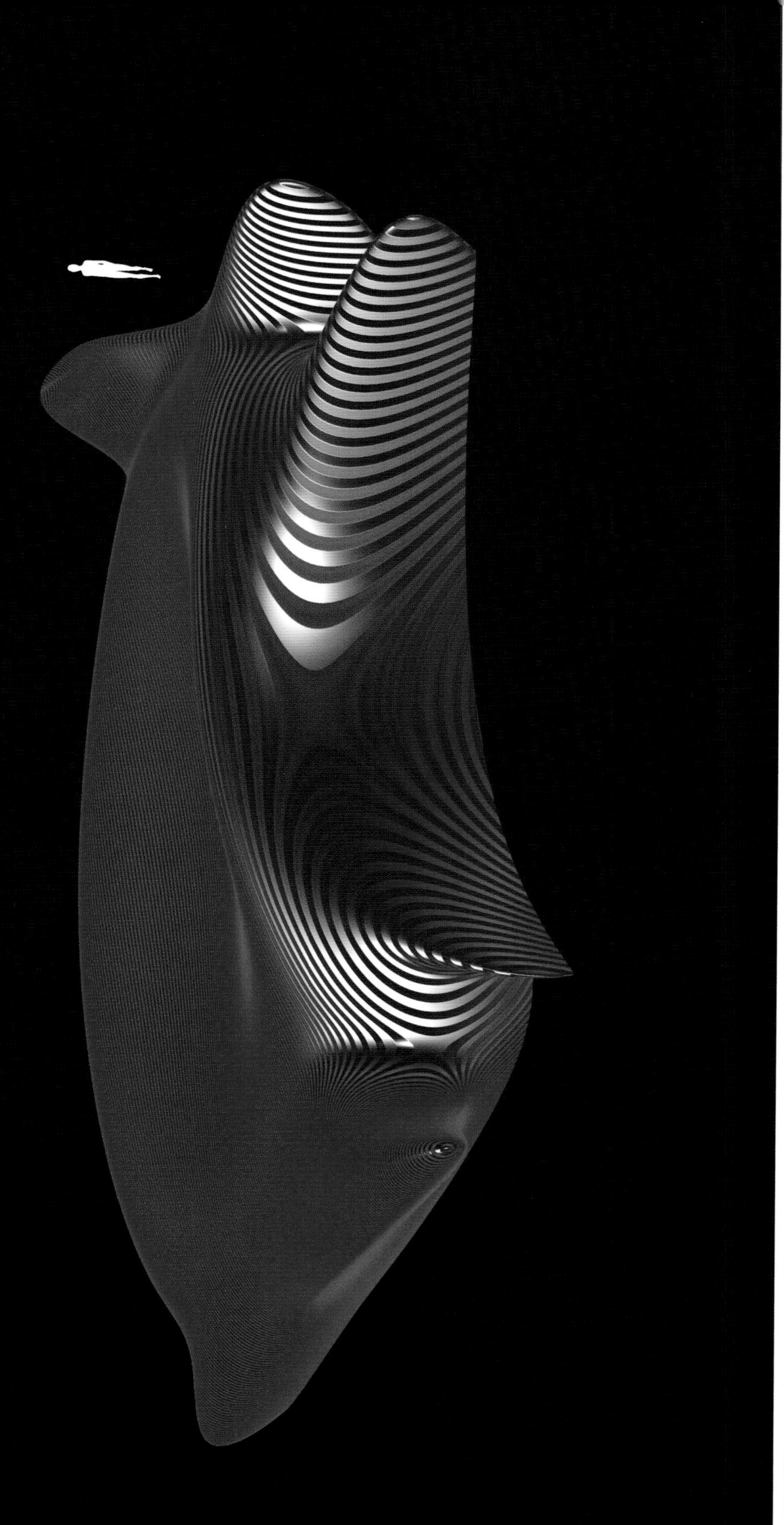

HOV · 076 · Multiversum

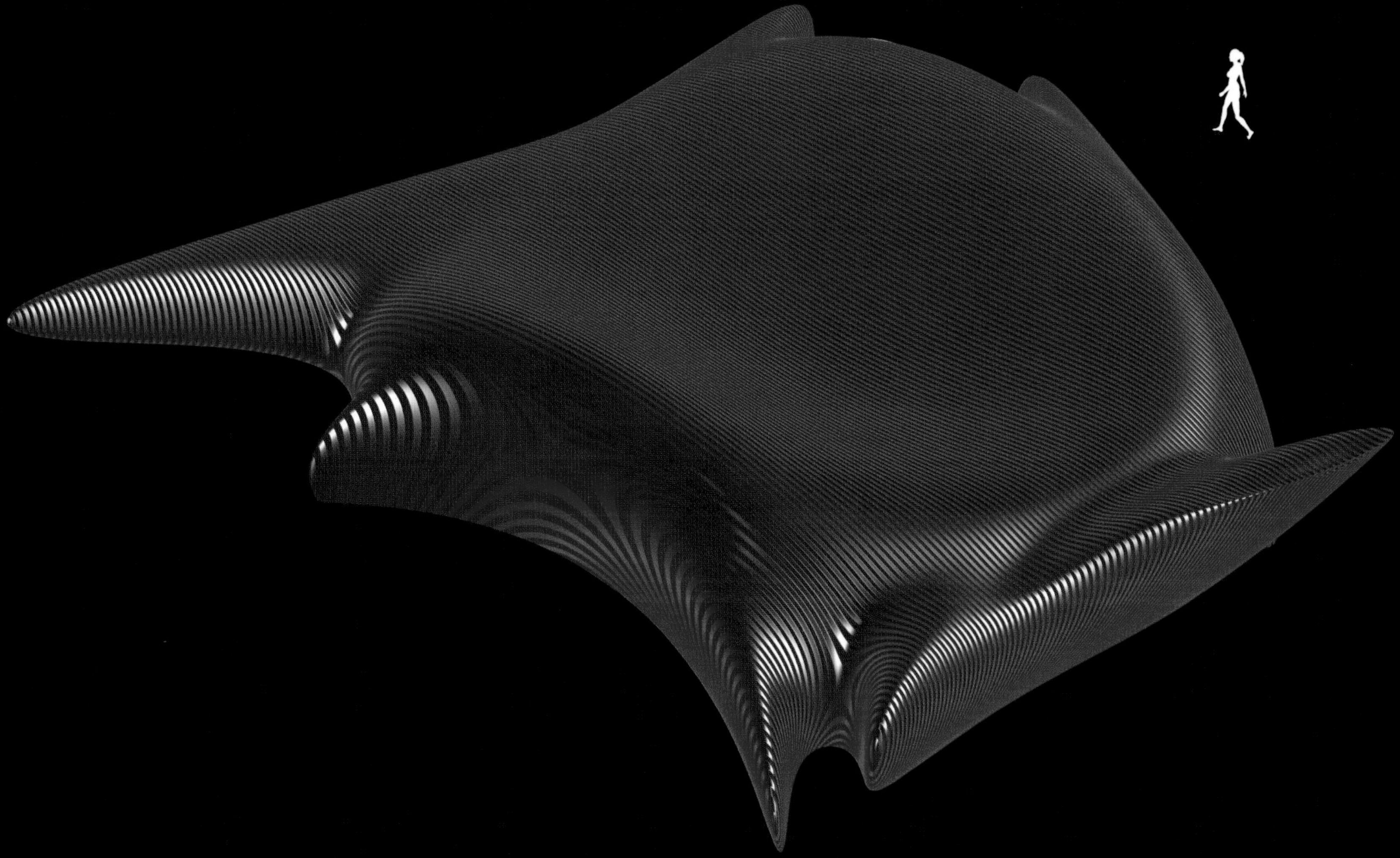

Pillow House represents a study about a residence with a radial distribution of the internal spaces following the archaic models which can still be found with some rural populations spread from the Equatorial Africa till the Amazonian area of the South American continent.
The central reference point, which is principally dedicated to an open-pit fireplace there, has been here associated to the collection and the first processing of meteoric waters, just summing up their two valences - usefulness and symbolism - within the same space.
The whole space has got variable conformations and the number of inhabitants is not pre-determined. Following the different cases in fact the internal space can receive one to about twelve people. The structure is made of a deformable thin section support net in composite material and of a double elastic layer of synthetic film: the outside is characterized by photovoltaic cells which are sufficient for the energetic needs of the minimal support equipments, the inside is made of transpiring fabric with strong thermal conservation capacity.
The two openings (entrance and central light) can be locked with two removable elements.
The external surface can be selected time by time according to the external environmental conditions and to the installation place.

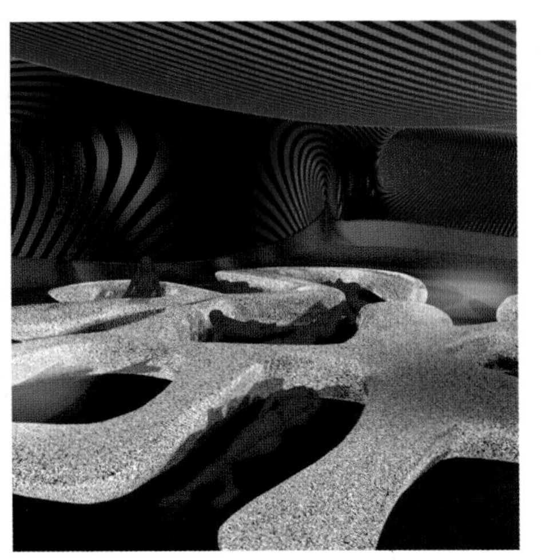

枕头房屋代表着一项关于居住室内空间呈发射性分布的研究，这种空间分布来自一种古老的模型，从近赤道的非洲地区到南美洲的亚马逊地区，现在我们仍然可以在这些农村人口中找到相应例子。
中心的控制点主要是提供了一个外露的壁炉，这里它也同雨水的收集与第一道处理联系在一起，这在一个空间体现了两个优点——实用性与象征意义。
整个空间包含了各种不同的构造，居住的人数也不是预先确定的。事实上，根据不同的情况，室内空间可以容纳一到十二个人。该结构包含两种材料，一是复合材料制成的薄断面可变支撑网，二是弹性双层人造薄膜——外层分布着光电池，足以满足设备的最小能耗需求，内层则由高热容可透气织物组成。
两个开口——入口和中央采光——可以用两个可移动的元素锁上。
外表皮可以根据外部环境条件和装置的位置进行选择。

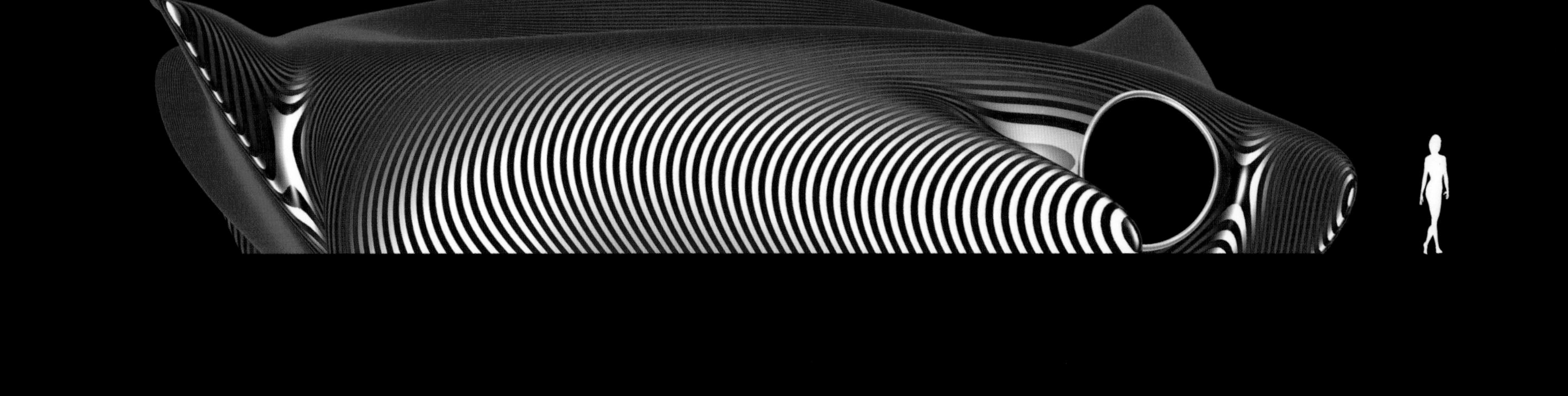

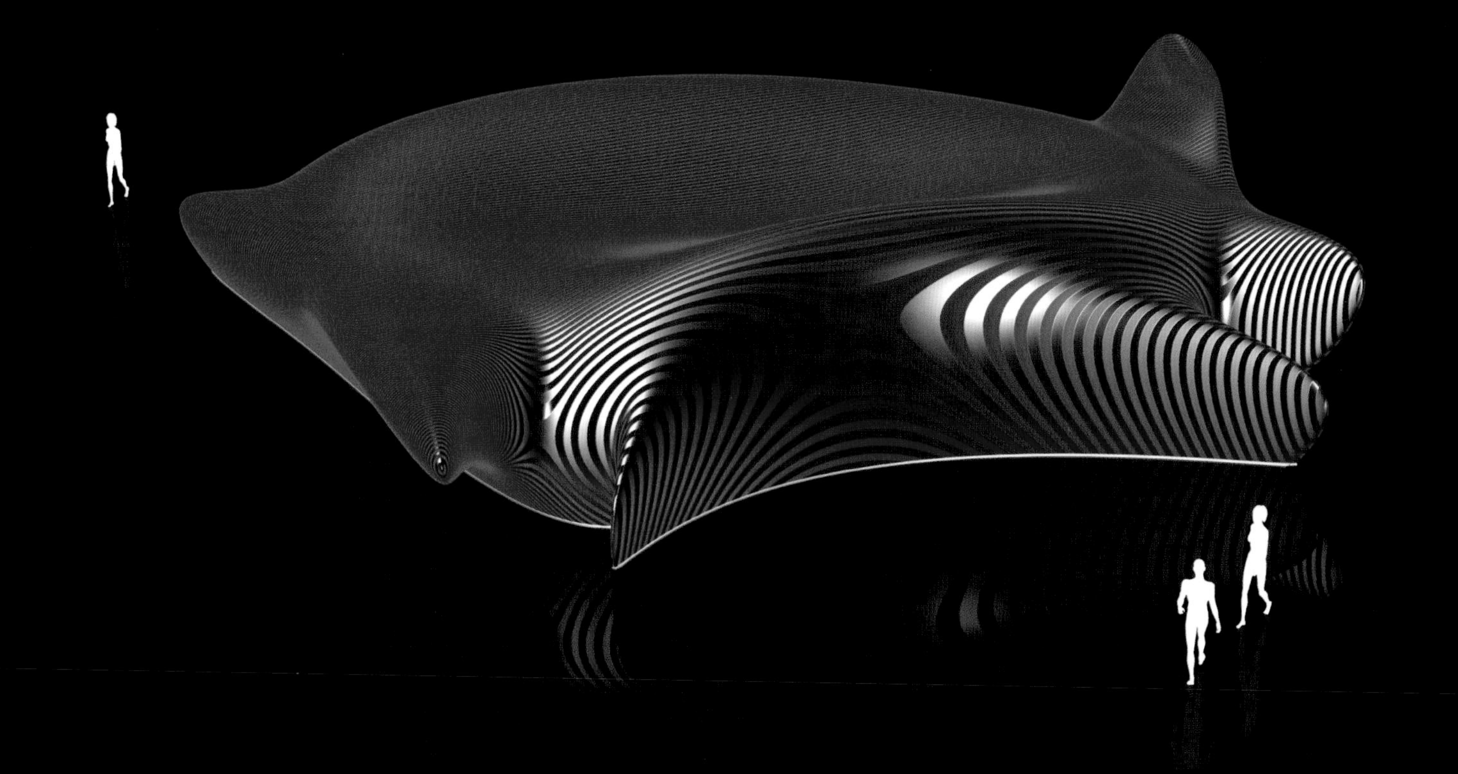

HOV · 081 · Multiver-sum

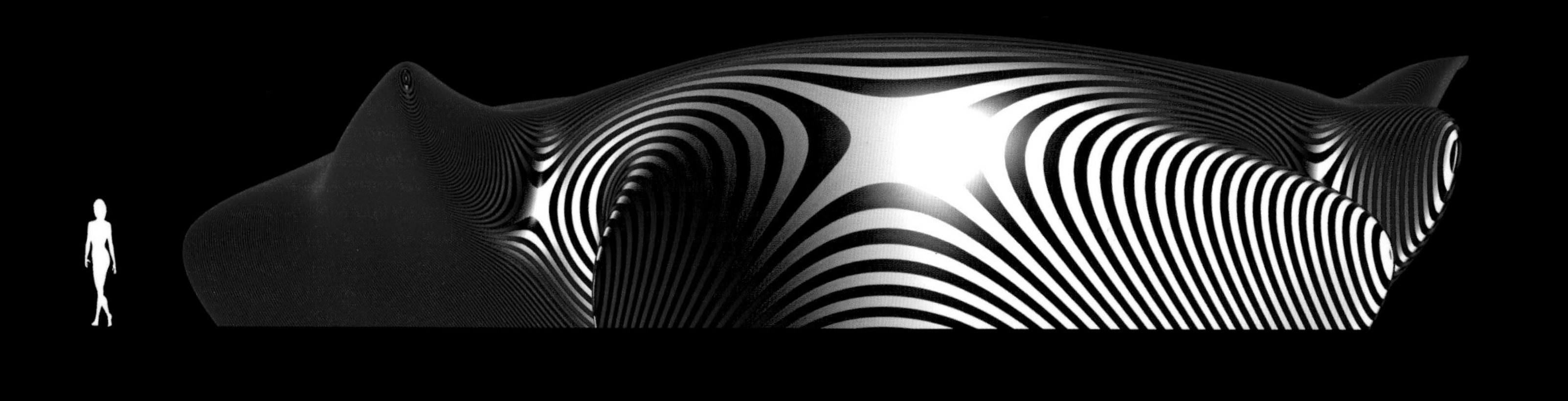

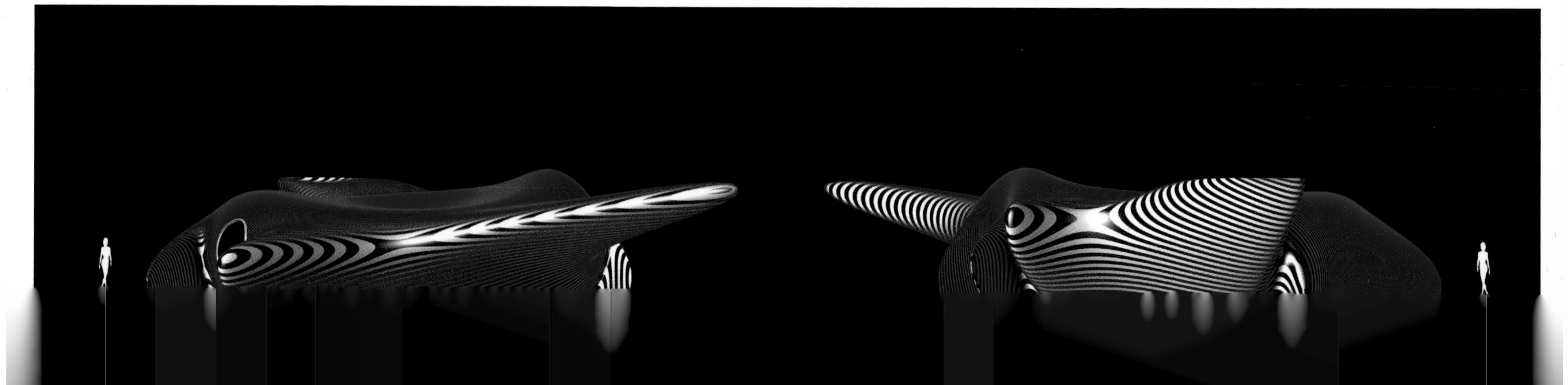

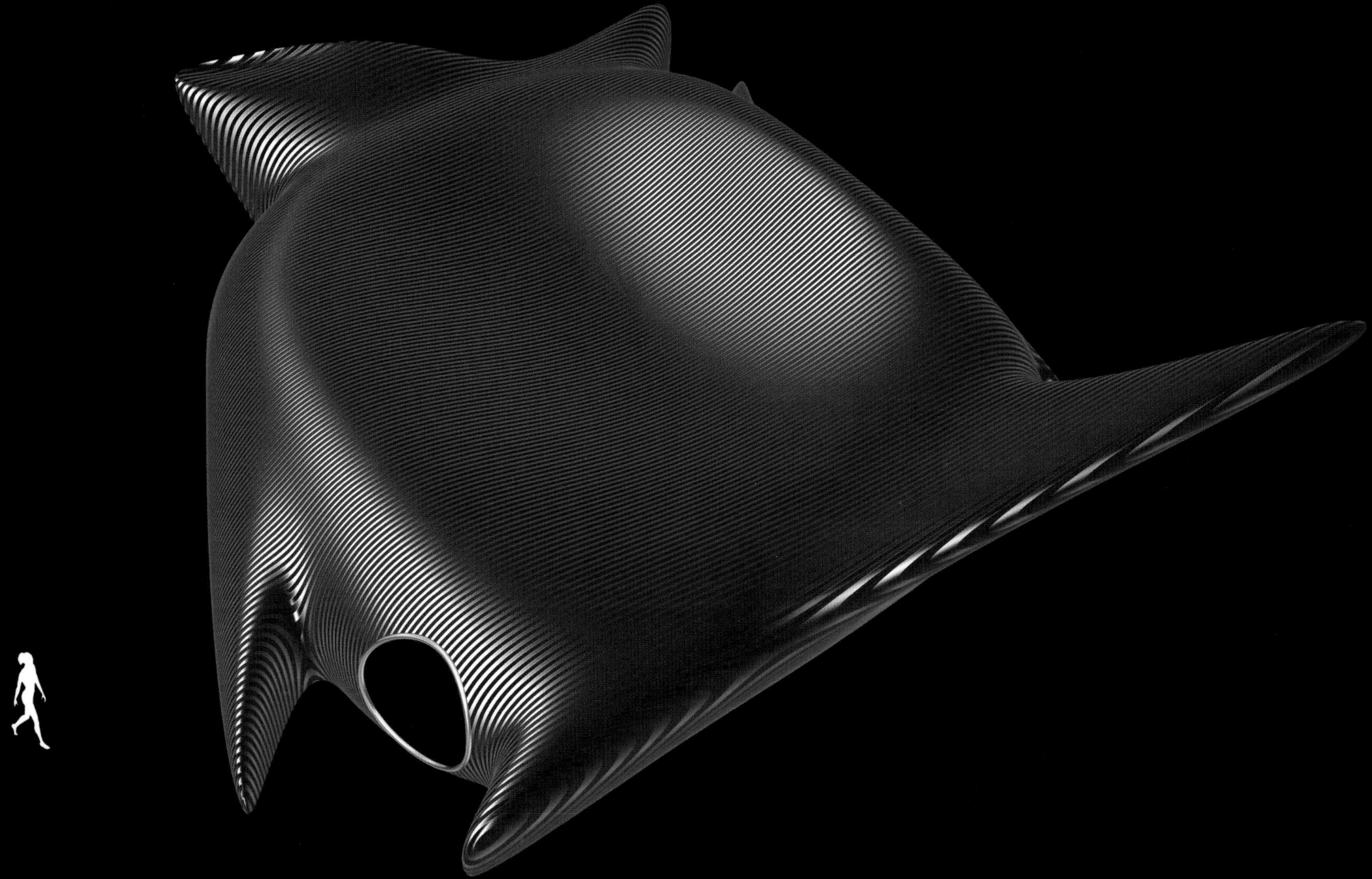

BUILDINGS

2000

"Turm für Giger"

"Turm für Giger" è un omaggio personale al grande artista svizzero H.R.Giger, creatore di straordinari paesaggi e di incredibili biomeccanoidi.

La struttura deriva da una serie di studi sviluppati per insediamenti simbolici, come le grandi costruzioni dell'antichità, dove lo spazio effettivamente disponibile è di entità trascurabile (qui circa il 2% del totale) al confronto delle dimensioni della costruzione, ed è rappresentato da un nucleo collocato nella lama discendente al centro della costruzione.

L'immagine è stata inviata all'artista il 5 febbraio 2000, in occasione del suo sessantesimo compleanno.

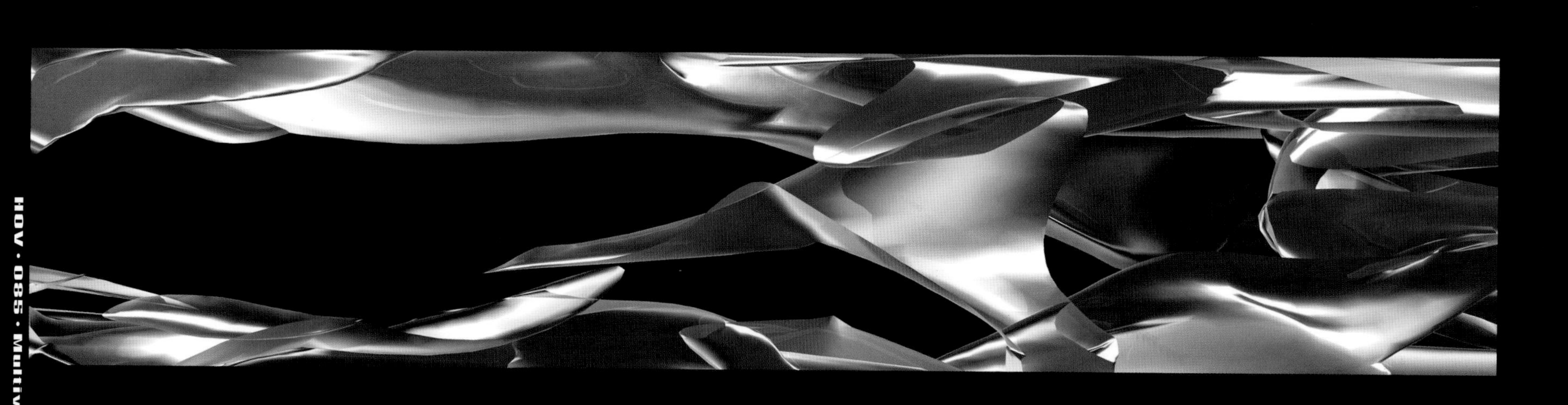

"Turm für Giger"表达了个人对瑞士艺术家H.R.Giger的敬意，他曾经设计了出色的景观和生物装置。

这个建筑来自一系列对于艺术家作品的研究，并具有象征意义地继承了它们的精神。就像伟大的古迹建筑，在那里可以到达的空间这里和整个建筑尺度比只是可以忽略的实体（大约是整体的2%），而且它被表现为处于萌芽的建筑中心的衍化物。

这幅图像已经于2000年2月5日，艺术家60岁生日的时候寄送到了他那里。

2001

NYC Tower

It is the project of a thin tower, especially meant for New York, its ideal location.
After 11th September, more than ever. In spite of its unconventional concepts of space and surface, the tower can be used as a normal building. it is also characterised by a deeply impressive force. Unlike most other celebrating monuments, sort of compensation for feelings of guilt, this tower and its aesthetics aim at reproducing the catastrophe as it really was, and still is, without any adjunctive grace.

2001

纽约塔

这是一座纤薄的塔，它的理想场所是911后的纽约。虽然这座塔的空间和表皮都是非常规的概念，但是它仍可以作为一个普通建筑进行使用。不同于大多数庆祝式的纪念建筑物，它们多少带有对愧疚感的补偿，而纽约塔和它的美学意义都致力于再现那场灾难的真正本来面目，不添加任何借口。

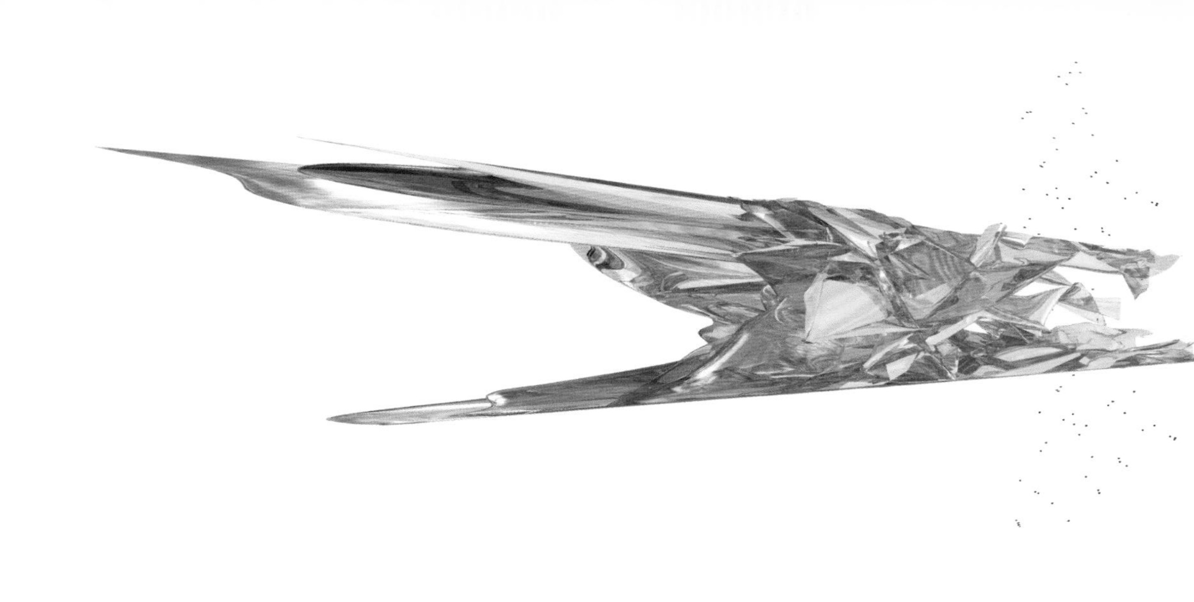

2002

Sea Tower

It stands for the big splinter of an unknown material coming from the past man will find in some millions years. Seized while emerging, it is now completely invisible. This sequence describes the transformation of the surrounding landscape during the millenniums since it first reveals itself.

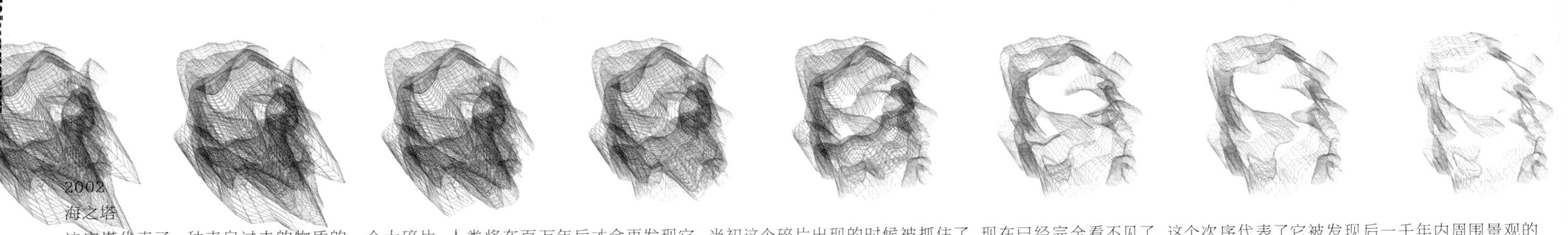

2002

海之塔

这座塔代表了一种来自过去的物质的一个大碎片，人类将在百万年后才会再发现它。当初这个碎片出现的时候被抓住了，现在已经完全看不见了。这个次序代表了它被发现后一千年内周围景观的变化。

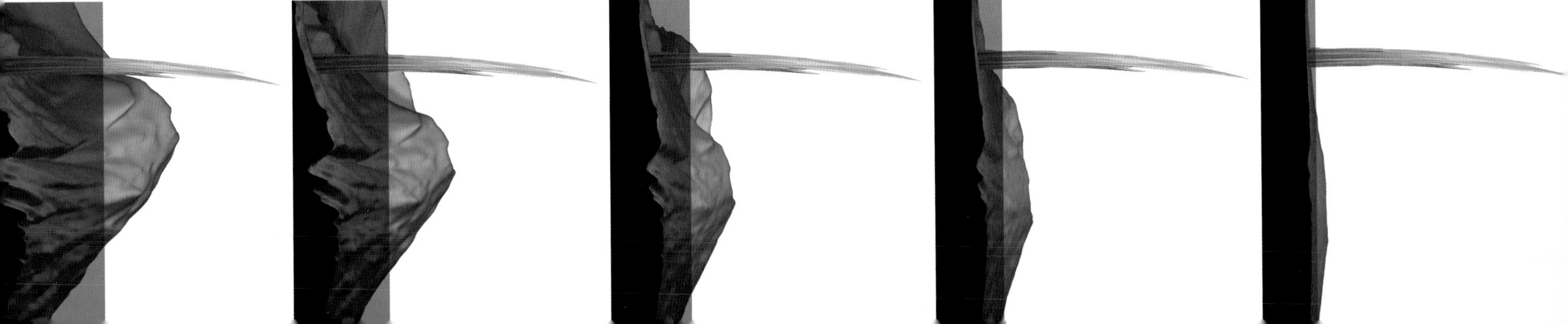

2003

HOV Tower

La torre di HOV è una costruzione immaginaria che è dedicata allo studio – il cui nome è ispirato a quello di una antica divinità egizia – al solo scopo di continuare la consuetudine che associa un nome o uno slogan (soprattutto per le torri) ad ogni progetto.

Non è certo una tentazione alla presunzione, semmai il riconoscimento, dopo molte dediche, all'icona ispiratrice dello studio.

Il suo profilo ha un richiamo drammatico che sembra incutere timore ed un senso oscuro di mistero. Sensazioni spesso presenti nell'indole dell'uomo e del progettista fondatore di HOV che, forse in base a tale analogia, lo ha voluto richiamare.

HOV塔

HOV塔是一座正在考虑中的想象的建筑物，它的名字灵感来自于古埃及一名神灵egizia，它延续了在把统一的口号联系到所有方案所有里去的传统，首先所有的塔就是这样。

它的外形有一种戏剧化的号召力，仿佛能激起恐惧和黑暗的神秘感。这通常是人类与HOV设计者的本性中的一种情感，这样来推断的话，也许这座建筑是有意激发这些情感的。

2002

Reggio Tower (or Suicide Tower)

A reinforced concrete skeleton seized while travelling by train through Reggio Calabria suburbs; the raising of metal nets to prevent suicides in a panoramic building in my hometown: these are the suggestions of a project that images an odd and rough change of the conventional social model for the deserted and isolated structure along the hill slope. As any dates and information are missing, I just relied on the recollection of what I had seen. The smelting of aluminium industrial refuse, along with the low quality of the concrete previously used, gives the structure its new figure.

2002

HOV塔

如果坐火车旅游穿过勒佐卡拉布里亚郊区，那可以看见一个钢筋混凝土的骨架。骨架上拉起了金属网，为了防止在我们家乡的这个全景式建筑发生自杀事件。这个原本孤零零地被遗弃在山坡上的结构，经由一个项目的建议改造，如今粗略地描绘着传统社会模型的变化。因为所有的时间以及相关信息都已经遗失，我只是靠我以前的所见来回忆。铝工业废料的熔化物加上先前用的低质量混凝土，它们赋予了这个结构一个新的形象。

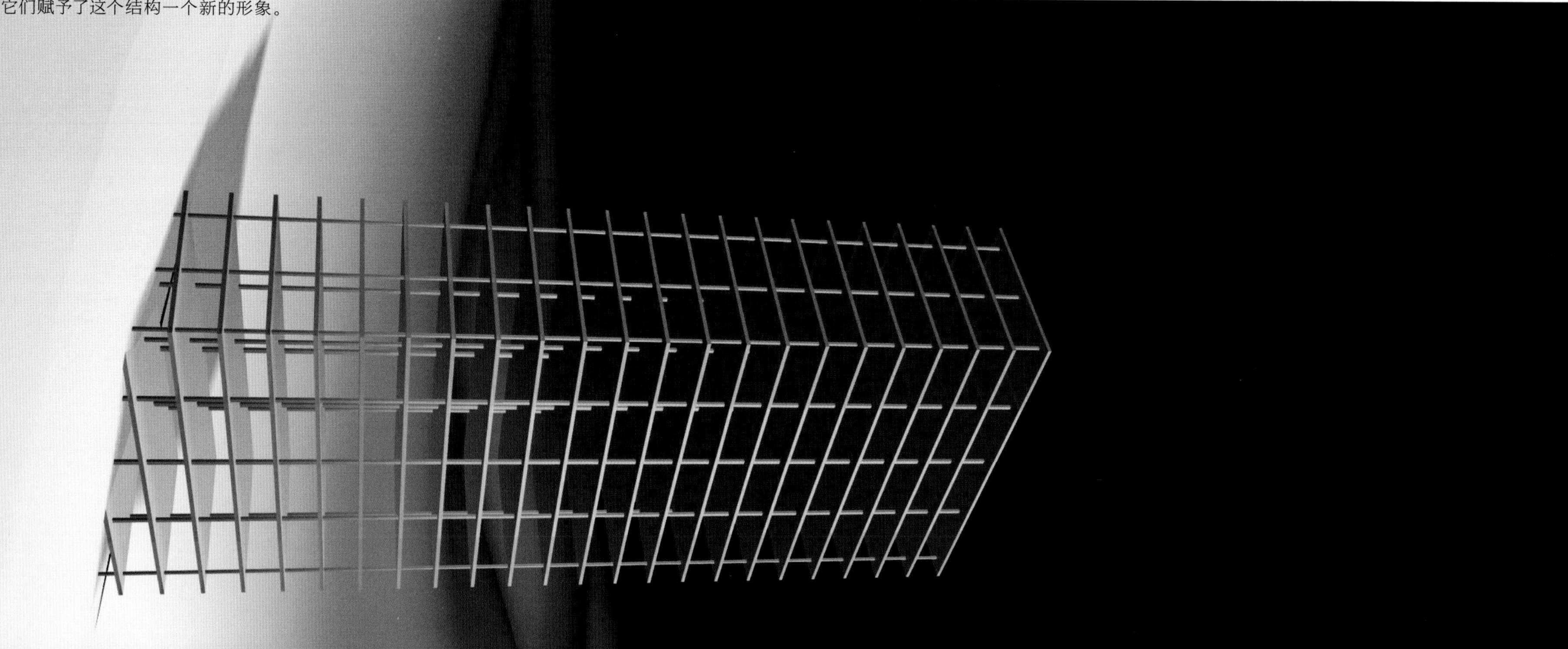

2006

Ice Tower

Within an arctic inhospitable landscape the Ice Tower represents a mirage and a vision which appears to the hypothetical observer out of any plausible predictability.

Nevertheless, together with the conception that among all living organisms, men are the most adaptable, HOV often prefigures hypothetical spaces for life inserted in environmental conditions that are completely different and extreme, without considering this operation a pure concept outside the possible reality.

2006

冰之塔

冰之塔处于北极圈内不适宜居住的荒漠景观中，对于假象的任何有可能出现的目击者，它代表了他们将看到的美丽幻象。

尽管如此，在所有活着的生物体的概念中，人类是最具适应力的。HOV经常假象处于完全不同的和极端的环境条件中的生活空间，他们并不考虑这些想法是纯粹概念的，完全超越可能的现实的。

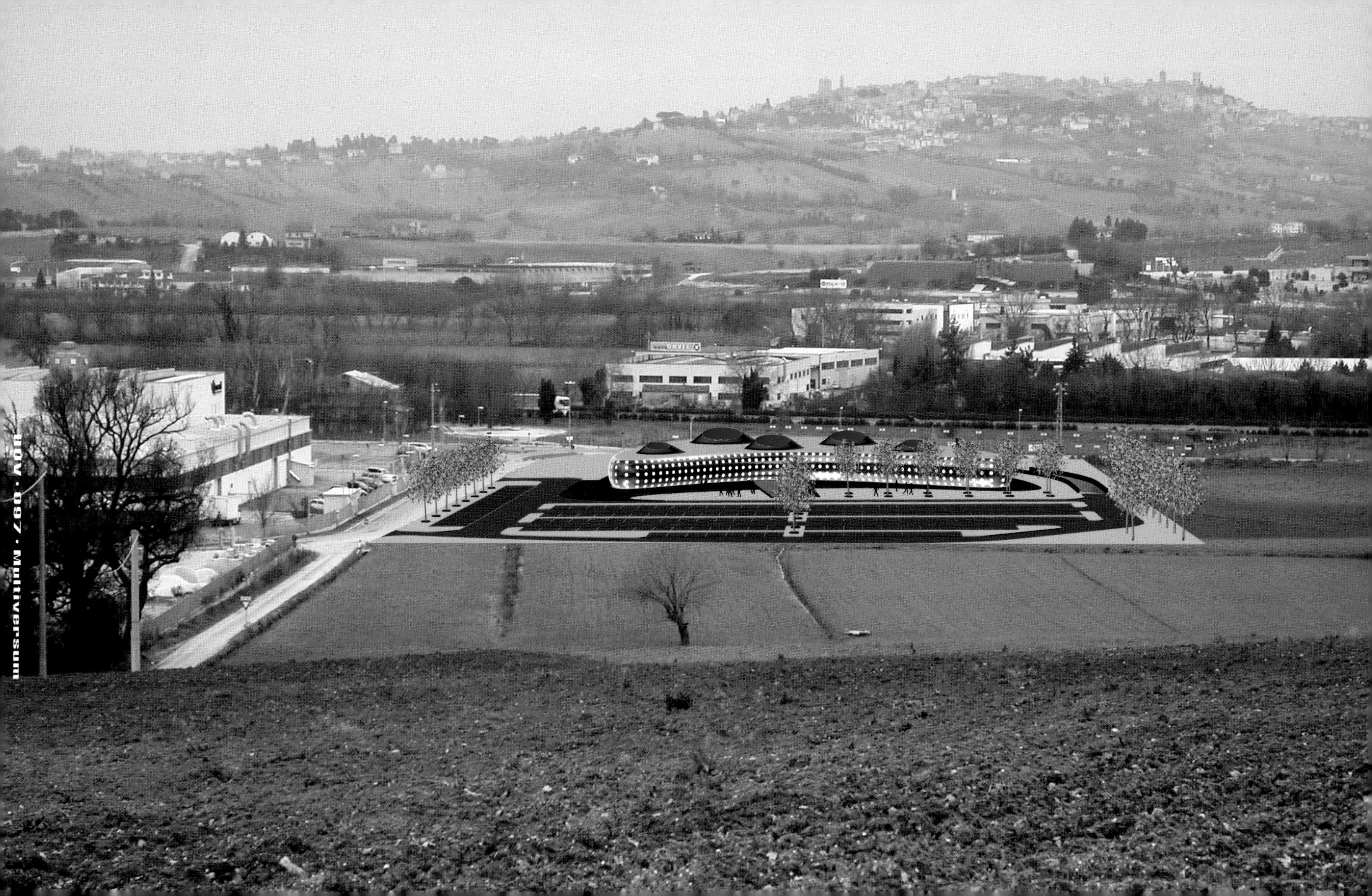
uov · 097 · Multiversum

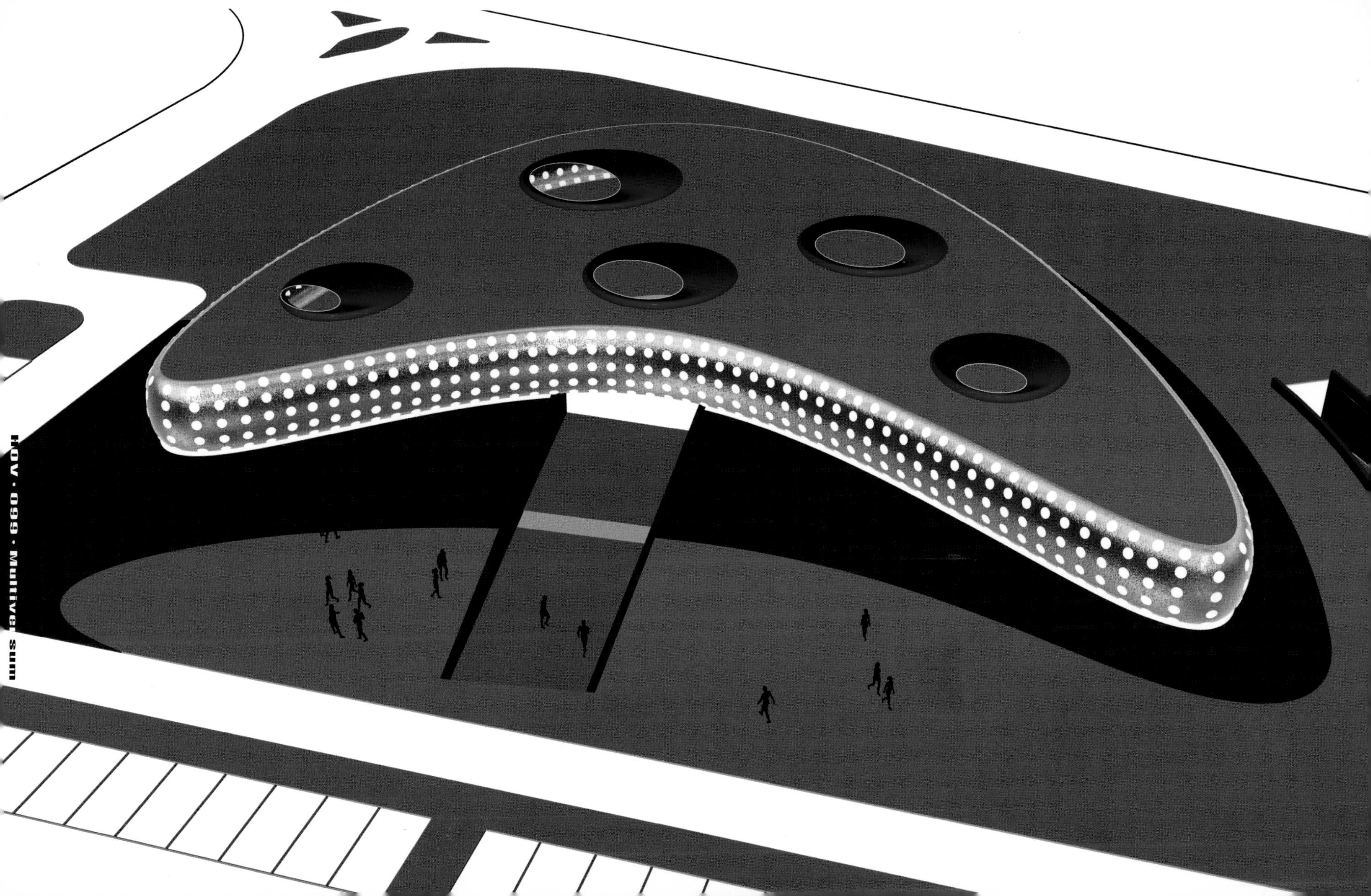

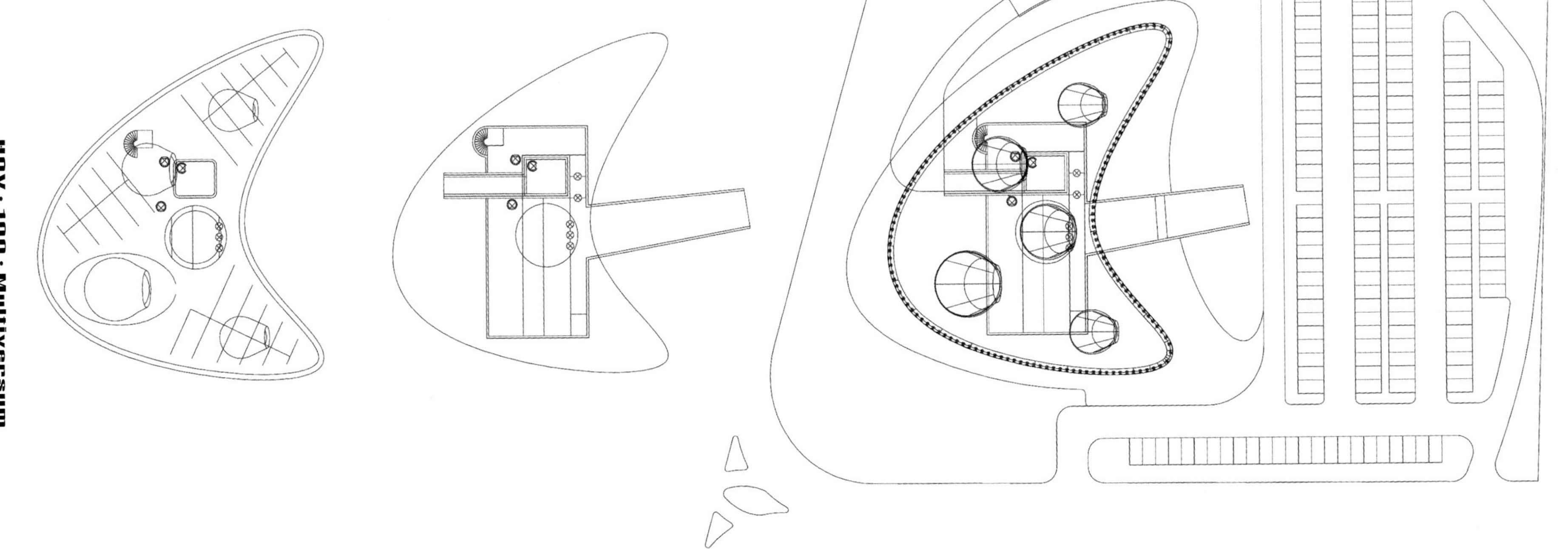

The project for a financial institute in a productive area is realised with an odd and very curious building. The around conditions, with lots of detractor elements, have suggested the emotional separation from the surroundings as well as a comparison with the original elements (to large-scale) of the landscape. In this perspective the building constitutes a new landmark. The construction is divided into two parts: the underground section contains the entry, the security area and the lobbies, whereas the first level is exclusively meant to administrative and public relations activities.
The highness of the building, without the wells of light (made of red glass-reinforced plastic), should be maintained under 4,50 metres because of local construction rules.

HOV为这所处于富饶地区的金融学院设计了一个非常奇怪的建筑物。有很多批评意见认为它和周围环境格格不入，大尺度上看和原有的景观元素上形成对比。从这个方面而言，这个建筑物建立了一个新的地标。建筑分为两部分：地下部分包含入口、保安区和门厅，地上一层则专属于行政区和公共活动区。
根据当地的建筑规范，建筑高度需控制在4.5米以下（不包括由红色玻璃钢制成的采光井）。

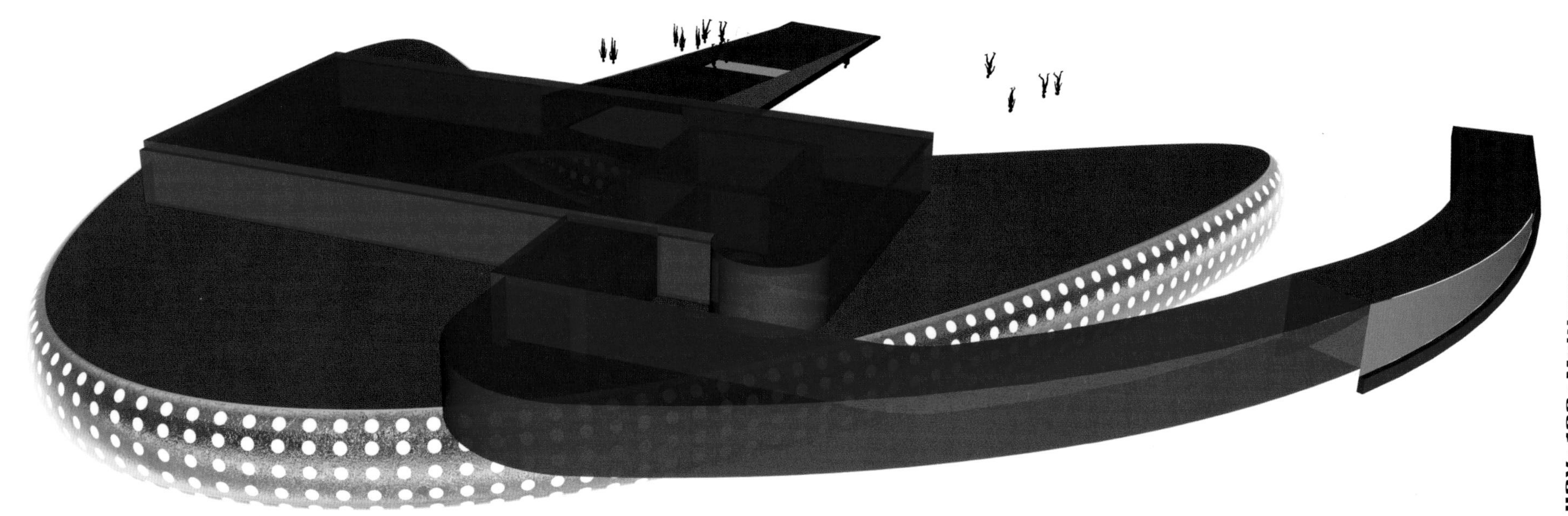

During a short visit to Bolzano, in North Italy, I noticed the austerity and the monumentality of some recent buildings far from the rich and lively design of the historical centre where, in agreement with the climate and the old European tradition, there is a vital and dynamic atmosphere at any time of the day.

Such a contradiction has brought about the idea of a drastic and alluring building whose destination is also brave: an amusement centre with love as a topic theme. A palace for the night or, better, for the Queens of the Night. A plan that, like others of hov's, defines itself and imposes its own condition independently from the clients, the contest, etc, as "necessary" idea.

我曾经在意大利北部的Bolzano短暂逗留，其间我注意到那里的历史中心设计得非常有活力，和近来的那些严肃的纪念碑式的建筑很不一样。这个历史中心与当地气候和古老的欧洲传统相符合。那里在任何时间都弥漫着生机勃勃的气氛。

这样的对比带来了一个概念——激烈并且诱人的建筑，它的目的也非常胆大——以爱为主题的娱乐中心。这是一座为夜晚而生的宫殿，用更好的说法则是为了夜晚的女王们。和HOV其他的项目一样，这个项目也脱离开客户、竞赛，宣称自己的概念是“必要的”。

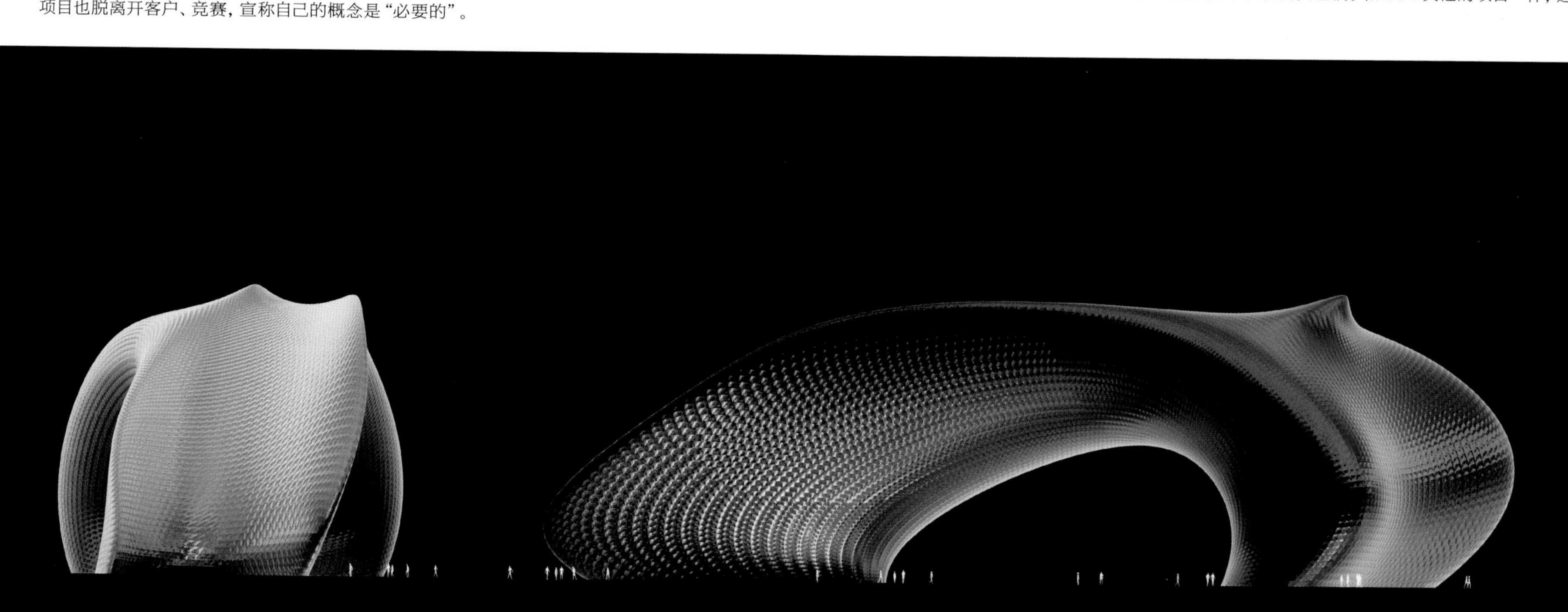

HOV · 105 · Multiversum

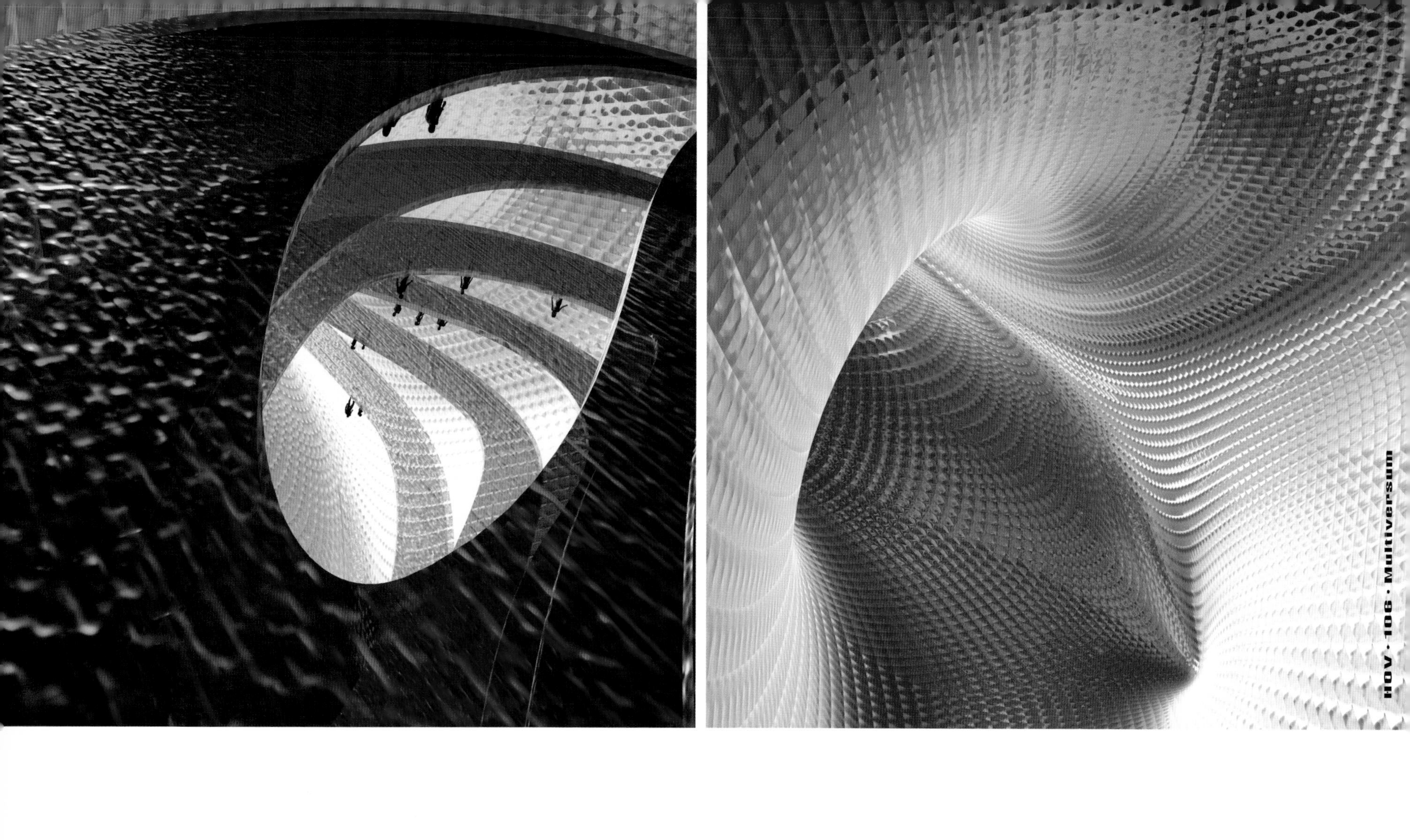

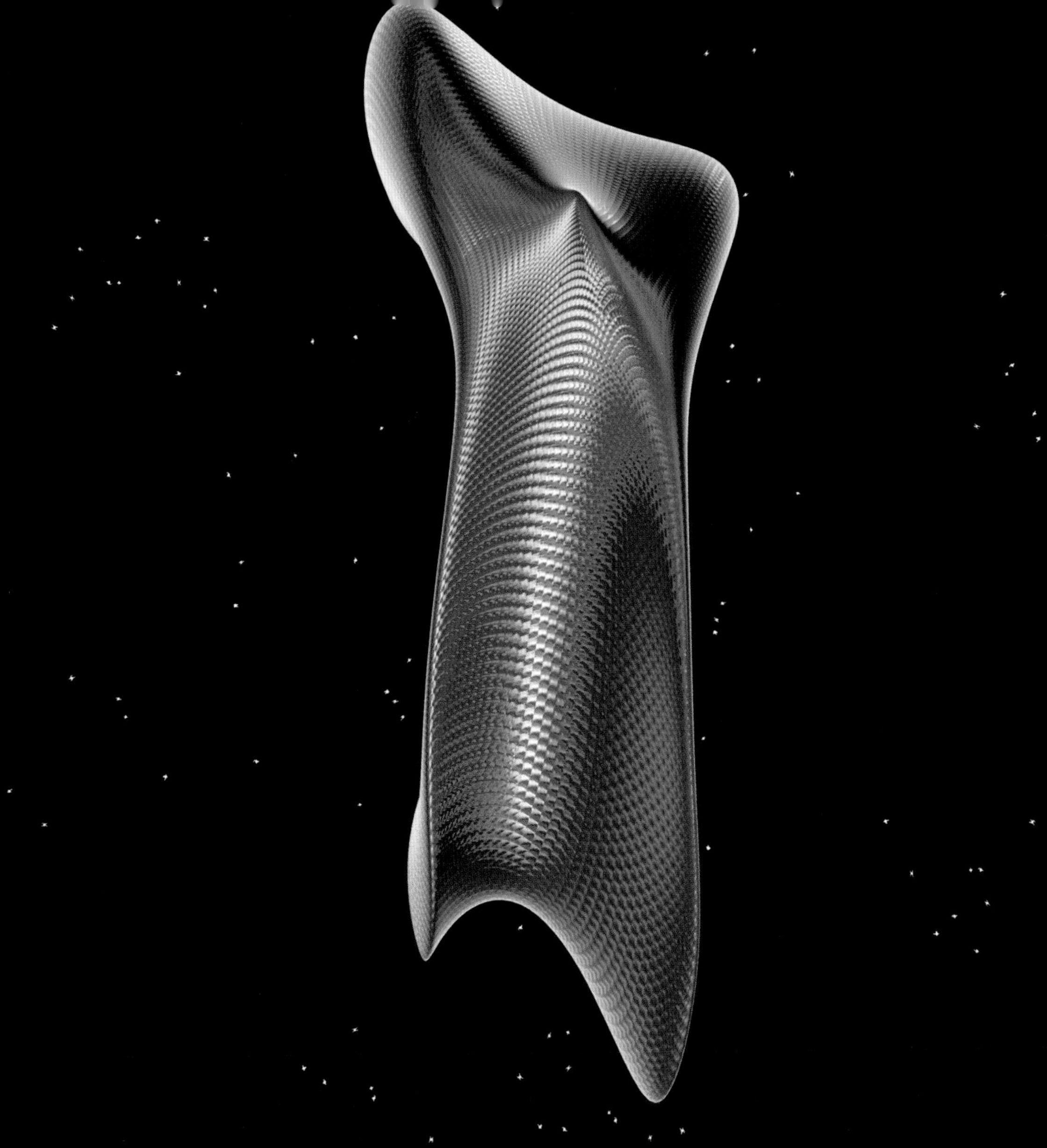

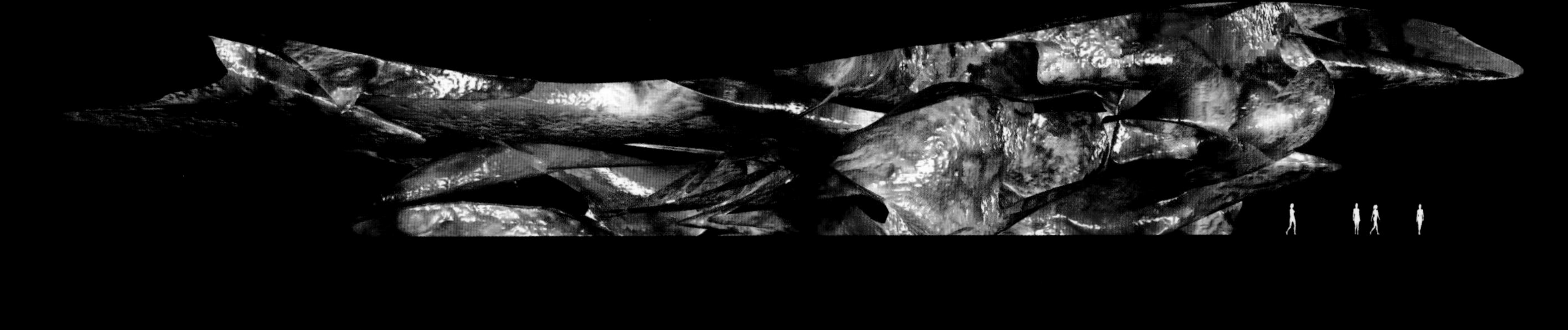

Mystery Palace is an object with a vaguely disquieting character, thought for the city of Ancona, where HOV Studio was born.
The idea is to create a night meeting centre for entertainments, similar to the project 'Palast für Bozen' (2003) in its spirit. Nevertheless the latter recalls a container with a biological nature inside and, even featuring an authoritarian aspect, it will turn into a fairly agreeable one when its interiority is discovered. On the contrary, the Mistery Palace is something uncertain and labyrinthic within the spirit of its conceiver, geometrically created by the superimposition of numerous topological transformations, just as many as the superimpositions of events and misteries concealed by the most symbolic sites in the city of Ancona. (cf. Found Space Theatre of 2003).
Hardly acceptable in the predictable social milieu taken for granted as a present reference model – which is not a typical feature for the city of Ancona only – the Mistery Palace will be able to receive all those people who can find the way to gentleness and secretness through sensitive, rich and secluded places, not necessarily sticking into the simplifications of 'Gothic Style' or bargain priced Satanism.

神秘宫是为HOV工作室诞生地——意大利的安科纳城——所设计的，它有一种模模糊糊令人不安的个性。
这个建筑的想法是为夜晚的娱乐活动创造一个聚会中心，这个精神和“Bozen宫”相似。然而后者令人联想起一个包含了生物学自然属性的容器，它的外观也很独特。它的内在特性一旦被人发现后，它将变得非常宜人。与之相反，神秘宫的创作者赋予了它不确定性和迷宫般的曲折，其几何形体由大量拓扑变形的叠加而成，正如这个安科纳城最具象征意义的场所隐藏了很多神秘事件。
不仅是安科纳城有这样的典型特征，我们可以用可预见的社会环境作为参考模型。也许很难让人相信，神秘宫将能使人们通过敏感、丰富、隐蔽的场所找到温和和幽静的感觉。要达到这一点，不需要再坚持哥特风格的简化或者廉价的恶魔崇拜。

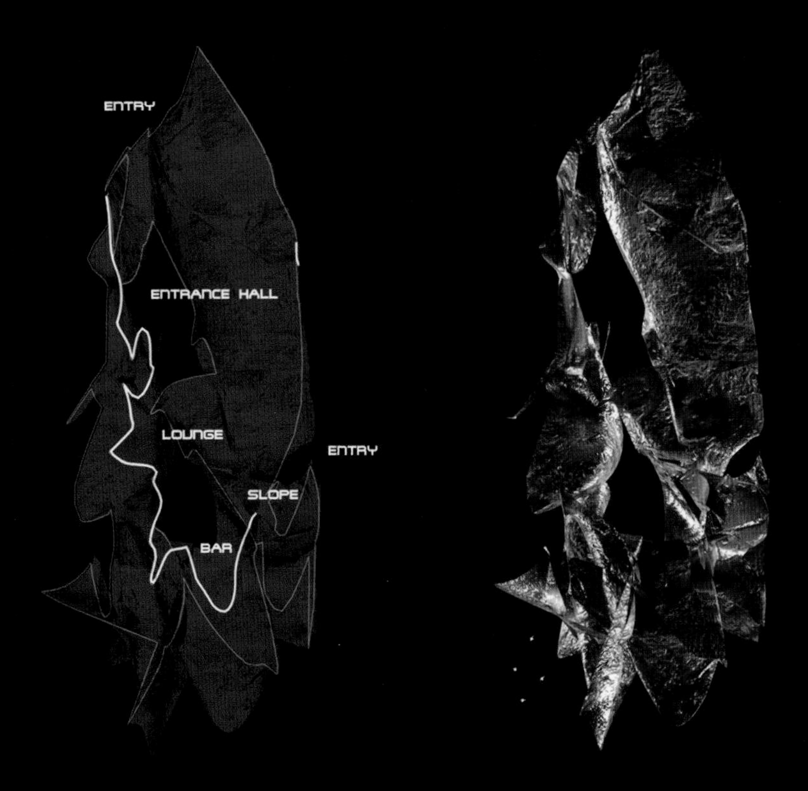
ENTRY
ENTRANCE HALL
LOUNGE
ENTRY
SLOPE
BAR

COMPETITIONS

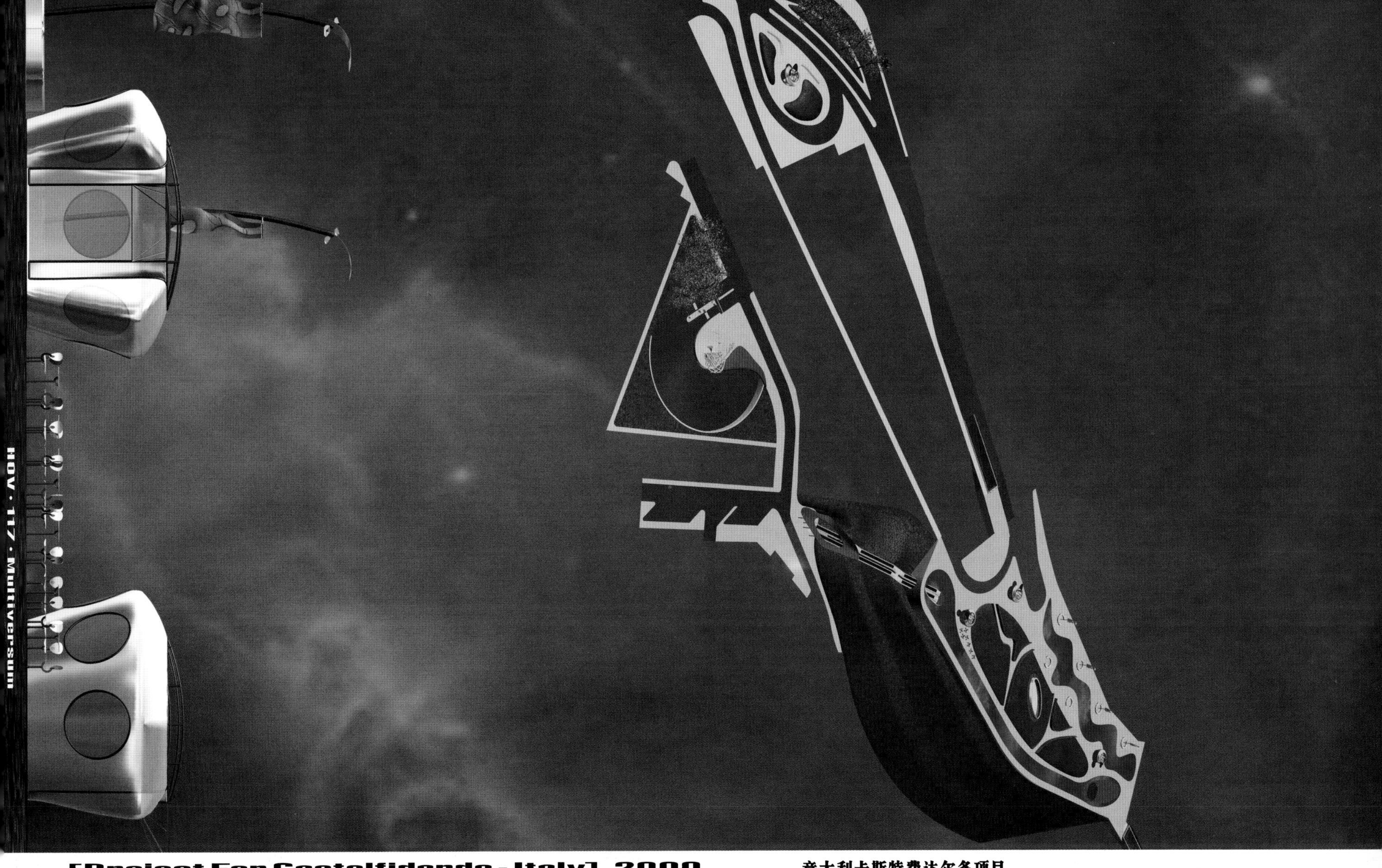

[Project For Castelfidardo - Italy], 2000

意大利卡斯特费达尔多项目

After the initial investigations of the square and acquaintance with the project theme, it became clear there were two levels to the project.
Although the general lines suggested by the Administration were very precise, the inner meaning of the competition made us relook at Piazza Don Minzoni, the greatest and the liveliest square of the town.
We consider that a town can not be expressed as either "typical" or "analogous" in itself model, but is the result of complexity and super-imposition, regardless of its territorial and demographic dimensions.
The project was meant to create processes and tensions refused by the tradition, rather than to exhibit the umpteenth architecture of an open space.
The emergence of an architectural requalification of the square was therefore as curious as it was clear that other spaces needed a deeper investigation.
Even if the square suffered from far too intensive traffic, the wonderful view and the arboreous species, with some interesting and healthful specimens, gave rise to the possibility of great flowering and fruition. The project therefore could not be solved by either a simple language or a paving restructuration. The central point seemed to be the accessibilty and the general qualification of the area.
Anything else was not important.
The garden - The new town garden is wider than the present one, although they share common elements.
All the tree-plantings are in fact mantained (for visibility reasons they have been omitted in our plans) and the pathways integrate with the present essences. Geometry derives from a sort of big pillow engraved by soft passages. The whole green area can be walked on: the lawn will be sown with a tough grass mixture which will require little watering (e.g. Festuca, Agrostis e Lolium). This grass will allow recreational activities to take place without ruining the appearance of the lawn. The fountain is re-proposed in a new version: it is larger with a changeable intensity directional recycle. It will be planted with new ichthyoid species, alongside the existing specimens. The edge is of sporting non-slip red rubber with a transparent security parapet of metacrylate. The confrontation with Nature, even if "natured", is always a central point of every project.
The side-boundaries of the paths are undifferentiated sitting places with sun or shadow: at will.
The square - The wide central space of the Piazza Don Minzoni, close to the town walls, may be organized according to the need. The mobile sitting places, so set, are just one of the possible solutions. The double sources of light (toward the walls or the lawn) are adjustable and create a scenographic sensation or an active illumination. The other sources of light are integrated in the paving, in the meadow, etc. Light supports function is metabolized during the day by information panels. The global space is like a table: to be set, according to the guests and the menu.
The structures situated there (a bar, a florist's, a newsagent's) are made up of a movable monobloc built in metal, plastic and rubber. In different colours or in the same one: at will.

在对广场进行了调查，以及对项目主题进行熟悉后，明确了这个项目的两个层面。
虽然组委会给出的纲要已经把项目描述得非常精确，这个竞赛的内在含义使我们重新关注堂明佐尼广场，它是这个镇上最伟大、最有活力的广场。
我们认为，如果不考虑一个城镇的领域和人口数量，城镇不能被描述为“典型”或者“类似”，而应该是复杂和叠加的。
这个项目并不想展示另一个熟悉的开放空间建筑，而是打破传统创造一些新的进程和张力。于是对这个场所进行建筑修饰得想法就显得很古怪，而其它场所则需要更深一步的调查。虽然这个广场交通问题很严重，但是这里的视野很好、树木种类多，其中还包含一些有趣且有益健康的品种，使得这里可以看见很多植物开花结果。因此，不能简单地用一种语言或铺路来解决这个项目。最重要的是这片场地的可达性以及它的整体修饰，其他的都显得不重要。

花园——新的城镇花园比现在的更宽敞，虽然它们都是由同样的普通的元素组成的。所有的树木植物事实上都被保留了下来（由于可见性的问题它们曾一度被我们忽略），铺路和现有的要素结合为一体。其几何形象就好像被一条柔软的小路刻过的大枕头。整片绿色区域都是可以让人走上去的：草地上将会播种一种硬的草混合物，这种草不怎么需要浇水（羊茅属、翦股颖 和 黑麦草）。人们在草地上休闲娱乐却不会破坏草地外观。喷泉被提议重建：它将被加大，并安装可变强度的有向循环。池中将保留现有鱼类品种的同时放新的品种。喷水池的边缘是运动型的防滑红橡胶，并安装有透明的甲基丙烯酸树脂安全护栏。即使是通过人工自然化，人与自然亲近总是每个项目的中心概念。道路的边缘是未加区分的座位，想坐在阳光下或阴影中，尽可随意。

广场——靠近城墙的堂明佐尼广场，其开敞的中心空间可以根据需要进行组织。可变的就座区只是可行的解决手段之一。双重光源（朝向墙或者草坪）是可调节的，可以创造出透视的感觉或者活泼的照明。其他光源则照在小路和草地等上。白天，光照可以通过信息通道支持功能运转。球形空间就像一张桌子一样：可以根据顾客和目录进行设置。

场地中还安置了一个构筑物，其中包含一间酒吧，一个花店和一个报刊亭。它是由金属、塑料和橡胶建成的一个可动的整体。想用不同的颜色还是一样的颜色，尽可随意。

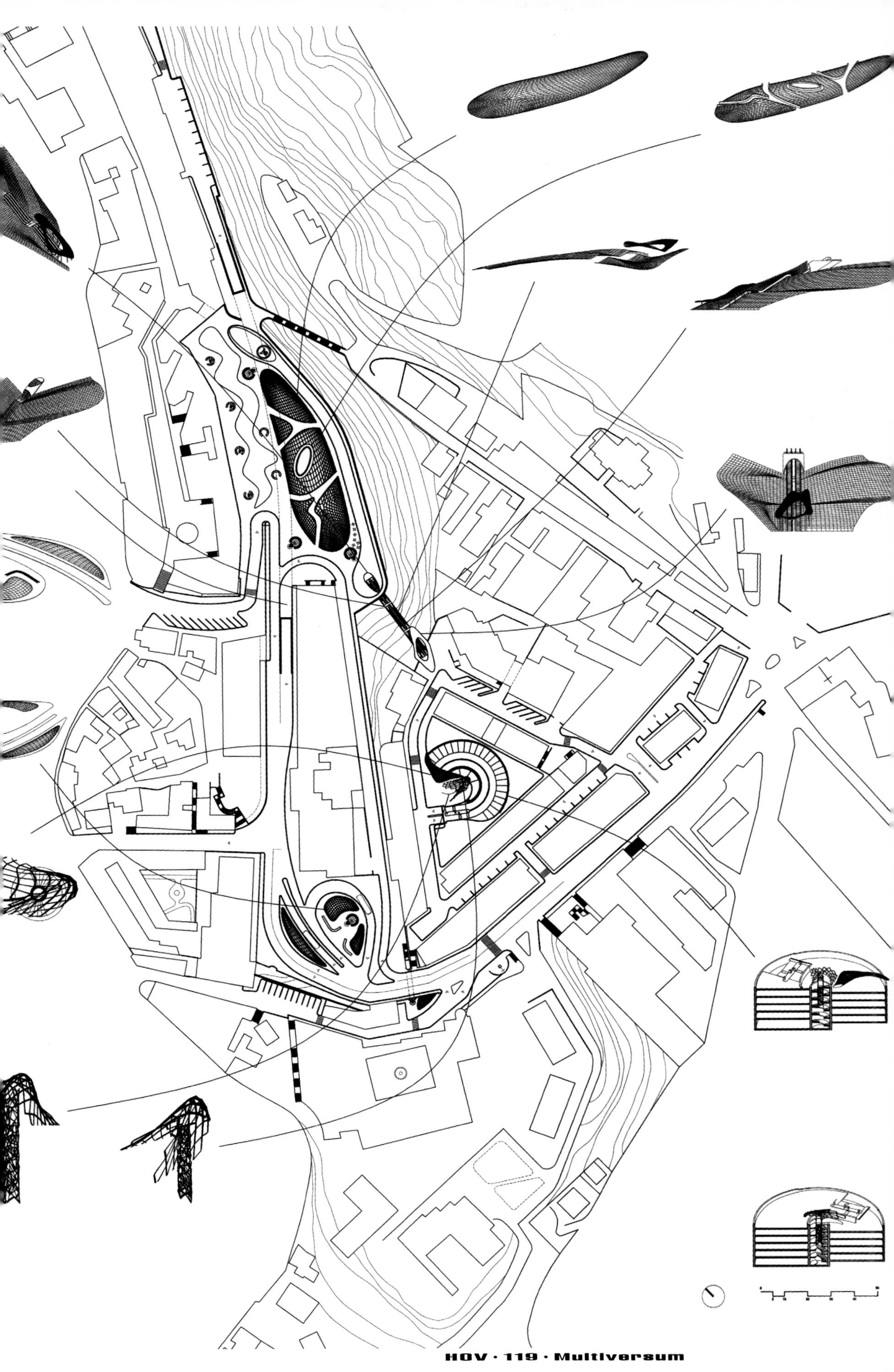

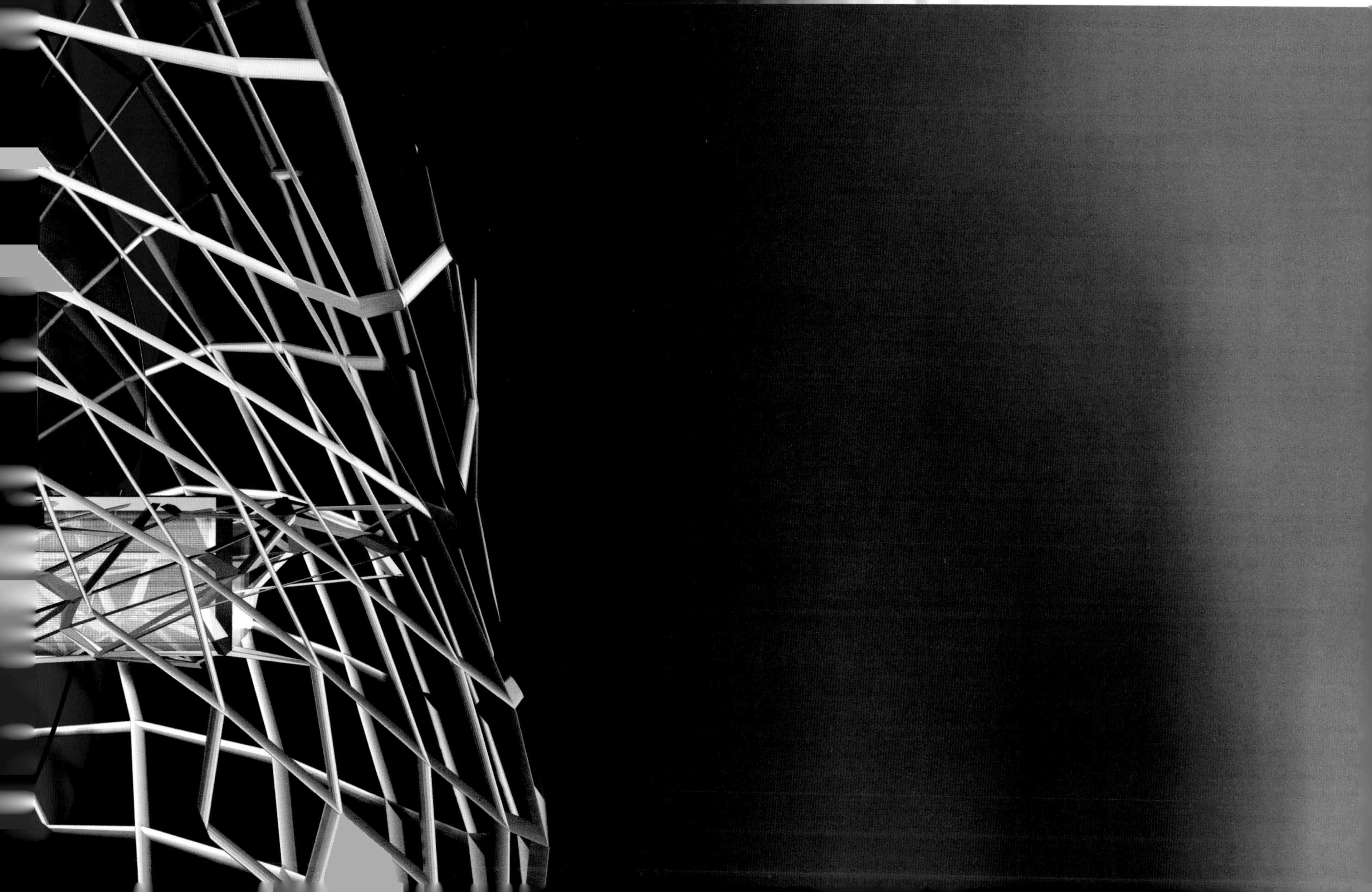

HOV · 122 · Multiversum

The "museum" of emotions is a project of a real space for virtual works. The works are represented by the same living organisms in their different feelings and emotional changes.
According to the theories of M. Maturana and his approach to the study of the biological systems, we are in a continual emotional evolution, fluctuating from one series of actions to another, within the interactions of our lives.
In this regard, emotion arises from the relationship between organism and environment, in the same way as walking is born from the movement of the legs in partnership with the ground. Furthermore, it is the emotion that defines the action. It is the emotional state, in fact, that specifies when, for example, a given gesture is an attack or a caress.
The "museum" bears witness to the emotional system of the living organism in its being.
The perimeters of the object provide the first variation in emotional state, that is APPROVAL for the arriving organism and REFUSAL for the departing. This is because a living system, in its dynamics of interaction with the external environment, is only influenced by those external elements that its structure allows and this is true for every emotional state.
The emotional flow in spaces without order or hierarchy — SURPRISE, FEAR, REGRET, DISGUST, RAGE, JOY, SATISFACTION, HAPPINESS, CARELESSNESS, PEACE, etc — is subsequently determined by external dynamics (sparked by the museum itself) which initiate a series of actions within which the organism moves and then evolves autonomously.
Certain dynamics are extreme, provoking (the performance of artists or actors, violent images, transformations and actions against the body), others are more natural and commonplace (lovers kissing, food, drinks, activity and areas of tranquillity).
A model of "art" where everyone is represented and which brings about a substantial change in the relationship between observed and observer, with the observer playing an integral part in that which he observes.

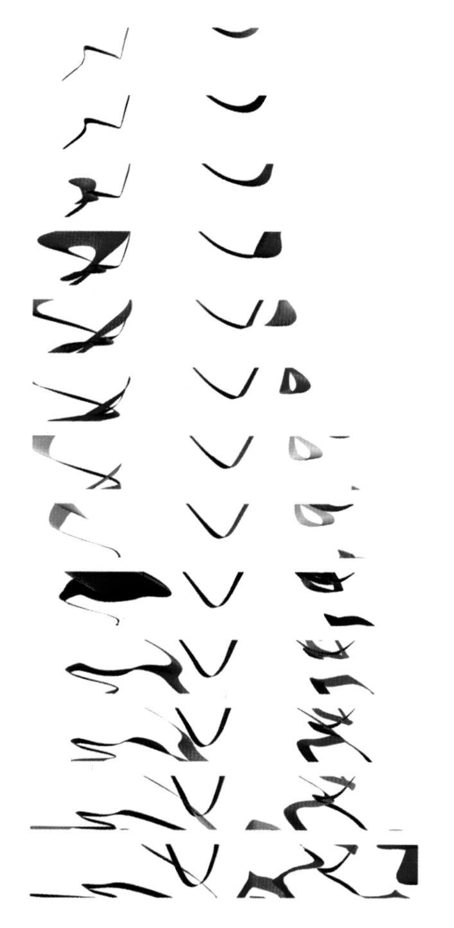

情感“博物馆”是为虚拟的作品而设的真实空间。这些作品描绘了同一个生物体不同的感受和情感的变化。

根据玛吐拉纳的理论和他的关于生物系统的研究，我们人类处于持续的情感进化进程中。人与人之间相互作用的同时，我们又在不同的行为中摇摆。

以这个观点来看，情感是来自于生物体和环境的关系，就好像走路是来自于腿的运动与地面的关系。此外，行为是取决于情感的。举个例子，某个特定的姿势是表示攻击还是关爱，是由一个人的情感状态决定的。

这个“博物馆”见证了生物体的情感体系。

物体的周长表现了情感状态的第一个变量，对于到来或离开的有机体是“批准”以及“拒绝”。因为一个生命系统在和外界环境相互作用的过程中，只会被它的结构所承认的外界因素影响，所有的情感状态都是这样的。

惊讶、恐惧、厌恶、愤怒、喜悦、满足、幸福、无忧无虑、平静等这些情感在空间中无次序、无层次地流动，随后它们将由外界动力决定。博物馆提供这个外界动力，这会激发有机体的一系列行为——移动，然后自主地进化。

有些动力是极端而且刺激的，比如艺术家的表演、暴力场景、打斗场景等。其他的则更为平静、自然，比如恋人亲吻、食物、饮料、安静的行为和地方等。

这样的一个艺术品描绘了所有人身上发生的事，它可以由观众控制展品，并给展品和观众之间的关系带来实质的变化。

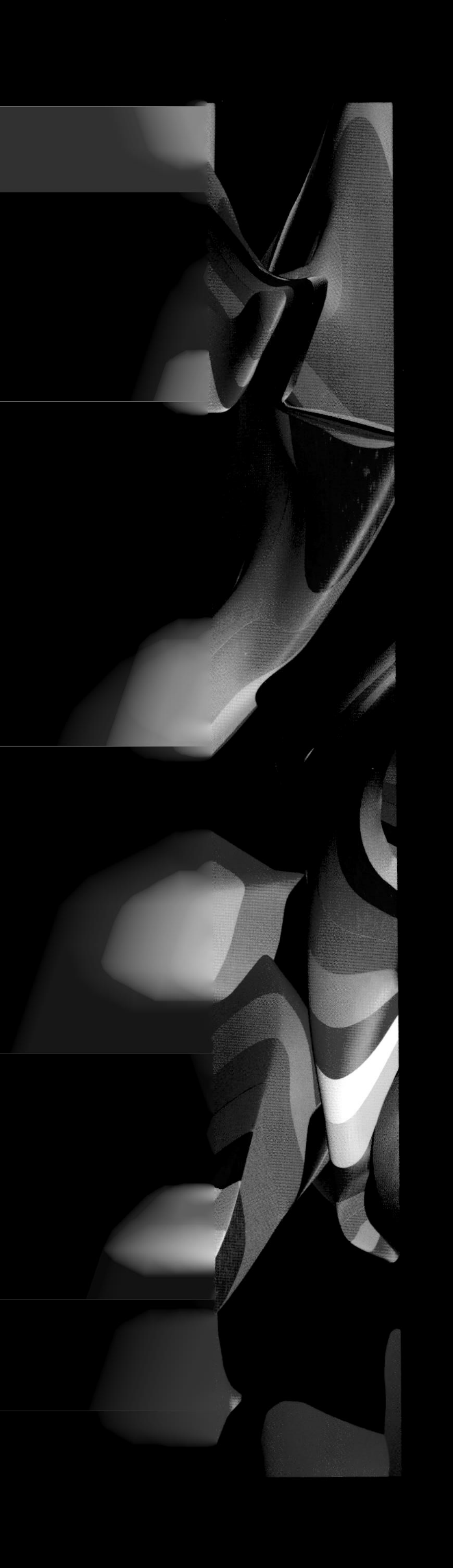

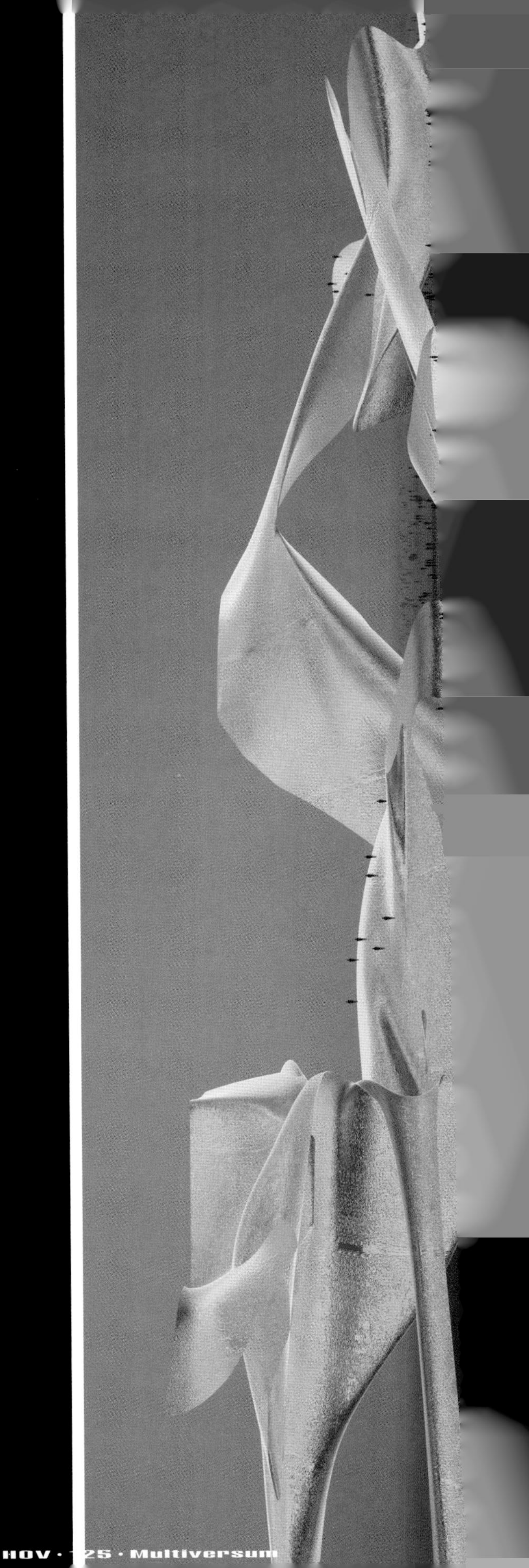

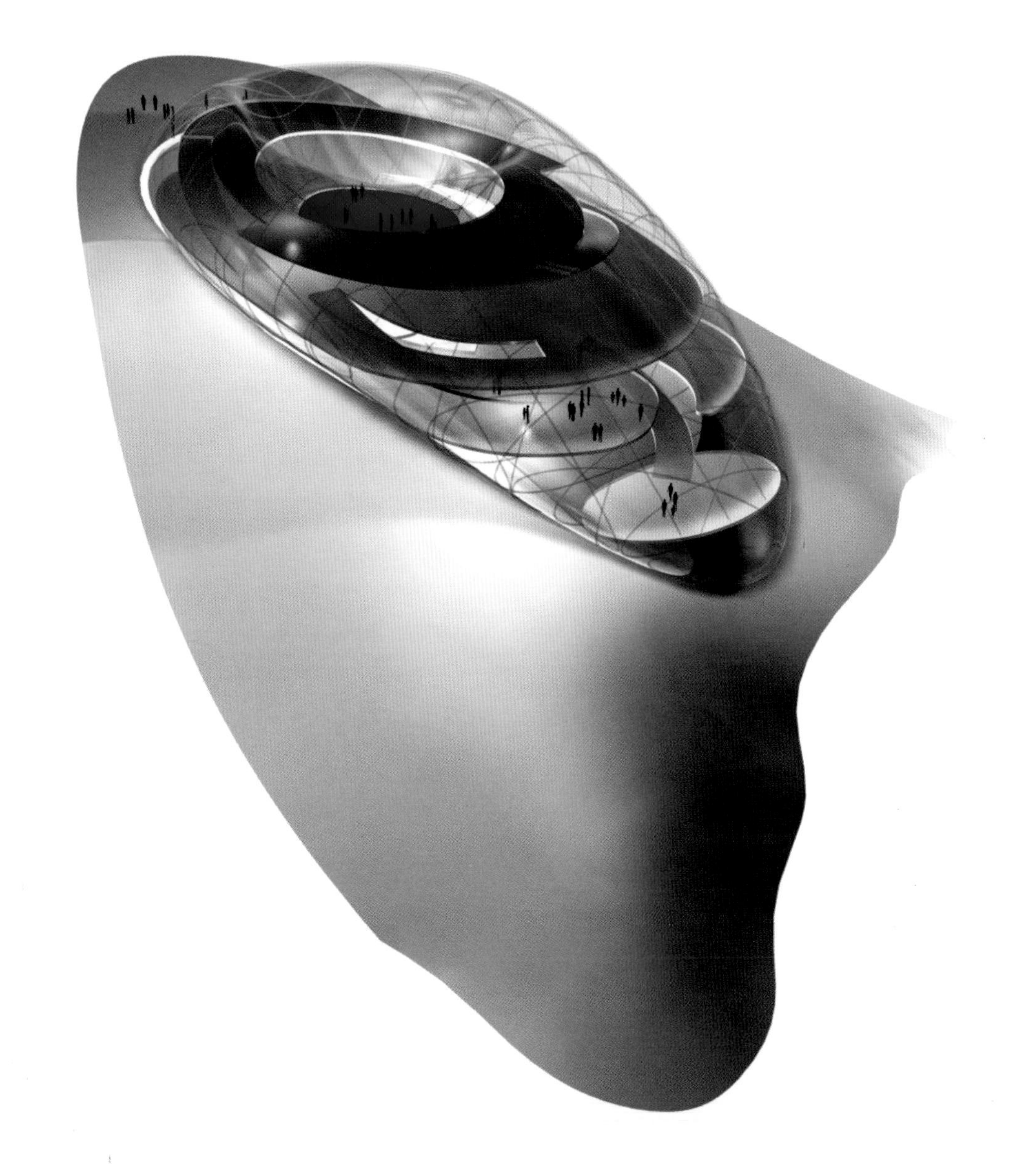

Pictures Notes
diagram of how the building developed in line with the natural slope in the land and sequence of main building elements.

图片说明：
这个图表说明了建筑物随着陆地的天然坡度生长，以及主要建筑物元素的次序。

Love of life and nature in spire Tomihiro Hoshino's shi-ga (poetry and painting) project. Hoshino, a most unfortunate former athlete forced to paint and write with his mouth following a serious training accident. Now, years later, his works touch the heart and soul of lots of visitors through the sense of peace and calmness they transmit. In homage to his brave work, this project treats visitors as never detached from the marvellous natural setting that inspires and mirrors the artist, making them ponder over and reflect on the most important things in life.
The building system is designed to meet the extreme needs of highly seismic environments. The main support structure is constructed out of a series of linear moulded wooden units combined with plastic cores and reinforced with criss-cross, joined together strips of high-resistance composite fibre.
The roof is made of a shell of separate panels-twin, transparent and made of thermo-moulded polycarbonate - that are extremely elastic and fixed with soft joints.
The inside floors are made of thin casts of conglomerate with added synthetic polymers and an integrated structure of high-resistance composite material. The entire system is compatible with stresses and strains that would cause deformations that other types of buildings could not cope with. All this is thanks to technological know-how already applied in special sectors of components design and ship building.

星野富弘曾经是一名运动员，在经历了一次严重的训练事故后，现在被迫只能用嘴绘画写作。多年以后的今天，他的作品所传达的安宁与平静，感动了无数来访者的心灵。设计者认为是大自然激发了星野富弘的灵感并且反映了他的品质。为了向他的勇气表达敬意，建筑让参观者们感觉始终和美丽的自然环境在一起，同时使得人们去思索生命中最重要的事情。
整个建筑体系设计可以应对地震环境中最极端的情况。主要的支撑结构包含一系列线性木模加塑料芯，并以十字形式交错加强，另外还加有条状高强度复合纤维。
屋顶由一层分离的双面板建成，面板的材料是透明的热成型聚碳酸酯。屋顶的弹性非常好，并且是用软性节点固定的。
室内地板包含了添加人造聚合体的聚结薄模板，结构由高强复合材料结合而成。对于会引起建筑形变或其他后果的压力和拉力，整个系统可以很好地应对。这是因为在建筑的一些特殊部件的设计和运输中引用了最新的科技成果。

aerial view showing a photomontage of the museum in its natural setting and overall redevelopment of the area.

这个鸟瞰图表现了建筑在其自然环境中以及该地区再开发的一系列照片

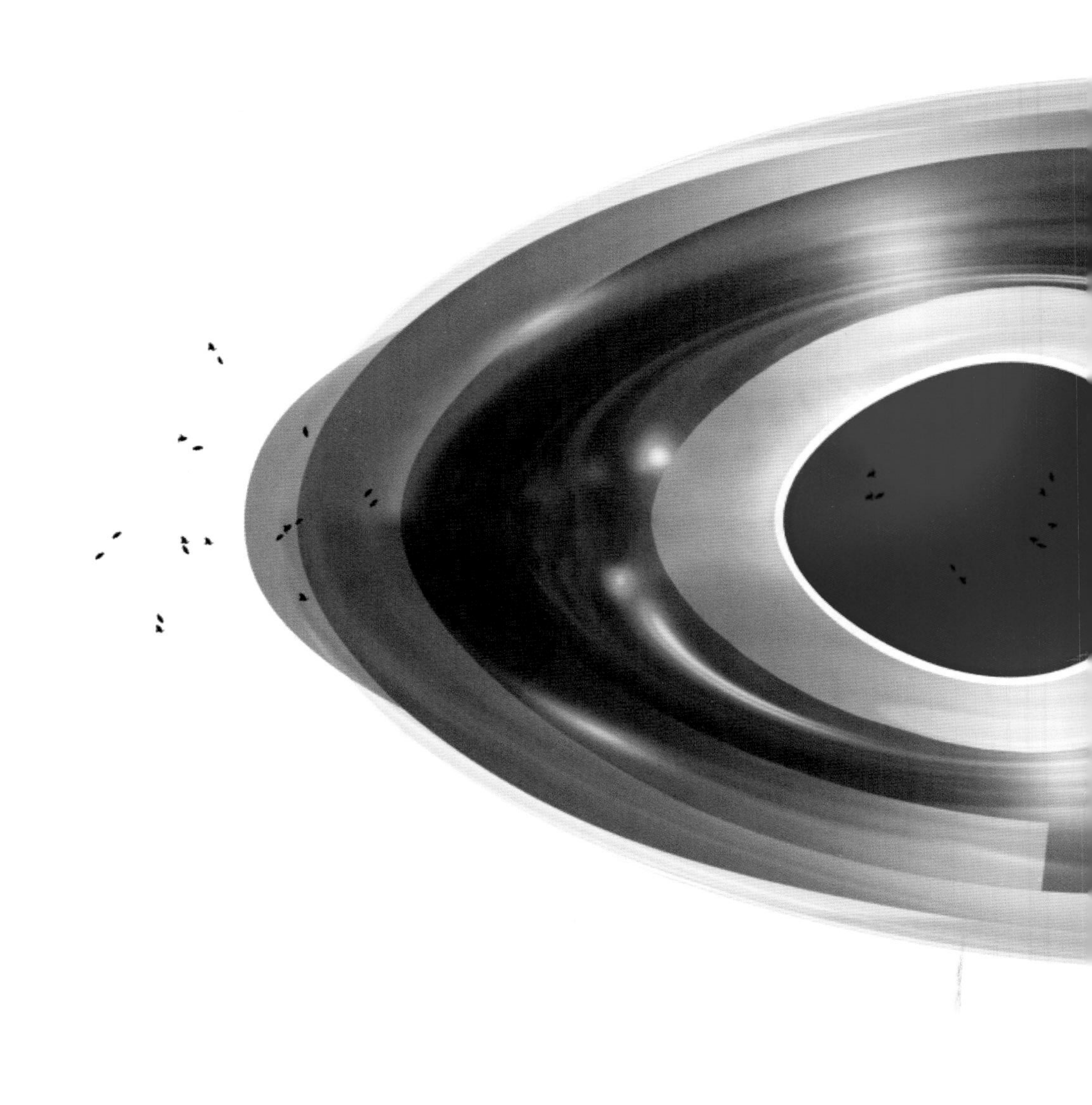

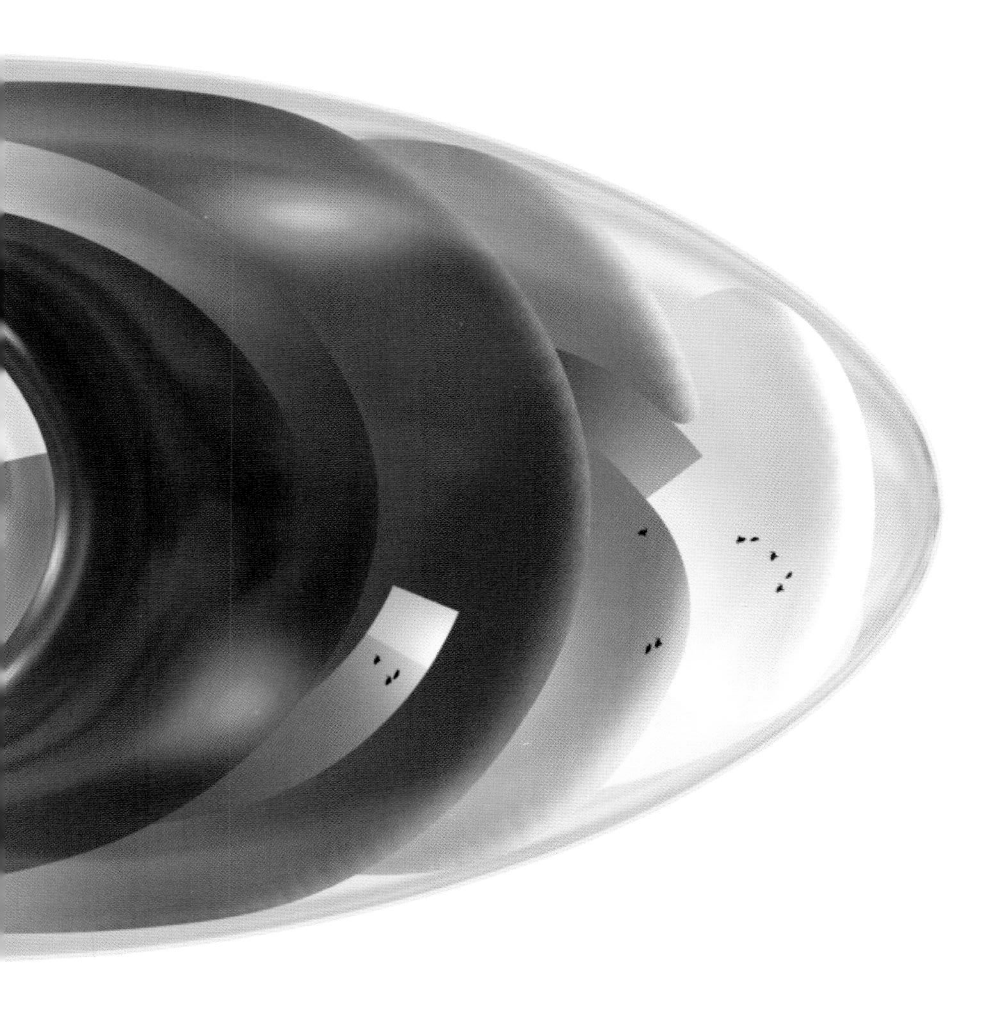

plan

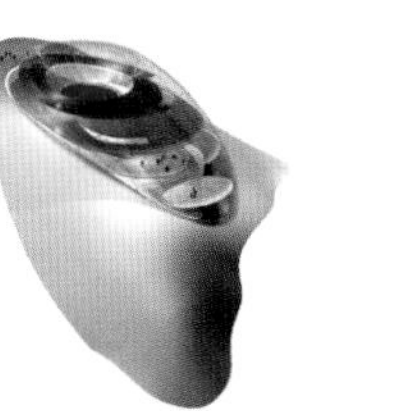

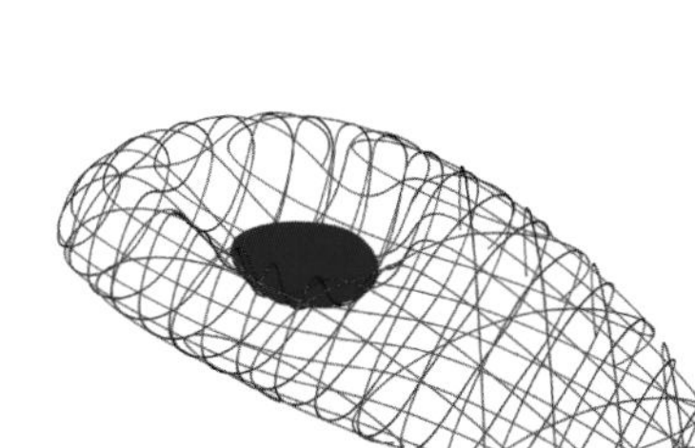

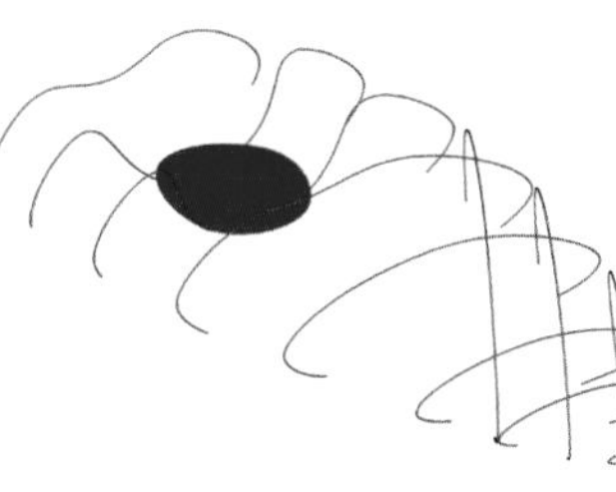

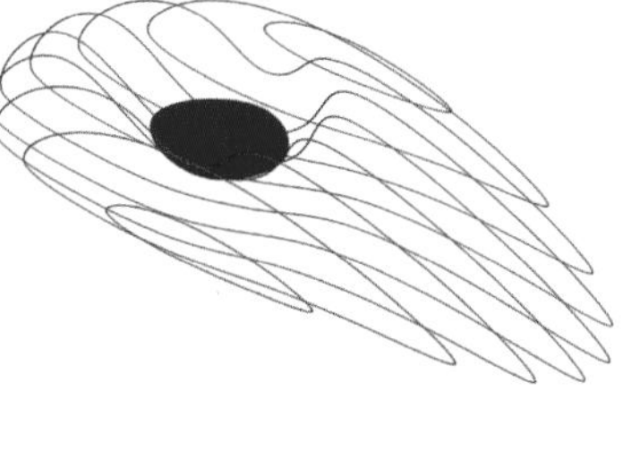

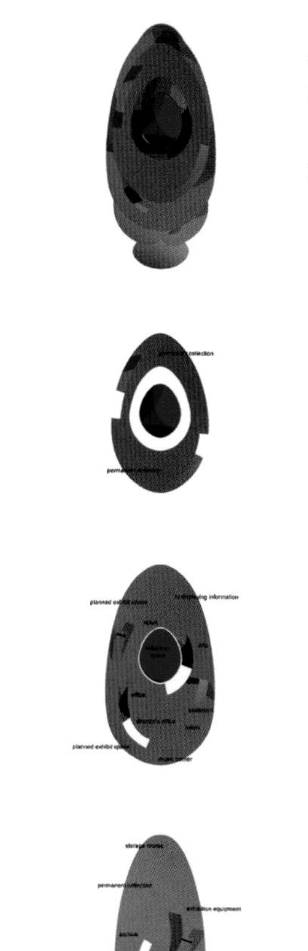

stratified sequence of distribution schemes.

分布设计的分层顺序

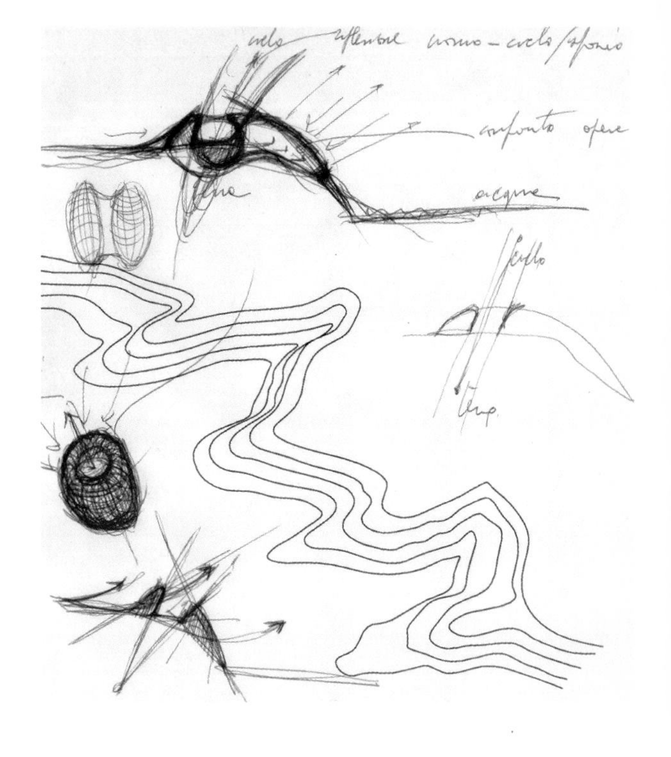

studies for the transversal and longitudinal layout, and the criss-crosses, reinforcements and circulation.

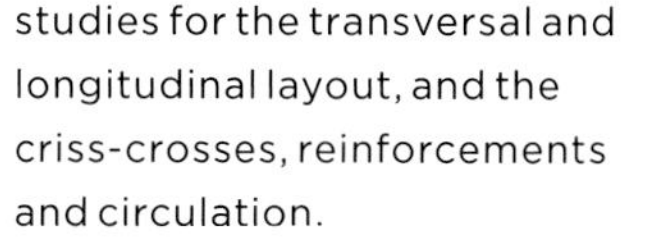

横、纵向布局的研究，十字形加强，环形流线

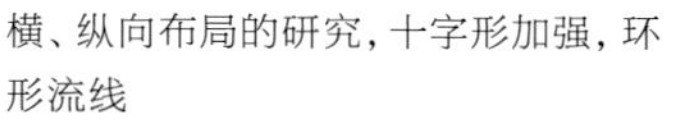

Pictures Notes
renderings of the complete
structure

图片说明:
整体结构的渲染图

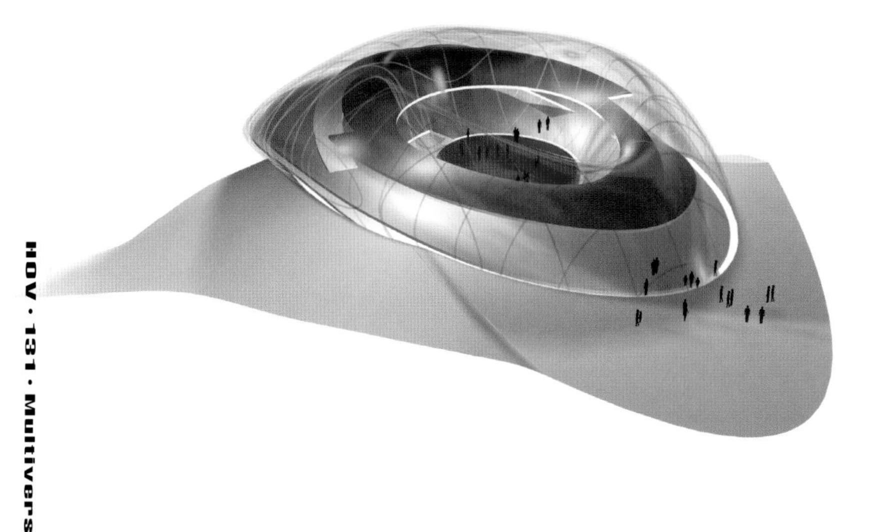

section

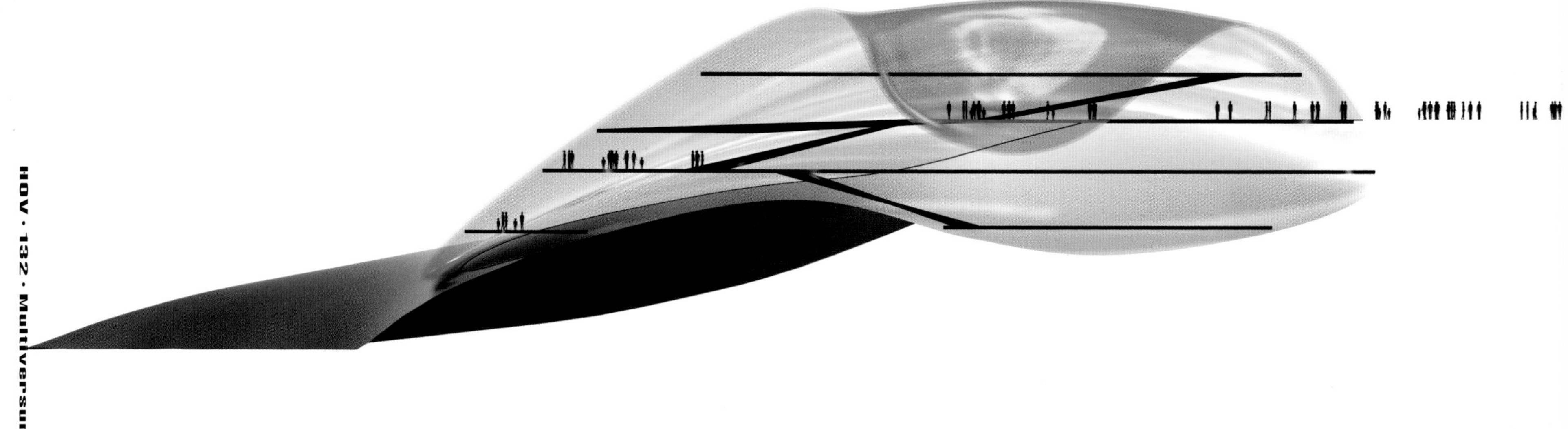

photomontage of the museum.

internal view

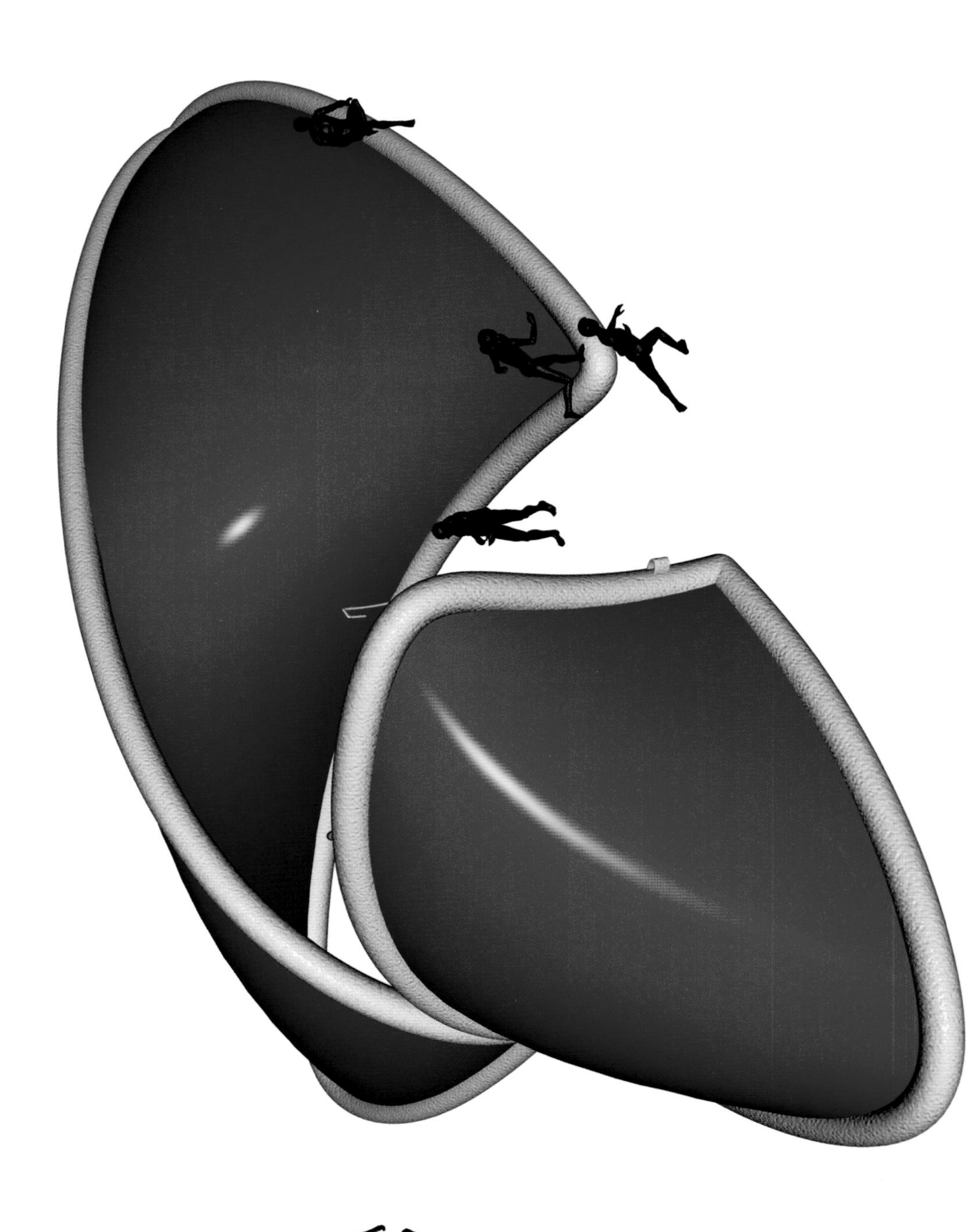

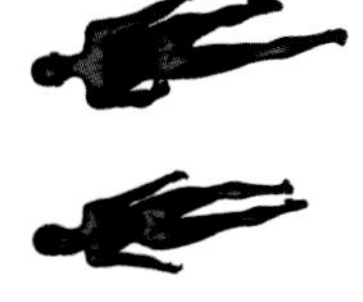

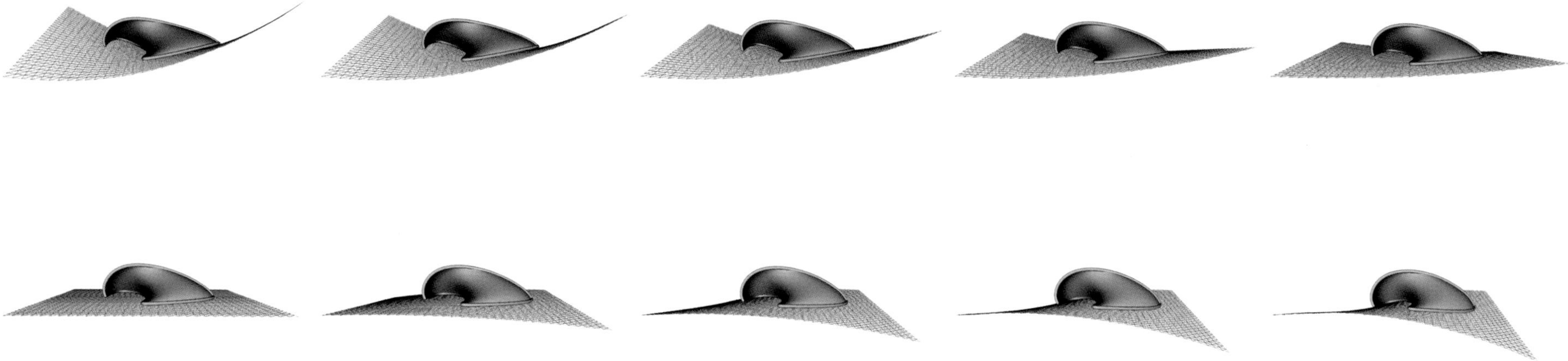

Design concept

The inflatable structure is a simple, coloured and versatile element, which can be installed in the city open spaces apart from their morphology or surface (lawn, paving, asphalt, water).

The concept is the use of a simple but intriguing object in the chosen areas, so that an interest might be stimulated without aggression or any particular devices.

The result is a system that can varies in dimensions and be used in different ways according to the different needs (illumination set, open-close kit, rigid metal structure, fire system, information system, etc)

Different versions of the same structure can be realised: a model with the external surface of semiconductor polymers cells that appears like a big display distorted for interactive plays or messages and information; or, the application of flexible photovoltaic cells for the prototype of an energetic unity.

The assemblage is realised by inflating the object. The water (which could be also used for the fire system, if included) in the element in contact with the ground, secures stability. This building technology is used for sea rescue boats of reinforced rubber or for protection pneumatic systems.

The two main support element are departmental and are realised in reinforced rubber with a thin net of mix material, tear-proof, fire-proof and very resistant to vandalism. Its thin plastic cover stretches when inflated and can be matched with any printed or designed film.

This allows a chromatic diversification, the application of logos or advertisements and even decorations by the visitors.

The structure can therefore be used both as a normal sitting/shelter and for more peculiar needs: meeting place, shows, projections, expositions, lounges, information point,etc.

Thanks to the statics deriving from the geometry and the building technique, neither anchorage nor even light modifications of the area will be necessary. The rough and resistant surface of the basic element, together with the structure own weight, once it is immersed into the water, provides the resistance to the sliding just through friction.

The assemblage phase requires an atmospheric compressor and a water inlet line, or a tank truck, as well as easy mechanical operations. The only fundamental suggestion is to preserve the dismissed structure in a soft container with mineral powder to be washed off before the next assemblage.

In the simpler version the absence of metallic components secures the greatest active reliability of the structure. Even if torn as a consequence of a traumatic accident, the material does not allow the damage to expand, so giving time to mend it.
The structure can also be fixed with poliuretanic foam. This operation is irreversible.

Technical description

Building system and materials - The basic structure takes its inspiration from the inflatable boats of nautical origin. Two different in material elements are cut and soldered into one: a thicker one for tubular sections, a thinner one for connection surfaces. No radial joints are used for the variable geometry of the structure. The cuts in the fabric are longitudinal and compensated in order to reduce the torsion on the tubolars. The pneumatic support section is internally divided into 8 independent rooms about 3,60 m long, the air pneumatic section being internally divided into 6 independent rooms about 3,10 m long.
Both of them are made of reinforced material with polyester fabric saturated by coating and calendering with mixtures of specific elastomers.
The different internal rooms allows for a constant balancing of the inflating pressure - about 0,2/0,25 bar - and contribute with their quenching effect to improve the resistance to the crashes, in particular thanks to the water filled section.
The material is resistant to any hydrocarbon and solvent. It has a limit breaking stretch of 20% and a use temperature ranging from - 40° to + 80°.
The control-valves for the inlet and the aspiration of air and water are movable and must be taken apart before the folding operations. The meteoric waters flow through passages opened in the collecting points on the cover surface.
Fire system - The basic fire system can be completed with a little automatic one: three sprinklers on the sides of the air tubular.
The abduction line is normally outside and it has a suitable junction, but in special conditions the water can also be taken from internal reserve of the tubulars through a little automatic or manual compressor. It will be then pressured into the sprinklers pipe. The use of this water does not harm the stability of the structure, whose tubulars will be later filled up.
Light system - The system can be integrated in the recess formed by the air tubular. The water-proof

luminous elements, fixed on a rigid plastic structure, are mobile and equipped with cold light lamps.
The connection to the mobile board is integrated in a screened and protected external channel along the basis tubular.
Closing Kit - Sittings, tables and shelves, along with a mobile board with net or connection cables can be kept in a closed part of the structure. It is realised with an additional element made of the same materials but with only air inflatable tubulars. The total weight of the closing system is about kg. 129.
The opening/closing operation is manual and consists of a crank demoltiplicator on the junction band of the closing system.
The latter is blocked up with a pin at whose end is a lock. Should the structure be particularly rigid because of the ground or the use, a steal support can be applied, which is variable in height according to the pressure of the basis inflatable ring.

Transport and endurance - The phases of loading, unloading and transport do not require special equipment. A motor-lorry with an oildynamical moving jib and a 5.30 (or more) metres long loading platform will be sufficient.
The stocking containers, provided with clasping handles, can be placed one upon another.
The implied materials and the tested technologies indicate an average endurance of the structure of about 10 years in a Mediterranean climate, apart from the numbers of assembling and disassembling operations, as long as they are realised according to the above mentioned indications. Possible damages, even serious ones, can be anyway mended with a cold sticking.
Estimated costs - Making a comparison with the costs of structures similar in technology and materials, a possible production amount for the basic model of the project is Đ 23.000,00. Since the industrial fields implied in the production have costs depending on the number of the pieces, the estimated values may vary. We have therefore thought of a limited production but not smaller than 5 pieces.

设计概念：
这个充气结构是一个简单的彩色的万用元素，它可以被安置在城市的开敞空间或城市表面——草坪、铺面、沥青、水面等。

概念是在指定区域运用一个简单但是可以引发人兴趣的物体，这样就可以不依靠任何进攻性行为或特殊装置来激发人的兴趣。

作品可以根据不同的需要改变大小，用于不同的用途，比如有照明设施、可开关装备箱、刚性金属结构、消防系统、信息系统等。

同一个结构可以变化出不同的样子。比如外表皮用半导体聚合单元制成，它就成为一个大型展示屏，用于消息与信息展示或者互动式游戏；或者安装上可变式光电池，它就成为一个能量体的原型。

这个物体靠充气完成组装。装置里的水和地面接触保证其稳定性，这也可以运用到消防系统里去。这个建筑物的技术也被运用于海上救援艇、强化橡胶和保护气垫装置。

两个主要支撑元件是分离的，由强化橡胶和混合材料结成的薄网安装而成。它可以防撕裂、防火并防止人为破坏。它表层的薄塑料可以随着充气而延展，并能和任何设计印刷的图像相配。

这样建筑物表面就可以有丰富多彩的变化，商标、广告甚至顾客的创作都可以成为它的装饰。

所以，这个结构不仅可以用作常见的座位或者遮蔽物，还可以满足一些特殊的需求：会见场所、表演、投影、展览、休闲、新闻布告等。

通过几何学与建筑技术所得的静力学，场地不需要给这个建筑增加锚固或调整光照。一旦它浸入水里，基础元件的粗糙表面和它的重量相加，足以靠摩擦力来抗滑动。

装备工作需要一台气体压缩机、一根输水管或一辆油罐车。这个过程就和简单的机械操作一样容易。唯一要特别注意的是，需要准备一个装有矿石粉的柔软的容器，装置卸下后保存在里面，下一次安装再把装置表面的粉末清洗掉。

简单说来，整个建筑不用金属元件，可以使得结构有最大的活动性。即使建筑物因为外力被破坏了，这样的材料可以避免破坏进一步扩大，这样就给了维修更大的余地。整个操作是不可逆转的。

技术要点
建筑系统与材料——这个基础结构是从海上充气艇得到的灵感。两种材料不同的元件被切割开来并焊接在一起：厚的用于筒形的断面，薄的用于表面的连接。结构的可变几何形并没有使用径向接缝。织物内部的纵向接缝被修补了起来，以抵抗筒的扭矩。气垫的支撑部分内部分为8个约3.6米长的空间，气垫部分内部分为6个约3.1米长的空间。它们都由聚酯织物强化材料制成，表面涂满涂层并以特殊人造橡胶混合物研光。

每个室内房间都可以保持充气的压强平衡，大约为0.2/0.25巴，加上它们的淬火效应可以增强对于撞击的抵抗力，而这要特别归功于充水部分所起的作用。

这种材料可以抵抗所有烃、碳氢化合物和溶剂。它被拉伸到120%，使用温度为－40°～80° C。

入口的控制阀和吸入的空气与水是可移动的，而且必须在折叠之前分离开。建筑物表面有雨水收集口，雨水可以通过收集口流入管道。

消防系统——一个小小的自动装置就能作一个基本的消防系统，在空气管的侧边安装上三个洒水器即可。

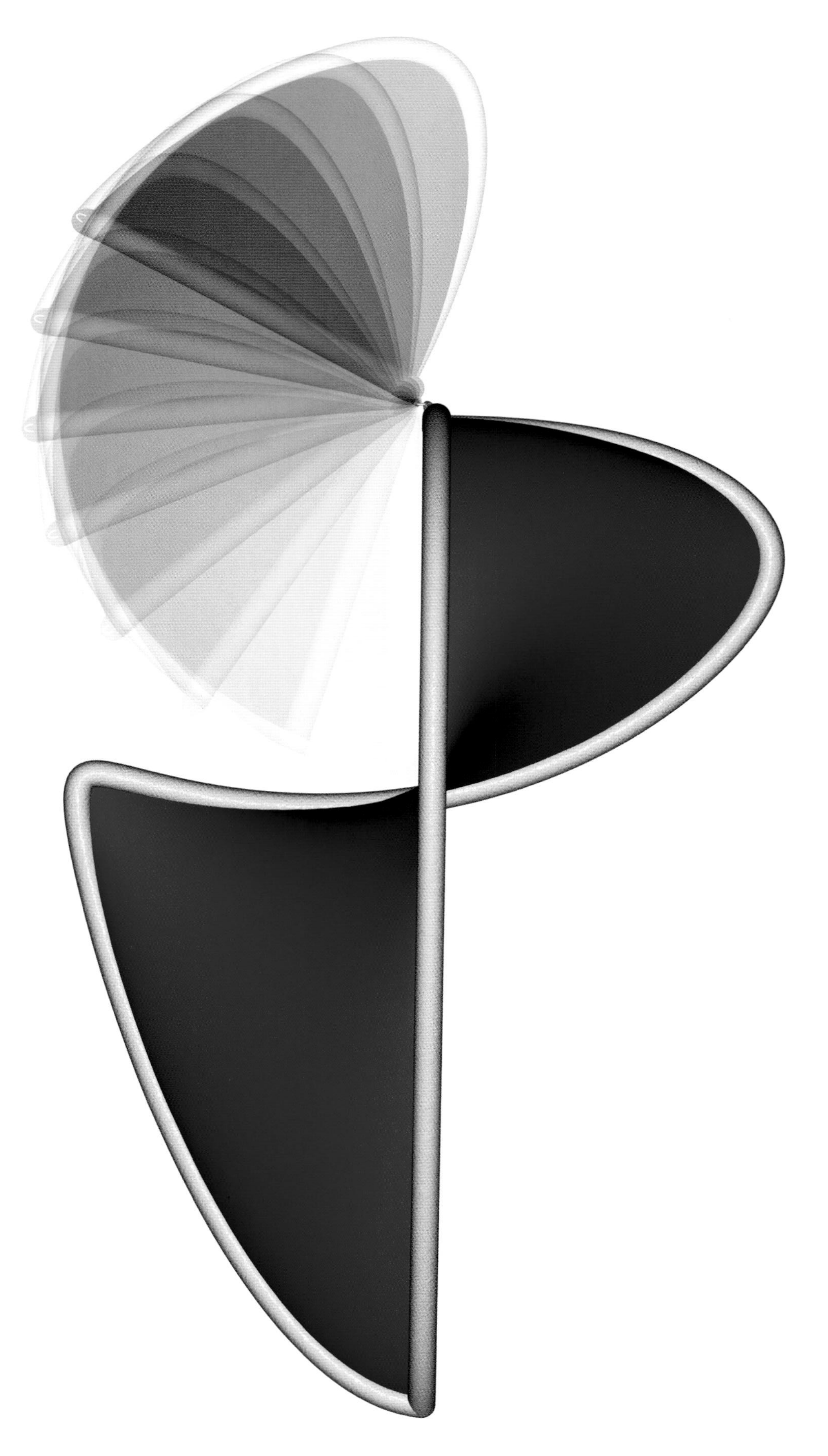

HOV · 138 · Multiversum

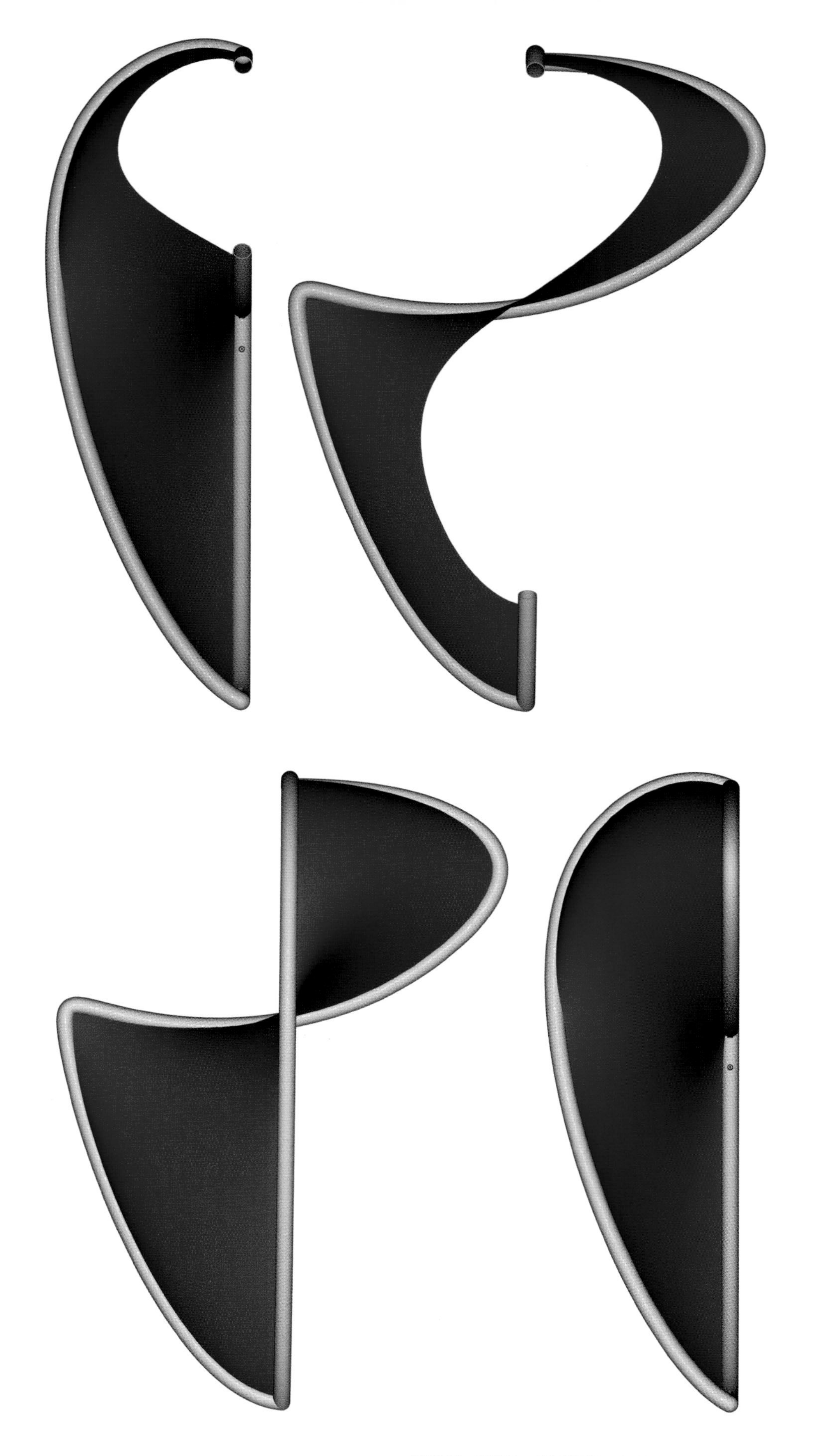

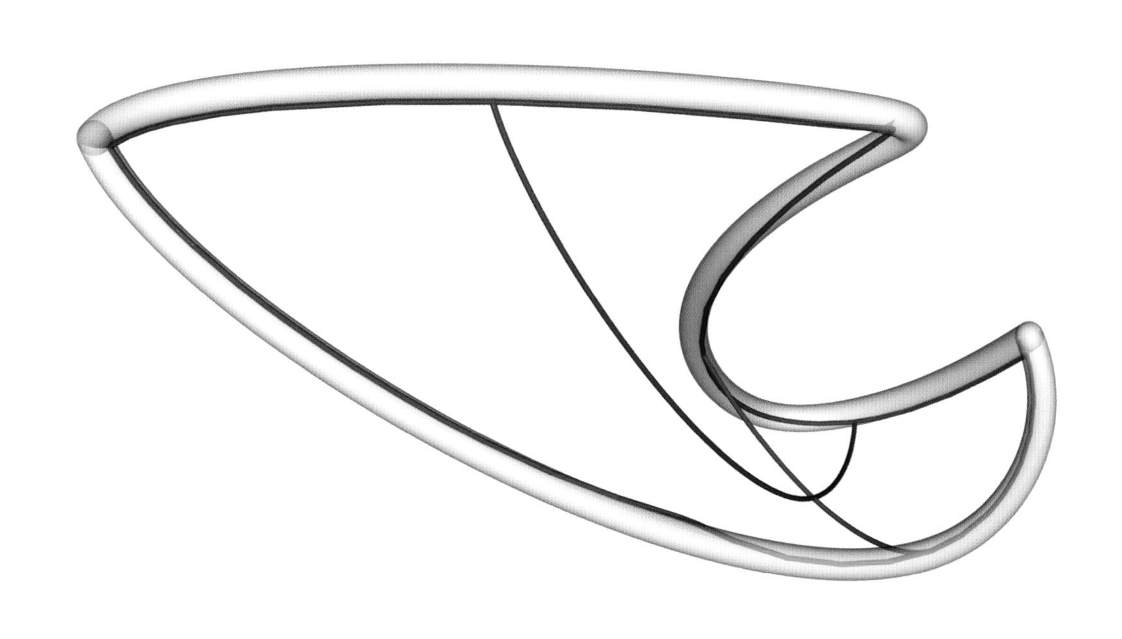

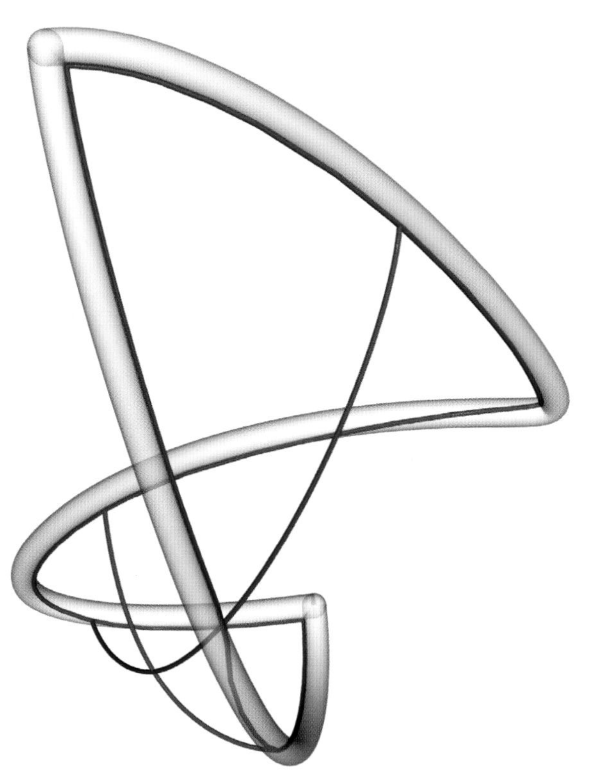

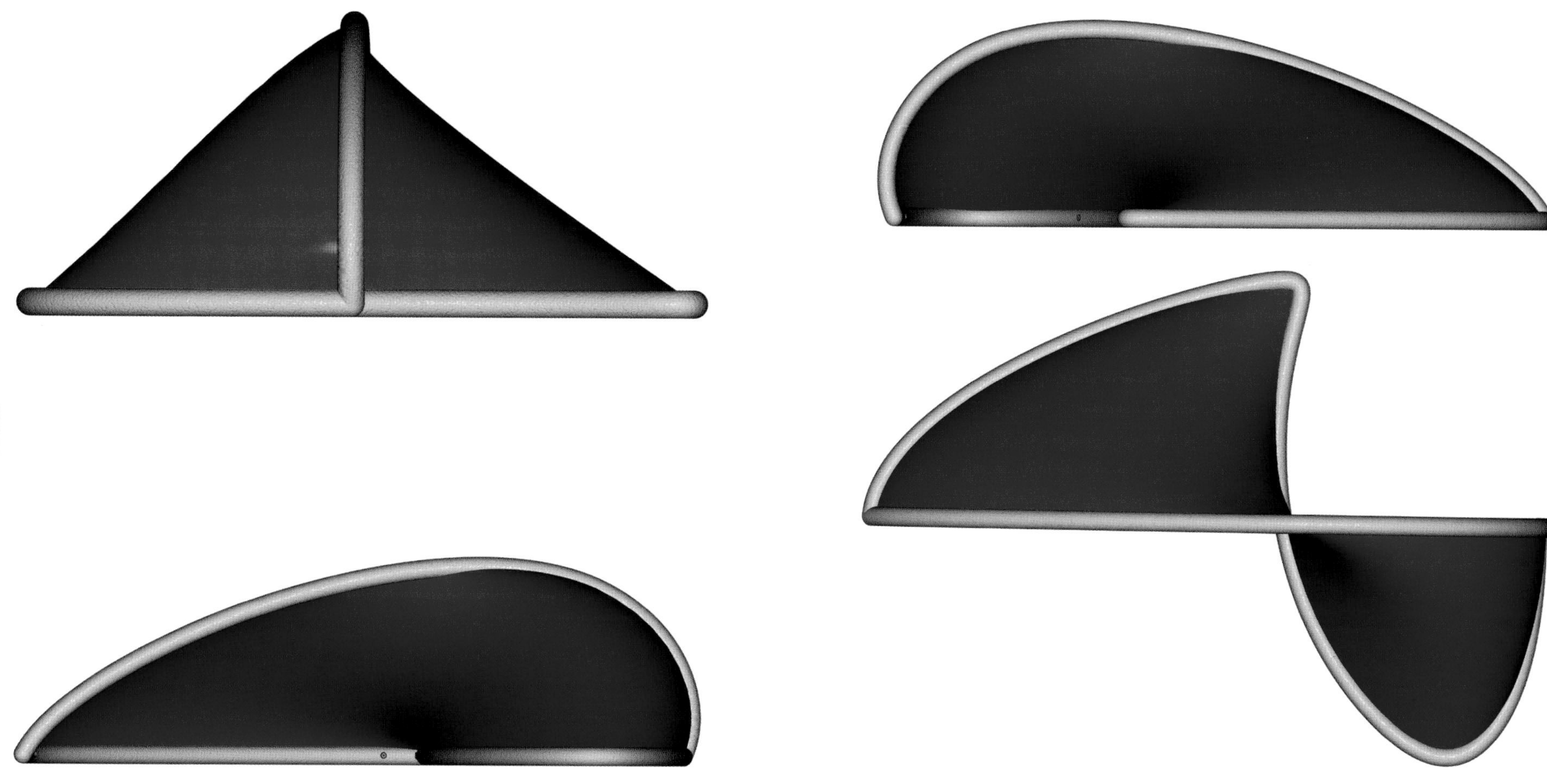

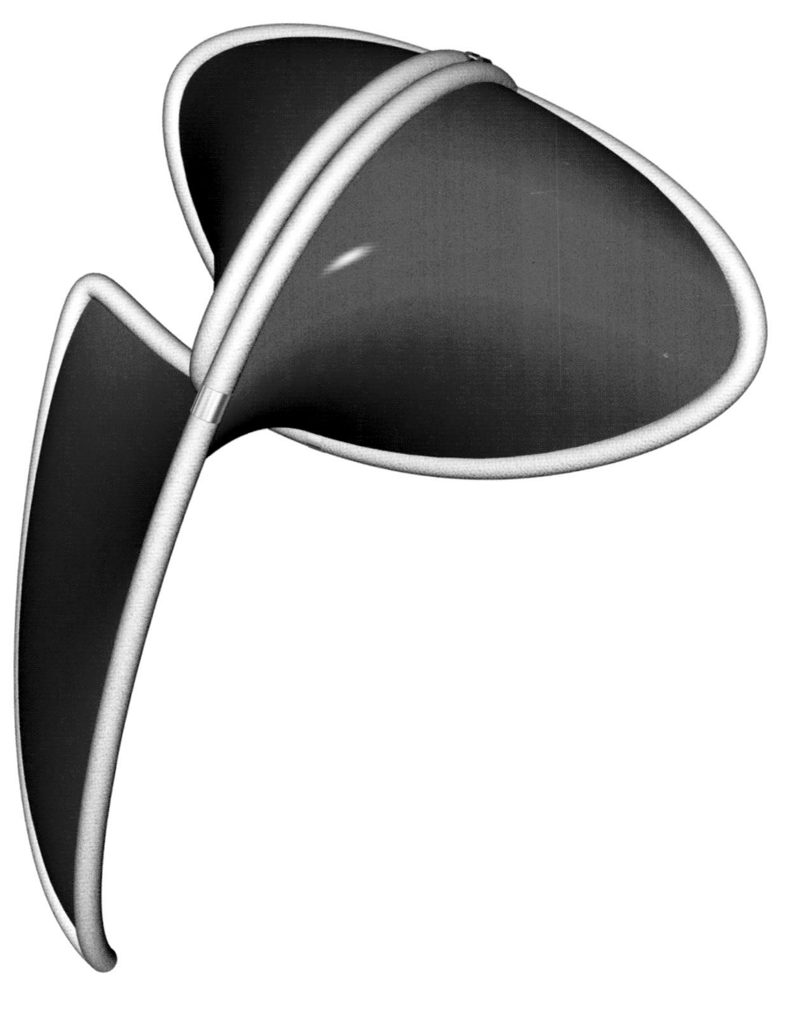

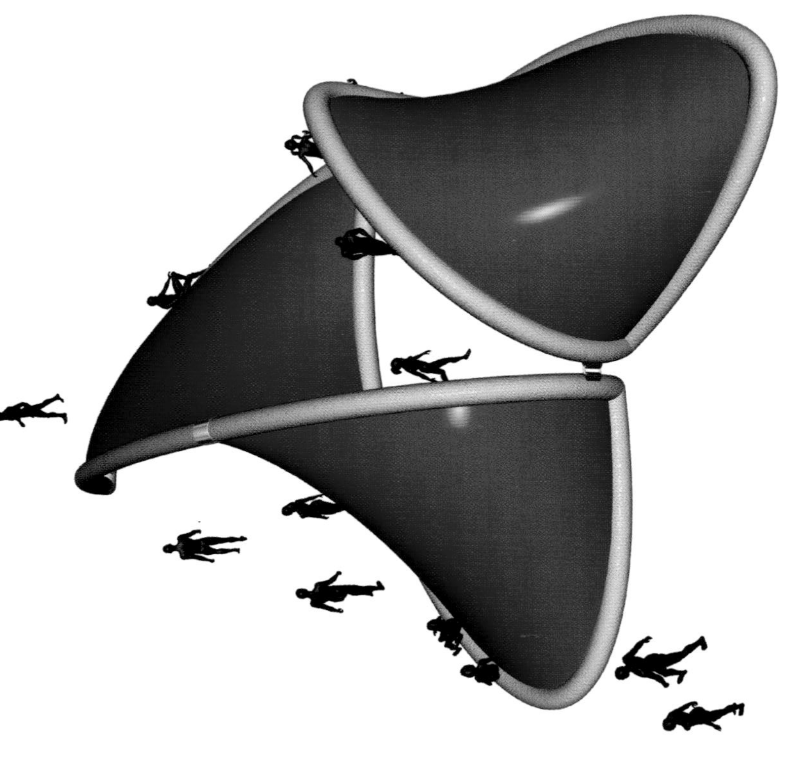

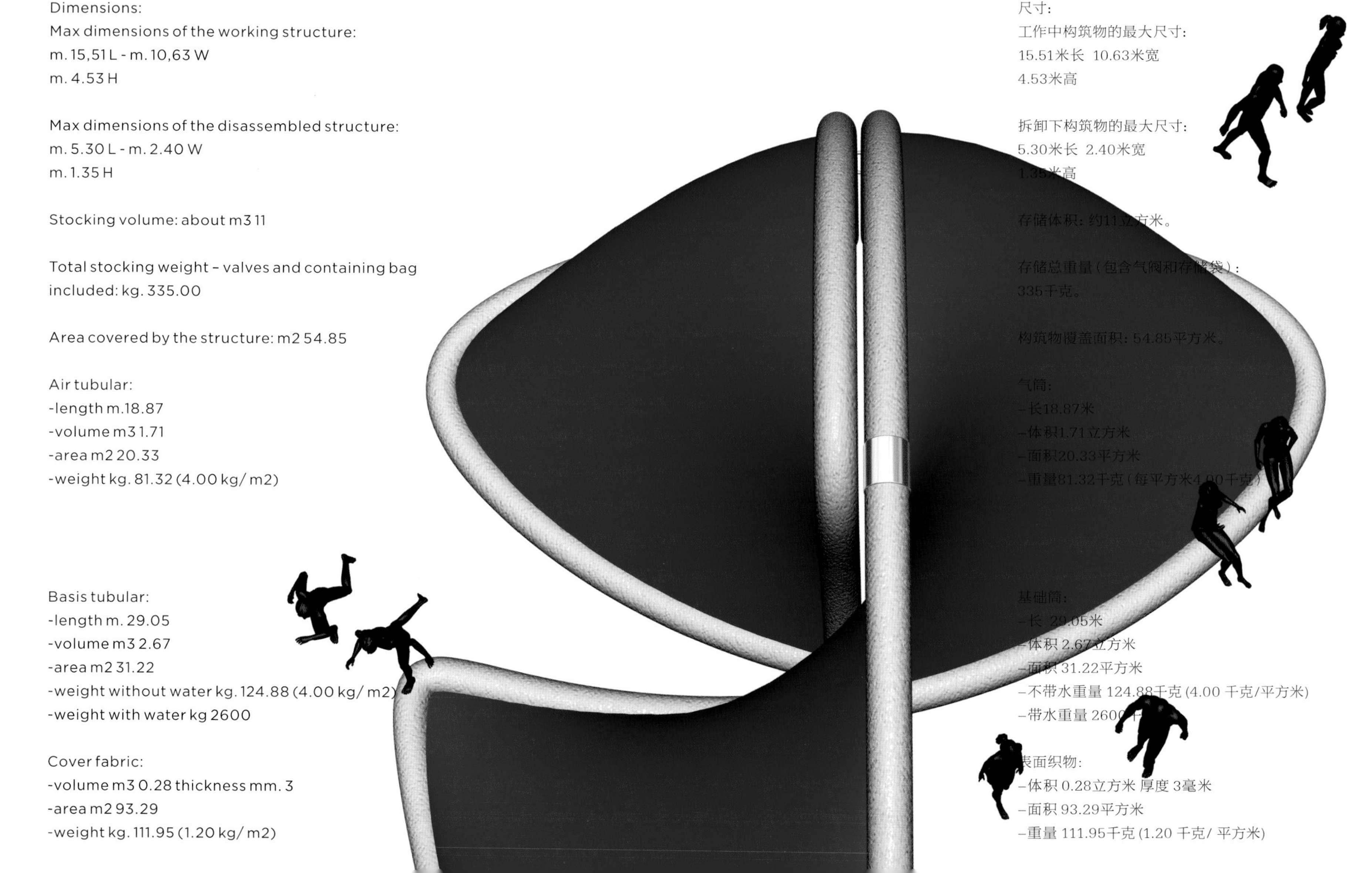

Dimensions:
Max dimensions of the working structure:
m. 15,51 L - m. 10,63 W
m. 4.53 H

Max dimensions of the disassembled structure:
m. 5.30 L - m. 2.40 W
m. 1.35 H

Stocking volume: about m3 11

Total stocking weight – valves and containing bag included: kg. 335.00

Area covered by the structure: m2 54.85

Air tubular:
-length m.18.87
-volume m3 1.71
-area m2 20.33
-weight kg. 81.32 (4.00 kg/ m2)

Basis tubular:
-length m. 29.05
-volume m3 2.67
-area m2 31.22
-weight without water kg. 124.88 (4.00 kg/ m2)
-weight with water kg 2600

Cover fabric:
-volume m3 0.28 thickness mm. 3
-area m2 93.29
-weight kg. 111.95 (1.20 kg/ m2)

尺寸：
工作中构筑物的最大尺寸：
15.51米长 10.63米宽
4.53米高

拆卸下构筑物的最大尺寸：
5.30米长 2.40米宽
1.35米高

存储体积：约11立方米。

存储总重量（包含气阀和存储袋）：
335千克。

构筑物覆盖面积：54.85平方米。

气筒：
–长18.87米
–体积1.71立方米
–面积20.33平方米
–重量81.32千克（每平方米4.00千克）

基础筒：
–长 29.05米
–体积 2.67立方米
–面积 31.22平方米
–不带水重量 124.88千克 (4.00 千克/平方米)
–带水重量 2600千

表面织物：
–体积 0.28立方米 厚度 3毫米
–面积 93.29平方米
–重量 111.95千克 (1.20 千克/ 平方米)

Approximate assembling time
4 workers

Unloading
40 “

Positioning
15 “

Inflating
30 “
(depending on the compressor power)

Water inlet
40 “
(depending on the pumping system)

Total
2h 05”
Approximate disassembling time - 4 workers

Emptying
60 “
(depending on the water drawing system)

Deflating
30 “
(depending on the aspiration power)

Wrapping
60 “

Loading
40 “

Total
3h 10”

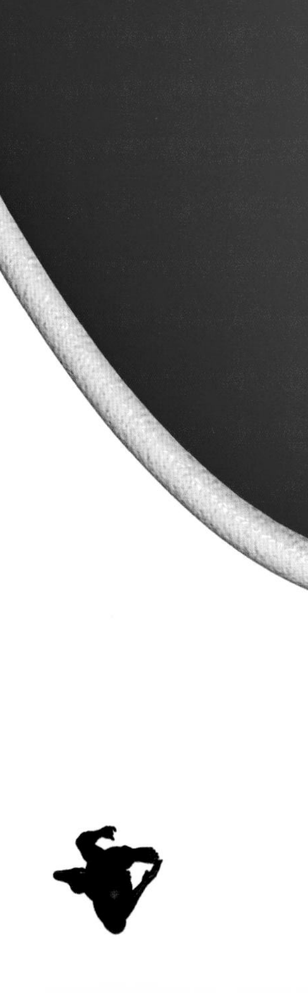

估计装配时间
四个工人

卸载
40分钟

定位
15分钟

充气
30分钟
（取决于压缩机的功率）

进水
40分钟
（取决于泵）

合计
2小时5分钟
估计卸载时间 4名工人

水倒空
60分钟
（取决于吸水装置）

放气
30分钟
（取决于抽气机功率）

包装
60分钟

装载
40分钟

总共
3小时10分钟

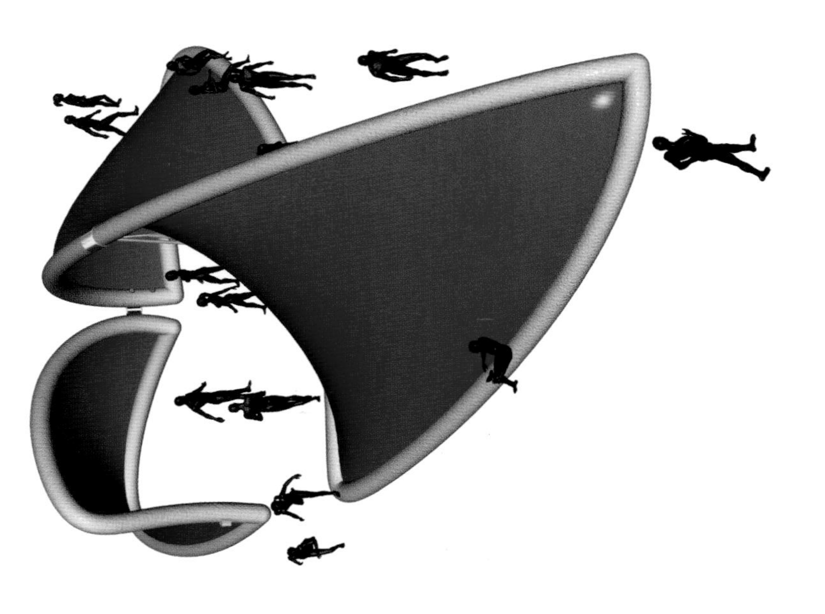

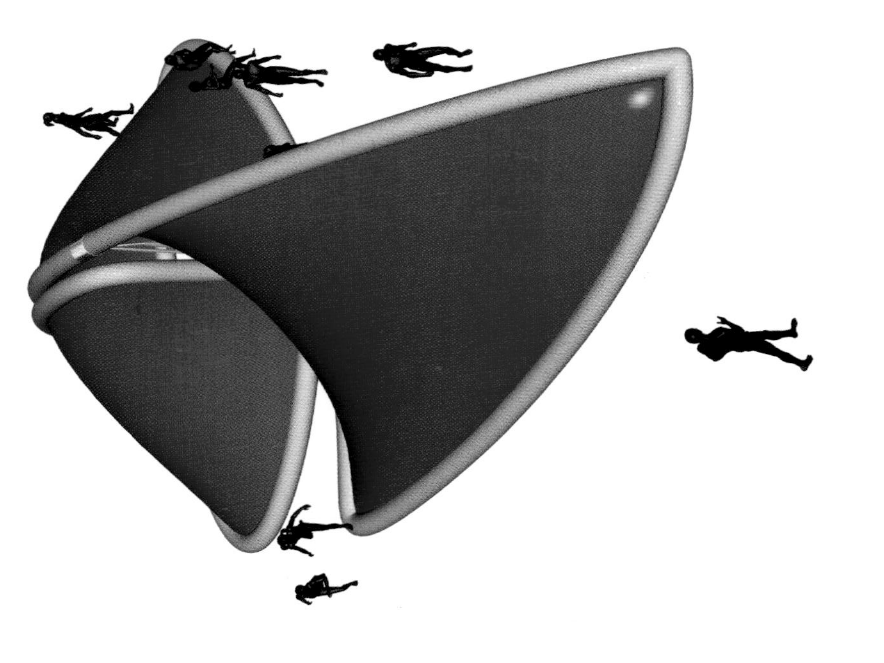

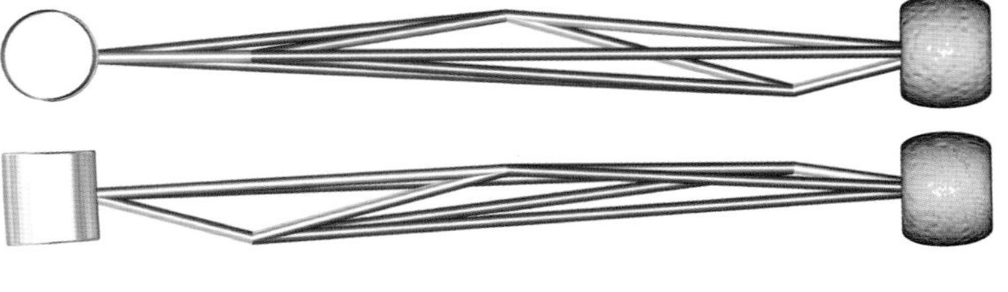

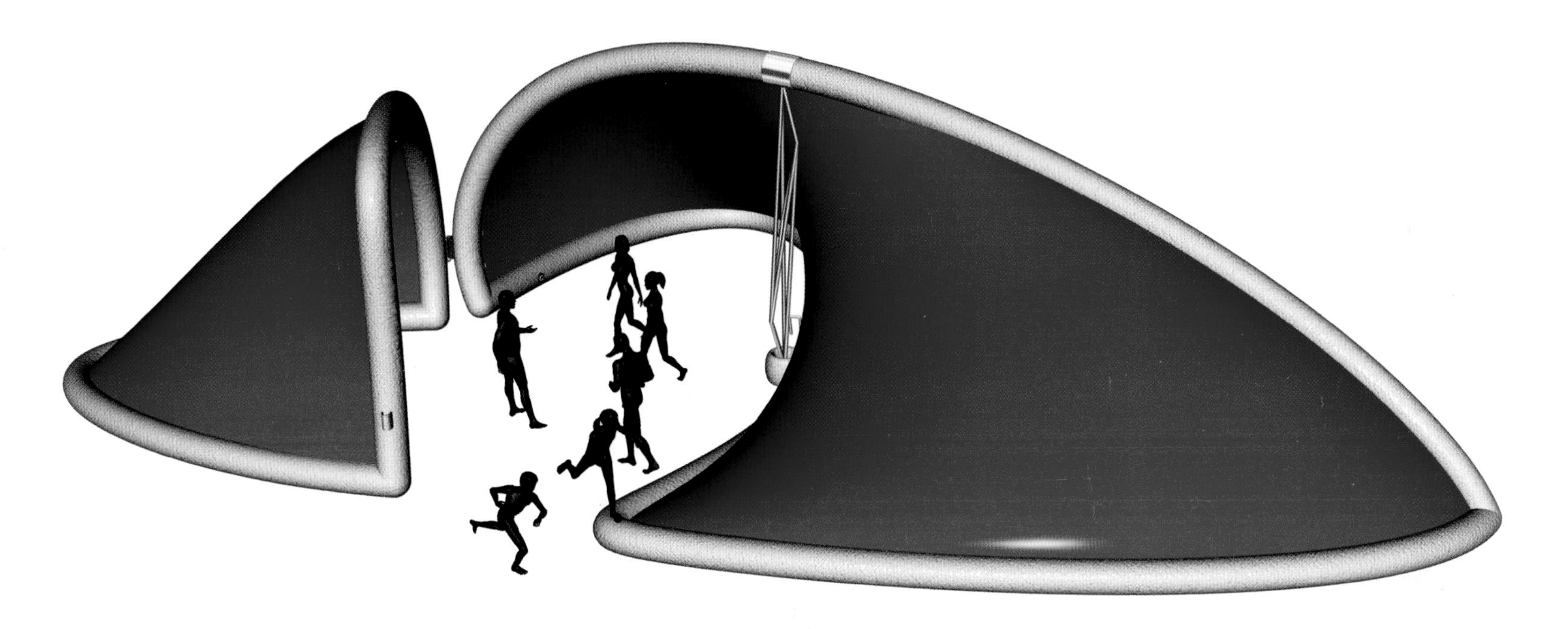

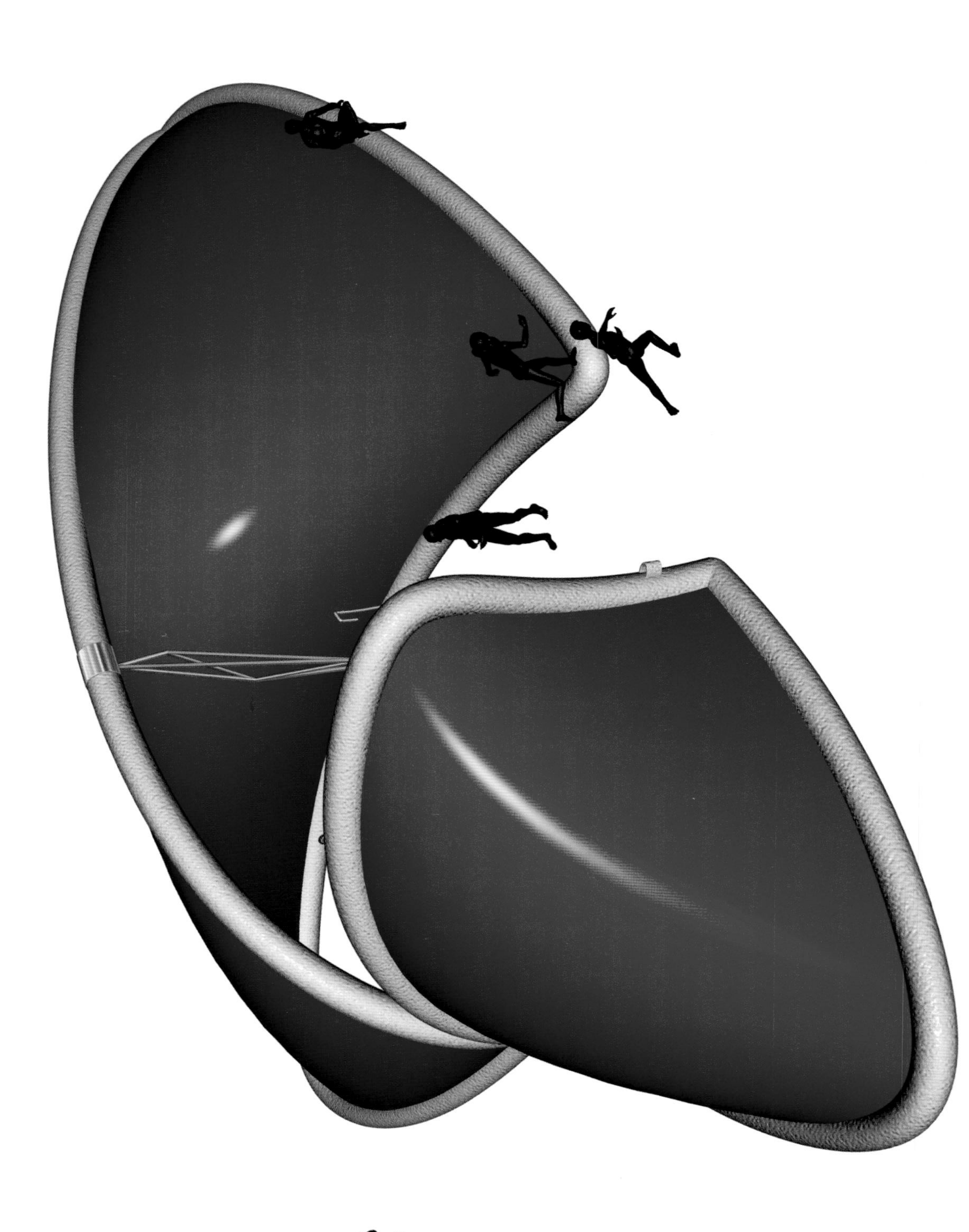

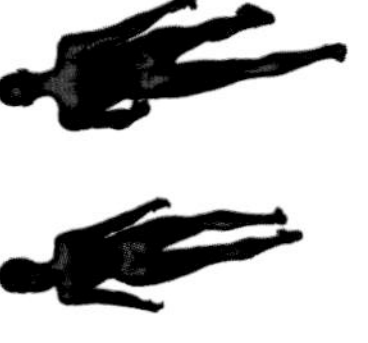

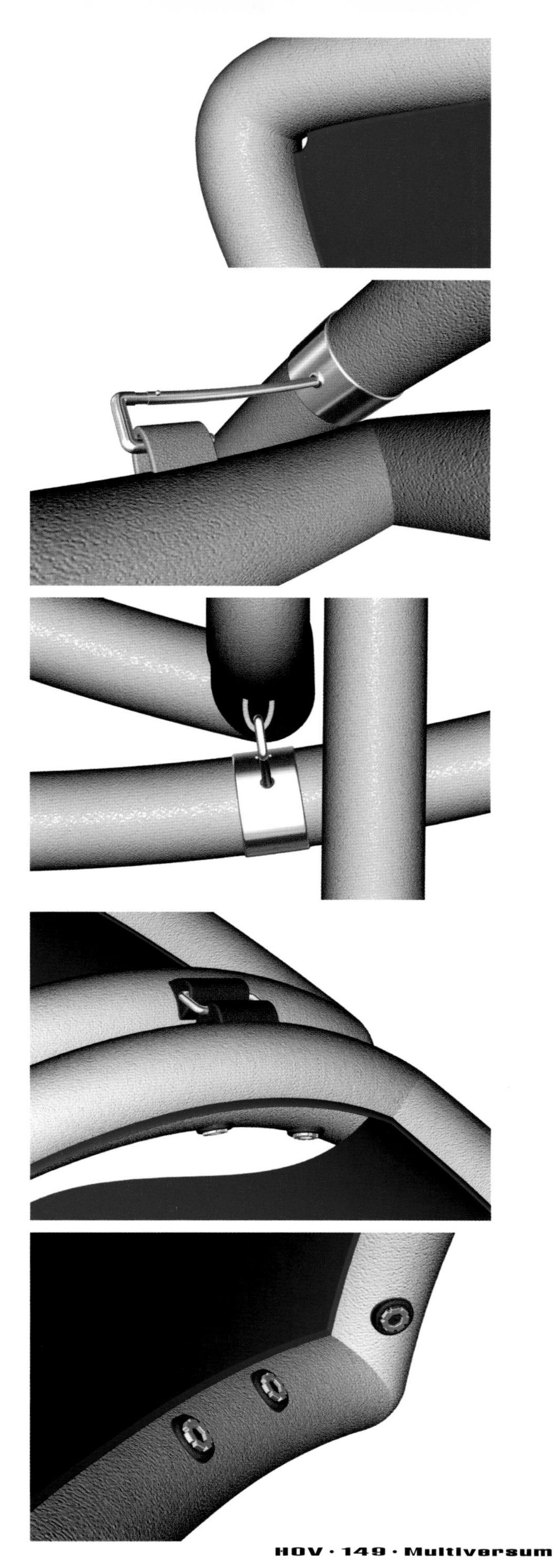

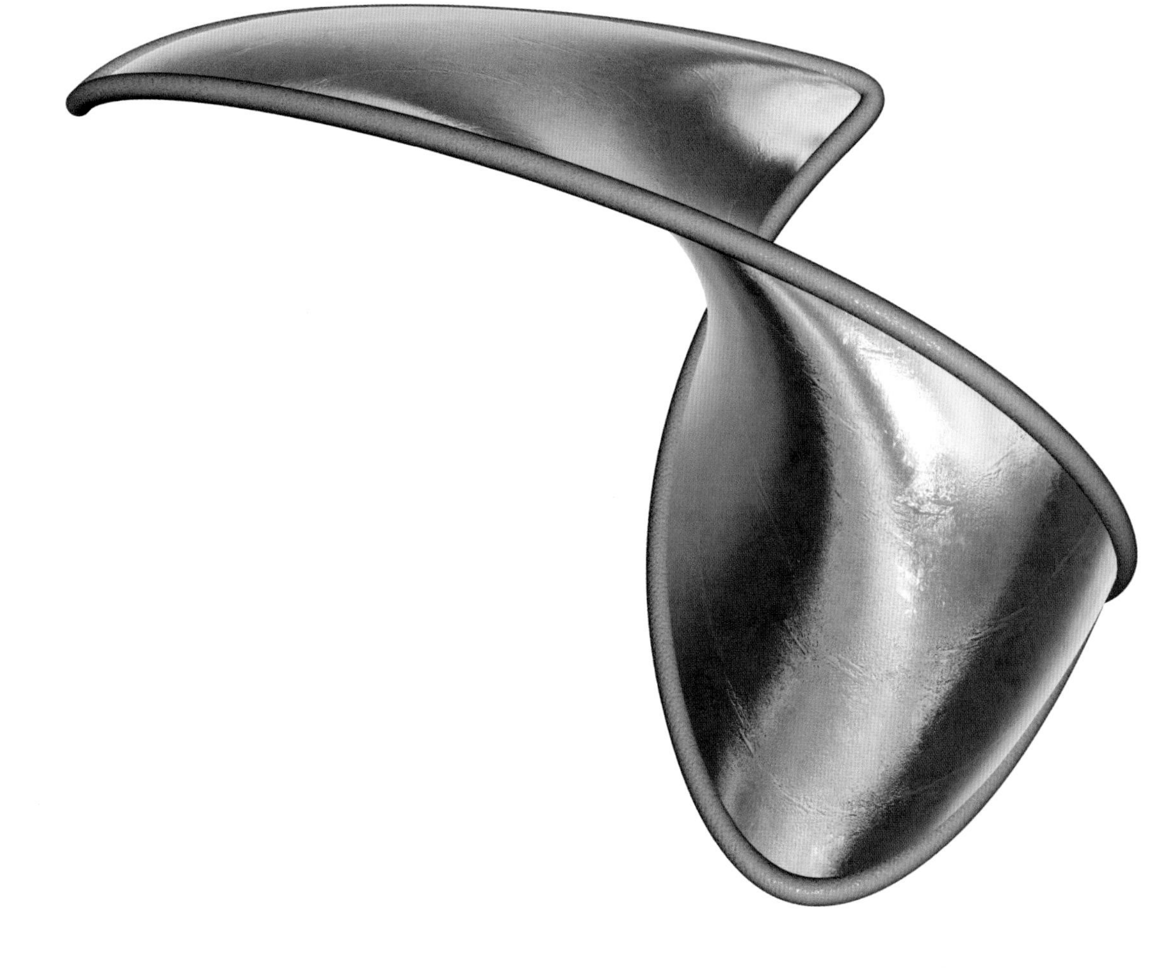

收集管线一般是放在外面的，并由合适的节点接在建筑上。但是在特殊的环境下，也可以用自动或人工压缩机取用筒内所存的水。然后水被压到洒水器的管道内。这样用水并不影响结构的稳定性，结构内的筒在用完水之后会再次被填满。

照明系统——照明系统可以安装在空气筒所组成的凹槽里。防水的照明元件被安装在刚性塑料结构上，这些元件是可移动的并与冷光灯装配在一起。结构管道旁，移动板被安装在有遮蔽的凹槽里。

封闭式套装用具——座椅\餐桌与架子，还有一个安装有接线电缆或网络的旋转板，设置在防灾结构内的一个封闭部分里。这个套装需要一个额外的装置，它和装置本身用同样的材料制成，但是只有空气充气筒。整个套装的重量大约为129千克。

开敞/封闭系统都是人工操作的，封闭式系统的连接带上有曲柄装置。

后者由一个销控制住，销末端有一个锁。如果由于地面的情况或用途的原因，结构需要格外刚硬，那就可以用一个钢制的支撑物，它可以根据充气环的压力来调整高度。

运输与耐久度——装卸的过程并不需要什么特别的装备。只要运货汽车上有油动力起重臂和5.3米长的运货平台就够了。

存放的容器上有钩状的把手，可以一个接一个叠放起来。

根据建筑所包含的材料以及经过测试的技术，可以推断出如果不算装卸的程序，并按照上文所提到的要点进行操作，它在地中海气候下的使用寿命为10年左右。

估计花费——把它和运用相似技术和材料的构筑物的花费相比较，这个项目的产品所有的元件花费为23，000欧元。因为这个产品里所涉及的工业元件的价格取决于产品的数量，所以这个估价可能有浮动。于是我们考虑进行小批量生产，但生产的数量不少于5件。

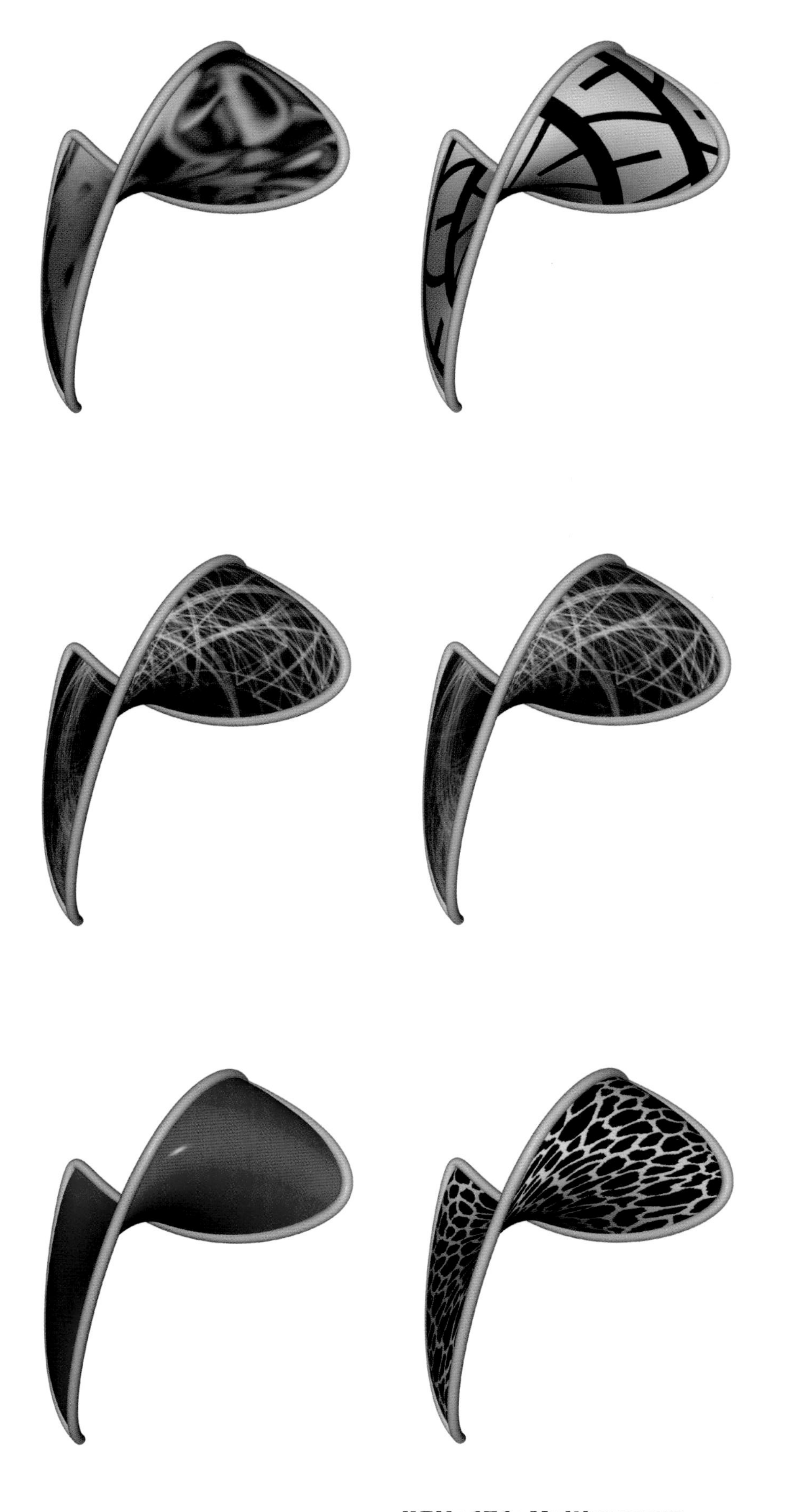

Ask any foreigner if he knows Ancona and the possibility is that you will be told of a port of shipment to Greece. Ask any Italian and perhaps you will hear of "that small size Adriatic town where Nanni Moretti's La Stanza del Figlio and Luchino Visconti's Ossessione were filmed."
Now: Ancona is just this, and at the same time much more.

It is nonsensical and at the same time profound: all depends on the individual reaction. Not much seems to happen. Like in a Beckett's play there is neither a plot nor a coherent action.
From its geographical appearance onwards, it is nevertheless very theatrical.

The chief town of the Marches, Ancona (110.000 inhabitants) lies as an amphitheatre on the hills of a promontory on the Adriatic Sea. Founded late in the 4th century b.C. by Greeks from Syracuse (Ancona < O. G. ankon, elbow), the city prospered under the Romans. In the 9th century it became a semi-independent maritime republic under the nominal rule of the popes, to whose direct control it passed in 1532. Part of the unified Reign of Italy in 1861, the town was badly damaged in World War II and during an earthquake in 1972.

A major role in Ancona's history is played by the port. It is the most important port on the middle coast of the Adriatic Sea, both naval and commercial, handling freight and passenger traffic to Yugoslavia, Greece, Turkey, Israel and Egypt. One of the main monuments in the town is in fact Trajan's Arch (another element of transition!), perfectly preserved and erected by the port in honour of the Roman Emperor who had ordered its enlargement (2nd cent. a.C.). This is the vital centre of the town, a sort of navel that gives nourishment and new lymph, besides opening doors to the Unknown.

This part of the Adriatic sea itself has peculiar physical features. It is only 35 feet deep on the average. The underwater visibility is nevertheless very limited because of suspended calcareous particles. Always regarded as a special way to the east world, in 1982 this sea was the scenery of a mysterious fact. A French sailboat with 5 persons on board disappeared off Ancona and no wreckage was ever found. A good closing scene, isn't it?

Nature revenge. Such is the feeling also while walking from the old lighthouse through the Jewish cemetery to the top of the sheer cliff behind the hospital Umberto I. Centuries long military occupation has preserved spots of savageness where rare vegetal species and protected animals live undisturbed though at very few metres from the busy town centre.

But Ancona is also rich in interesting works of art, the most outstanding of which is the Cathedral of San Ciriaco. A former pagan temple dedicated to the Goddess of Love, it has a Romanesque structure with Gothic and Byzantine influences. It lies on the highest hill of the natural amphitheatre and dominates both the sea and the other historical places. The Roman arena, the old lighthouse, the Napoleonic fortress, the Adriatic all around, the port: all of them contribute to make the town historical centre an ideal scenery for something "on the threshold": in-between East and West, Night and Day, Good and Evil, Fire and Water, Nature and Civilization, Sickness and Health. So, where could the tragedy of an Hamlet type character have taken place but in a transitional town like Ancona, whose old hospital, among historical buildings and deserted natural areas, is also being moved somewhere else?

如果问一个外国人他是否知道安科纳，那他可能会告诉你这是希腊的一个装运港。如果问一个意大利人，可能他就会说那是“亚得里亚海沿岸的小镇，南尼·莫莱蒂的电影《儿子的房间》和卢奇诺·维斯康蒂的电影《沉沦》的拍摄地”。
现在：安科纳城确实如此，而且不仅如此。

这里既显得毫无意义同时也意义深远，一切都取决于个人的反应。看起来这里没有什么大事发生。就好像贝克特戏剧中的那样，这里既没有阴谋也没有深谋远虑的行动。

安科纳城是马凯省的主要城镇，人口110，000，坐落在亚得里亚海海角的山坡上，呈阶梯状。公元前4世纪晚期，来自锡拉库扎的希腊人创建了这个城市，随后古罗马人的统治使它富饶起来。公元9世纪，在教皇有名无实的统治下，它成为一个半独立的海上共和国。1532年，它正式成为独立共和国，随后于1861年被统一入意大利。第二次世界大战和1972年的地震都曾使这个城镇受到严重的伤害。

港口在安科纳的历史中扮演了重要的角色。它是亚得里亚海海岸线中部最重要的港口，军商两用。它控制了通往南斯拉夫、希腊、土耳其、以色列和埃及的货运与客运交通。图拉真拱门是城镇里一个重要的纪念碑，它记录了一次历史上的转折。港口的人民竖立起这个纪念碑，是为了纪念那位于公元后2世纪下令扩大安科纳的古罗马皇帝，这个纪念碑至今保存完好。除了向未知世界打开的大门，这个纪念碑是镇上最中心的部分，就像给整个城镇提供营养的地方。

靠近这里的亚得里亚海本身也有特变的物理特性。它平均只有10.7米深，水下的可见度却十分有限，因为水中悬浮有石灰质粒子。这里一向被看作是通往东方的一条特殊通道，1982年这片海域上发生了一起神秘事件。一艘载有5人的法国帆船在离开安科纳后消失在海上，遇难人员没有被找到。以上是有关安科纳的故事，这是一个不错的结尾吧。

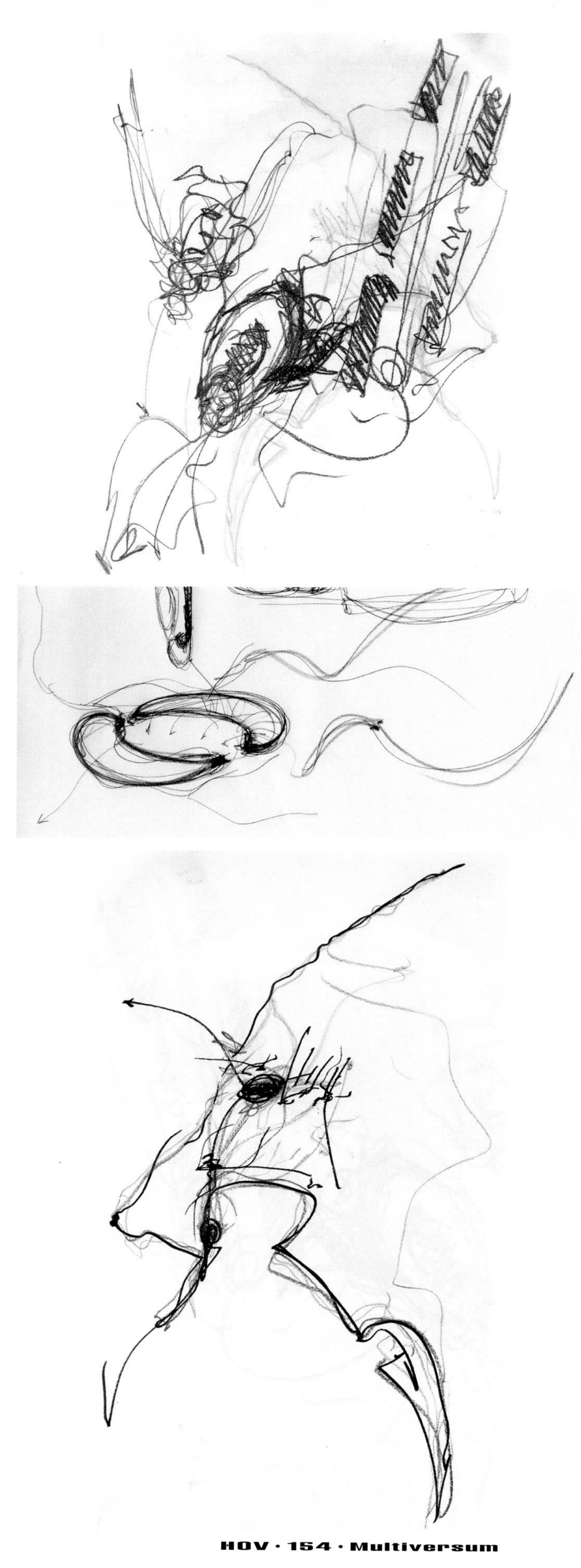

难道这是大自然的报复？我从古老的灯塔出发，穿过犹太人的公墓，来到了陡峭的悬崖顶，前面就是翁贝托一世医院。几个世纪以来，它一直作为军用。这里保存了一些荒野的景色，虽然离繁忙的镇中心很近，但是这里有一些稀有植物和保护动物，它们都不受干扰地安然生活在此。

安科纳也有很多有趣的艺术品，其中最杰出的就是圣齐里亚克大教堂。它的前身是拜祭爱之女神的教堂。它的结构是罗马式的，风格上受到歌特和拜占庭的影响。它位于自然阶梯地形的最高的山坡上，可以俯瞰到大海和其他的历史古迹：古罗马竞技场、古灯塔、拿破仑时代的堡垒、亚得里亚海、港口……这些组成了一幅“边界处”的理想景色——东方与西方、夜晚与白天、善良与邪恶、火与水、自然与文明、疾病与健康。安科纳正是这样的一个过渡性的城镇，不正像一个哈姆雷特式的悲剧发生地吗？而处于历史古迹和荒野自然中的古老医院，也已经被搬迁走了。

A

by Michele Gabbanelli

(with acknowledgements to William Shakespeare, James Joyce, Pier Paolo Pasolini, John Donne)

Ancona former hospital Umberto I appears as the ideal location for an event that goes beyond any theatrical dimension but the etymological one (e.g. theastai, to watch).
We better talk of a RITE, as ancestral as the sea surrounding the promontory on which the hospital lies; as pagan as the temple dedicated to Venus on the opposite hill (now the Cathedral of san Ciriaco); as fierce as the battles of gladiators that took place in the near Roman arena; as deadly as the natural terrace dominating the town historical centre, where medical garbage has been accumulated for over a century; as pure as the intact Mediterranean bush separating the chosen area from the sheer cliffs.

Our hypothesis is that all the pavilions are being moved to the new suburban hospital except this last one. Here, hundreds of Hamlets gather to perform one after another their paternal deprivation. While waiting their turn, they lie in bed watching on screens NATURE VERSUS MATERNAL KNOT. On the polluted terrace Everybody faces the A -topics in a literally tearing monologue:

abort me
symbiotic mother
or
let me leave let me live

Barbarians (in the etymological meaning of the term: foreigners) used to come from the sea. So does Horatio, whom Hamlet refers to as father, friend and foe:

Batter my heart, three-person'd God:
Divorce me, untie, or break that knot again,
Take me to you, imprison me, for I,
Except you enthral me, never shall be free,
Nor ever chaste, except you ravish me.

A wise playwriter/director would have not granted such an exiled character happiness.
But the temptation was too big:

flights of angels sing us to our rest
and the rest is silence

A

by Michele Gabbanelli

（感谢威廉莎士比亚、詹姆斯乔伊斯、皮埃尔·保罗·帕索里尼、约翰·邓恩）

安科纳的前医院——翁贝托一世医院是可以发生最最戏剧化的语源事件的场所。
我们最好谈论一下这里的一种习俗，如医院所在的海角周围的那片海洋一样古老，如拜祭维纳斯女神的教堂一样属于异教，如古罗马竞技场里角斗士的搏斗一样激烈，如俯瞰镇上历史中心的自然梯田一样死气沉沉，如陡峭悬崖与场地之间的地中海灌木一样纯洁。

我们的假想是留下最后这一个亭子，其余都搬迁到郊外的新医院里。在这个亭子里，成千上百个哈姆雷特聚集在一起，一遍一遍地演绎父王对他们的盘剥。排队等待的时候，他们就躺在床上看屏幕上的“与自然相抵的恋母情结”。在脏兮兮的台地上，每个人都面对着重要的题目，念着伤心的独白：

遗弃我
共生的母，
或者，
让我离开让我生存

野蛮人（根据语源学这个单词的意思是外国人）曾经从大海上来。哈姆雷特的父亲、朋友、仇敌、霍雷肖也是从大海而来。

打击我的心灵吧，三位一体的上父：
使我脱离你的敌人，使我自由或拆毁那个结合，
带我去你那里，把我禁锢，为了我，
除非你使我成为你的奴隶，我永远得不到自由。
也不可能变为贞洁，除非你把我奸污。

一个聪明的剧作家/导演不会给这样一个放逐的角色以幸福。但是诱惑实在太大了：

天使的飞翔像我们歌唱，祝我们安息，
安息即为沉寂。

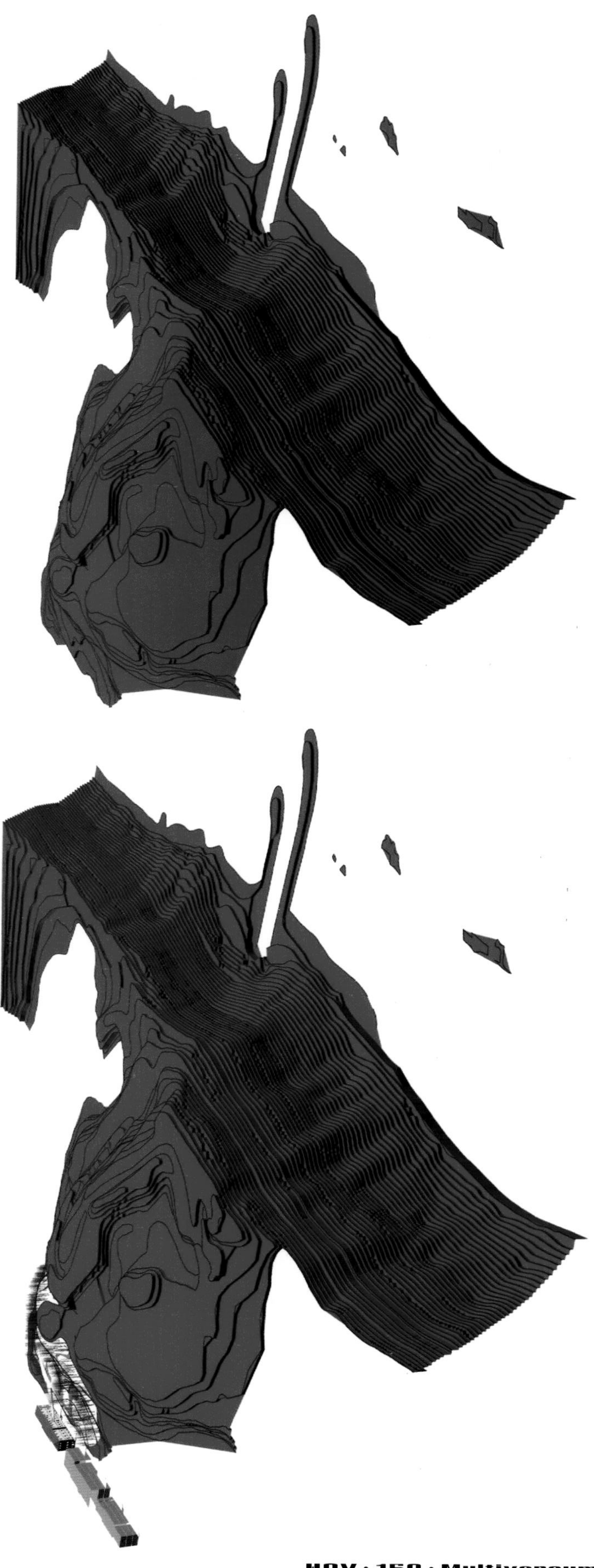

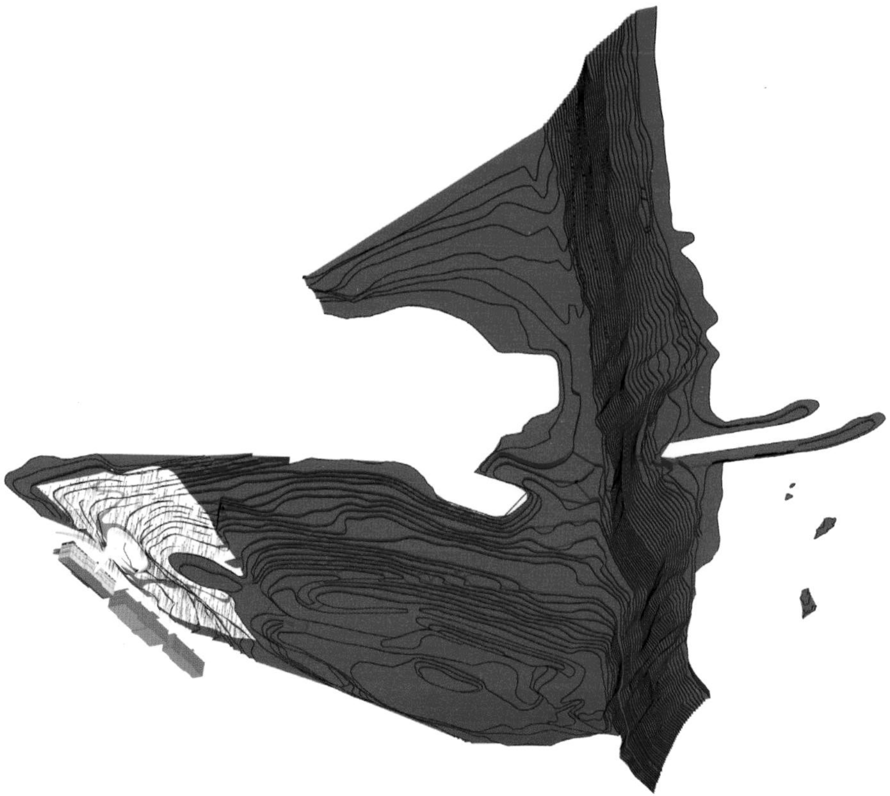

Ancona hospital "Umberto I", meant as a health reference point for the whole Marche region, was built in the second half of the 19° century.
It presents a "pavilions structure", which is typical for the period and consists of single buildings each dedicated to a branch of medicine.
It has almost doubled its dimensions over the years, so that in the early 80s the whole side of the Cardeto Mount, the one towards the town centre, has progressively been occupied.
Since the replacement of the major national health centres began, the different departments of the hospital have been progressively moved to a new suburban structure. The last administrative offices are also going to follow.
The plant is therefore going to be deserted, and the owner, "Azienda Sanitaria di Ancona" (Ancona health services) is looking for proposals and suggestions about its possible use.
The town-planning scheme provides for not more than 50% of the buildings to become residential and about 20 % to be transformed into offices and commercial areas, the open spaces and part of the buildings being at disposal for public use.

The hospital logistical structures (fuel, heating and lighting systems, storehouses, maintenance, waste material, etc) have been assembled in the up part of the area (complex. 35.000 sq m) that is not accessible to the public and almost invisible.
The long isolation accorded to this area through the surrounding pavilions of the hospital, allows now for perspectives and views of the town that are unexpected even to experts.
When the military zones (that in the photographs, according to the law, are covered in thick green) are dismantled, a well preserved naturalistic area dominating the sea with intact Mediterranean bush will be enjoyable too.

The garbage area, previously used also as a parking-place, is the centre of a symbolic and relational system. In the architectonic perspective it becomes the very heart of the performance, where the two characters meet.
The audience settles down at the last two floors of the former infectious diseases pavilion. These undergo no changes, neither in the room distribution nor in the bathrooms and in the lavatories. At both of the floors the audience will be either lying in the beds just like patients (up to 60 persons) or sitting on benches (up to 408 persons).
The footbridge connects the second floor with the stage; besides, an exit for the actor on duty is on the opposite side of the building, in the dressing-rooms area.
The implied technology and all the materials derive from the field of navigation: the main structure is made of resin-glass with the surface final touches of opaque putty; the movable transparent surfaces are of thermosetting polycarbonate; the access, of soft plastic.
Should the whole hospital area be taken into consideration for a recovery, the old store-houses near the area chosen for the performance will be removed. A parking will take their place.

安科纳的翁贝托一世医院建于19世纪后半叶，它是为全马凯省的人提供医疗服务。
它是“穹顶结构”结构，在那个年代是很典型的。它由若干个建筑单体组成，每个隶属于一个部门。
这些年来它的规模扩大了两倍，所以在20世纪80年代早期，Cardeto山朝向镇中心的那一边渐渐被占了。
自从国家医疗中心开始兴建，医院的各个部门开始往郊区的新楼搬迁。现在最后一个行政部门也准备搬走了。
现在这个建筑要被遗弃了，它的所有者——安科纳公共医疗卫生服务——正在征询有关该建筑再利用的提议。
城镇规划提议该建筑的50%用作居住，20%用作商业办公，其余部分和开敞空间则作为公共用途。

医院的后勤部分（燃料、取暖、照明系统、储藏室、维修、垃圾等）被安排在建筑的上层。该地区它们由多个单元组成。公众无法到达那里而且不会看见它。医院周围的亭子曾长期使它与外界隔绝，现在可以让人们在那里欣赏镇上的风景，连专家都没有预料到会有这样的美景。

垃圾区原先也被用作停车场。使这个从建筑的角度来看，这里是演出的中心场所，是两个角色见面的地方。
观众就坐在原先传染病部门建筑的一、二层楼里。在这两层楼里，观众可以像病人一样躺在床上（最多60人），或者坐在长凳上（最多408人）。
二楼和舞台之间有人行天桥相连接，另外，楼的另一边是更衣化妆区，那里有一个供演职人员使用的出口。建筑运用了航海领域所用的技术与材料，主要结构由树脂玻璃制成，表面是不透明的抹灰。可移动的透明表面材料为热硬化聚碳酸酯，入口处则使用软性塑料。
如果整个医院都要进行修复，那场地边用作表演的储藏室就会搬走，并以一个停车场取而代之。这样在房间分布和洗手间的安排上都没有变化。

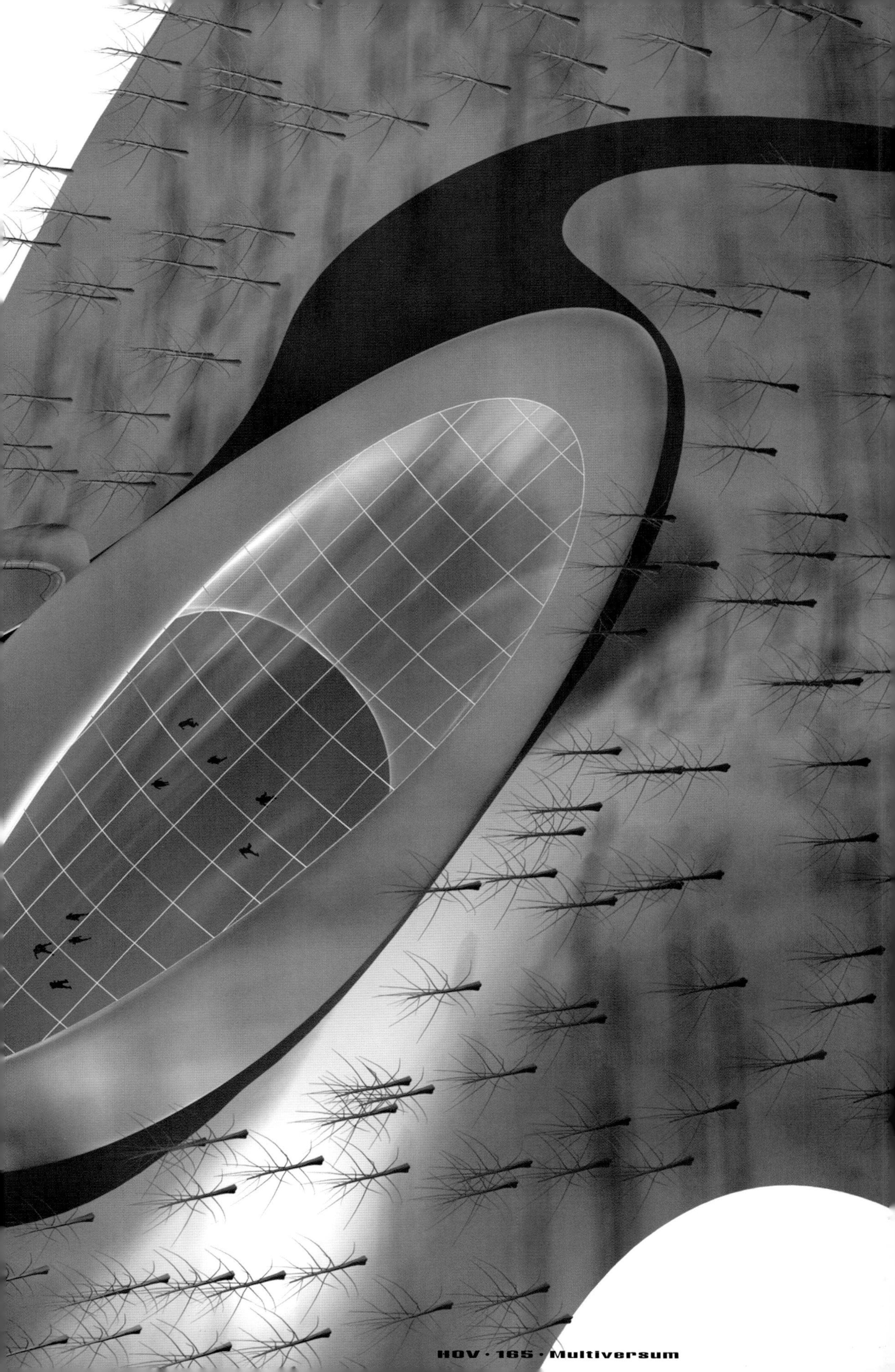

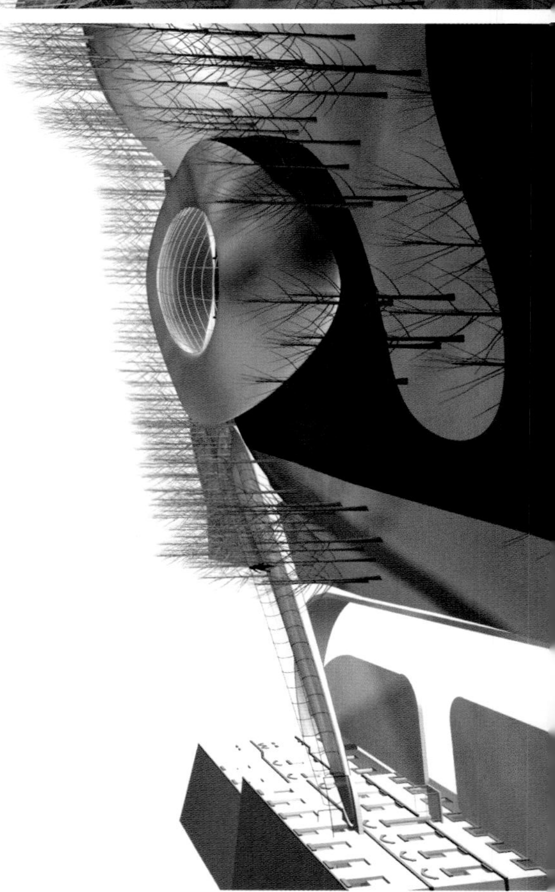

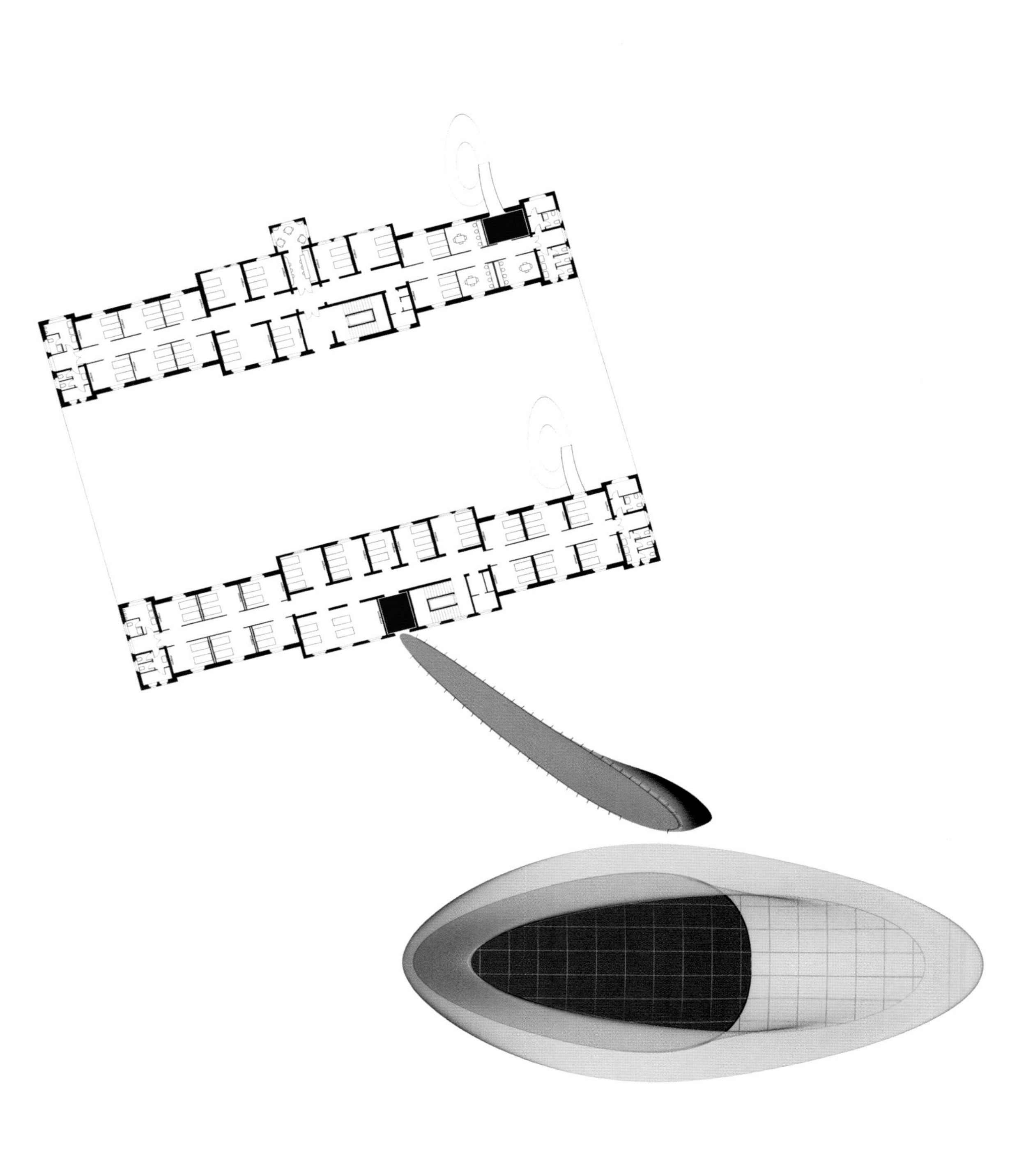

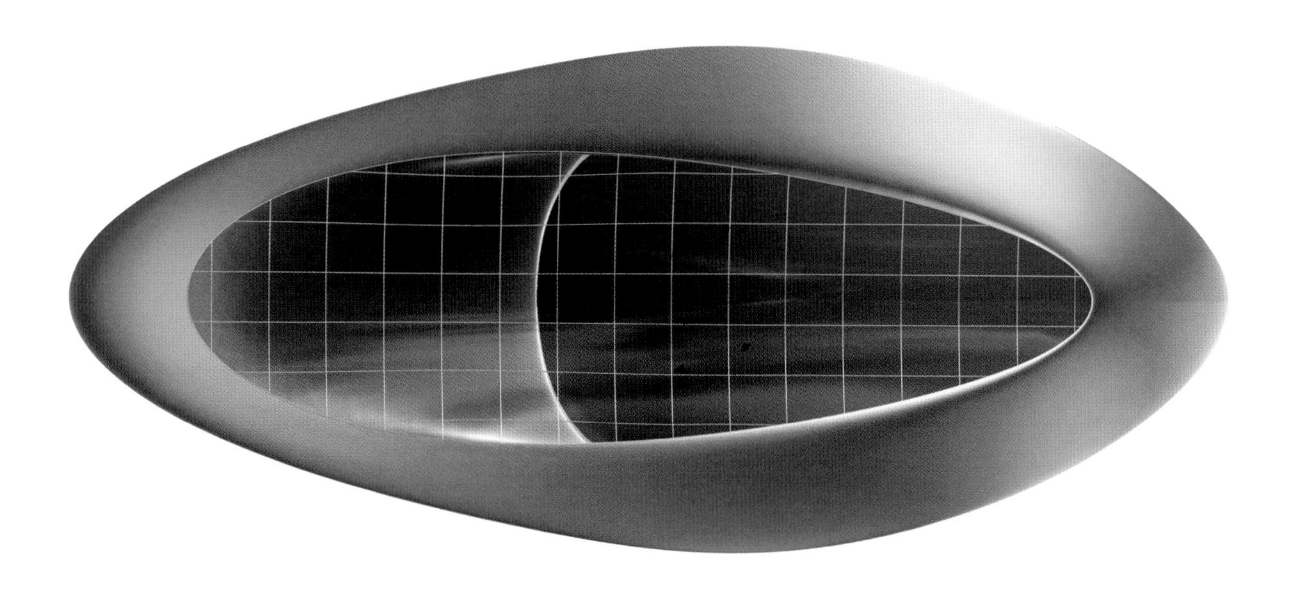

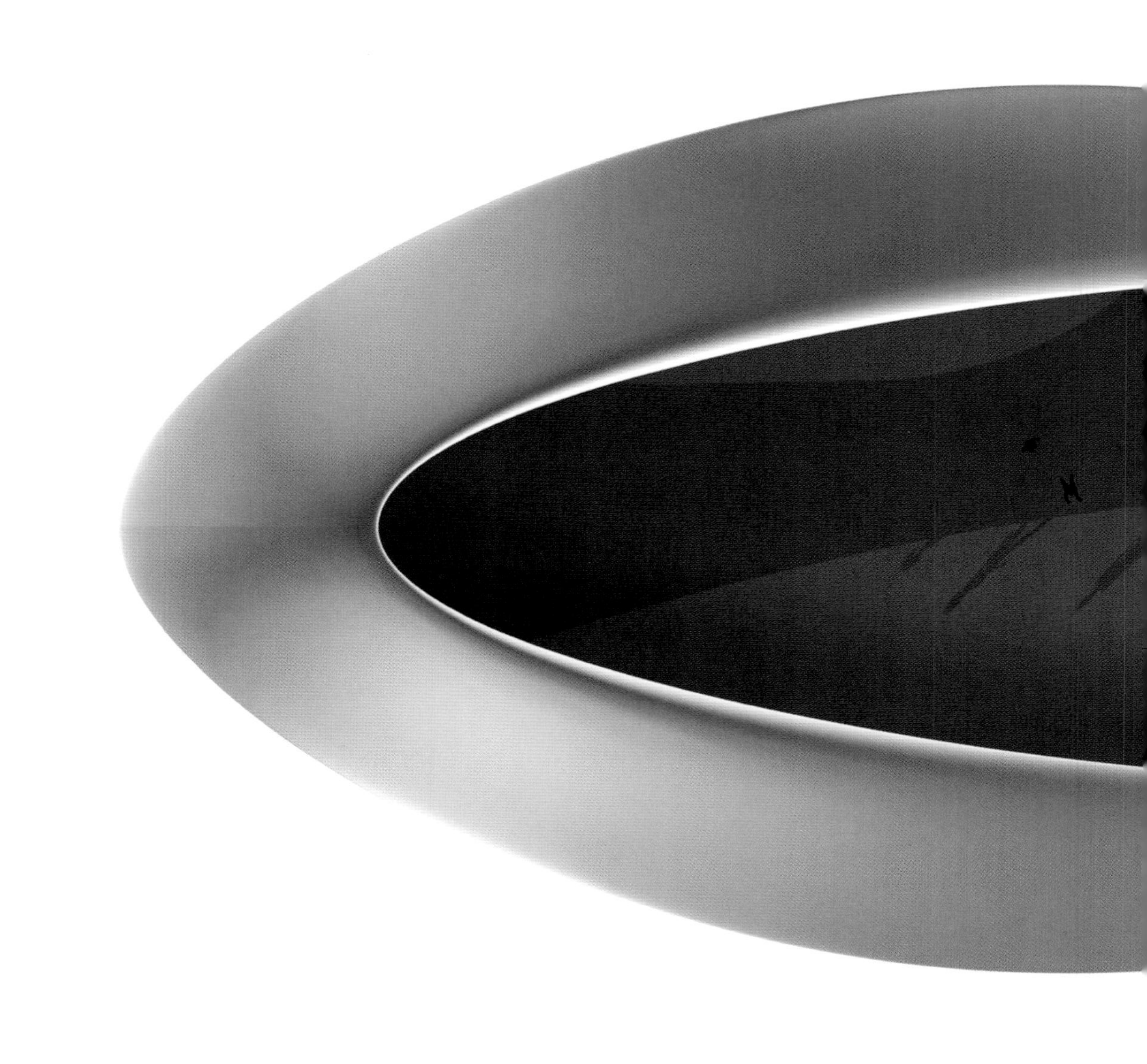

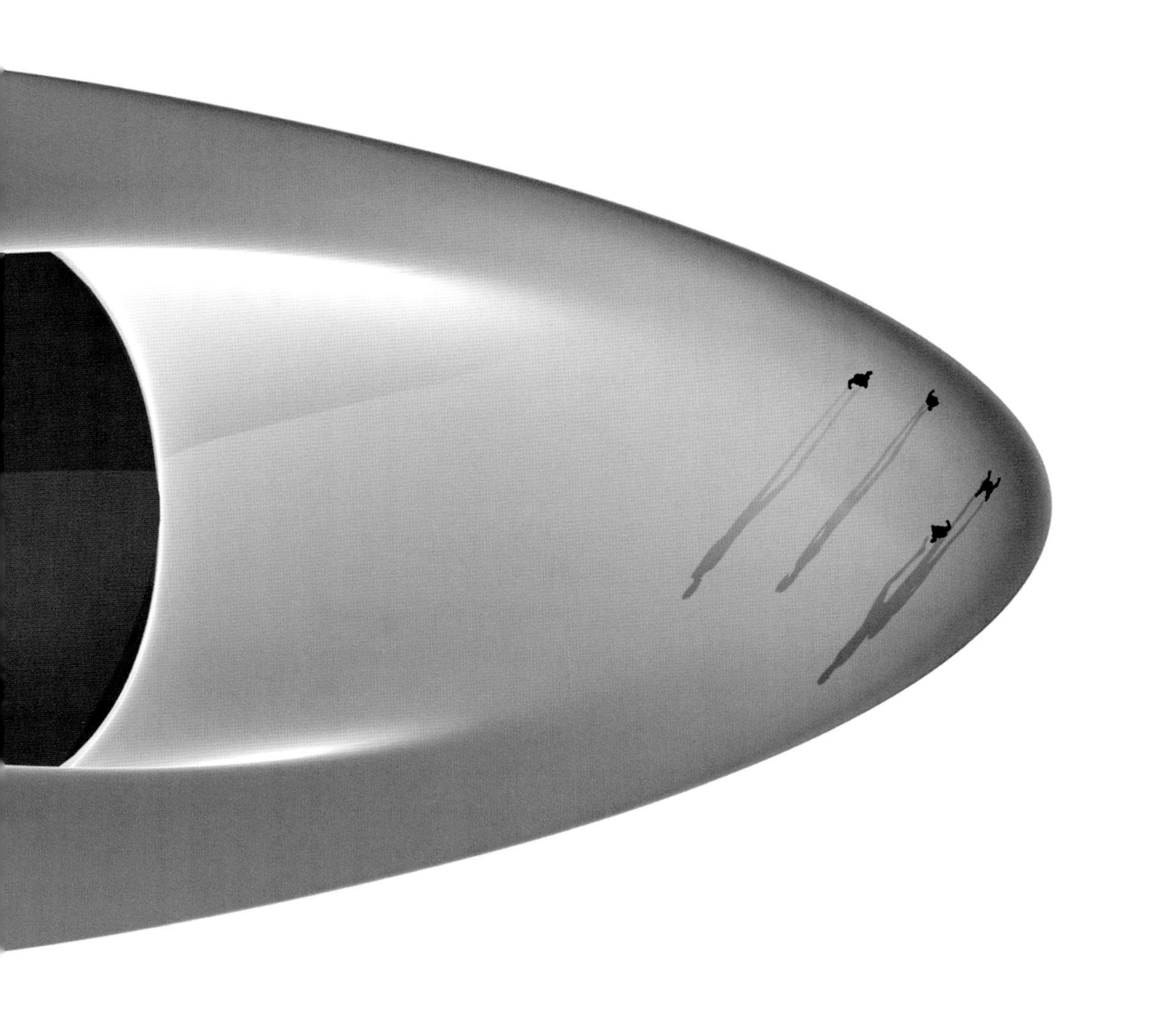

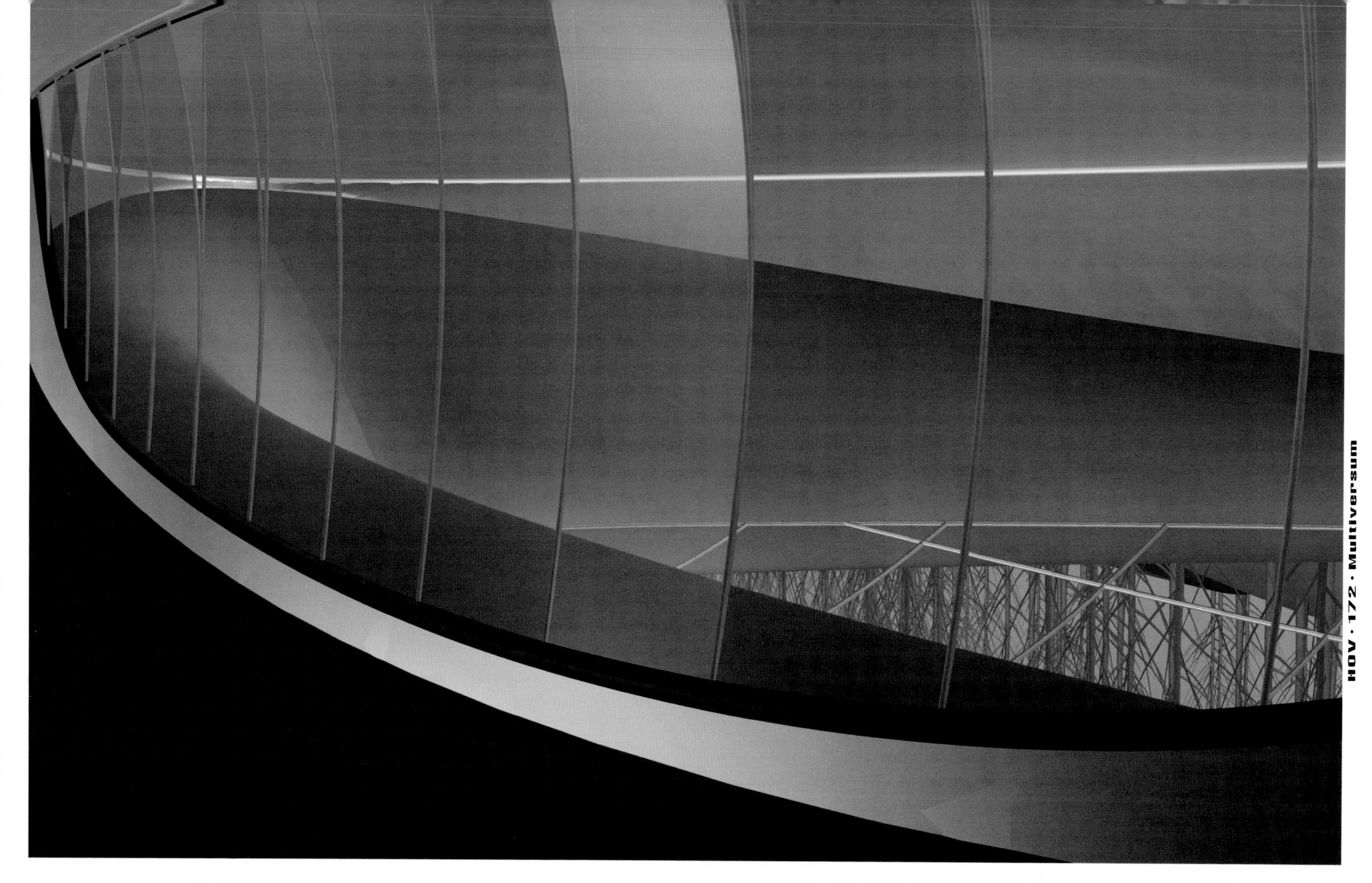

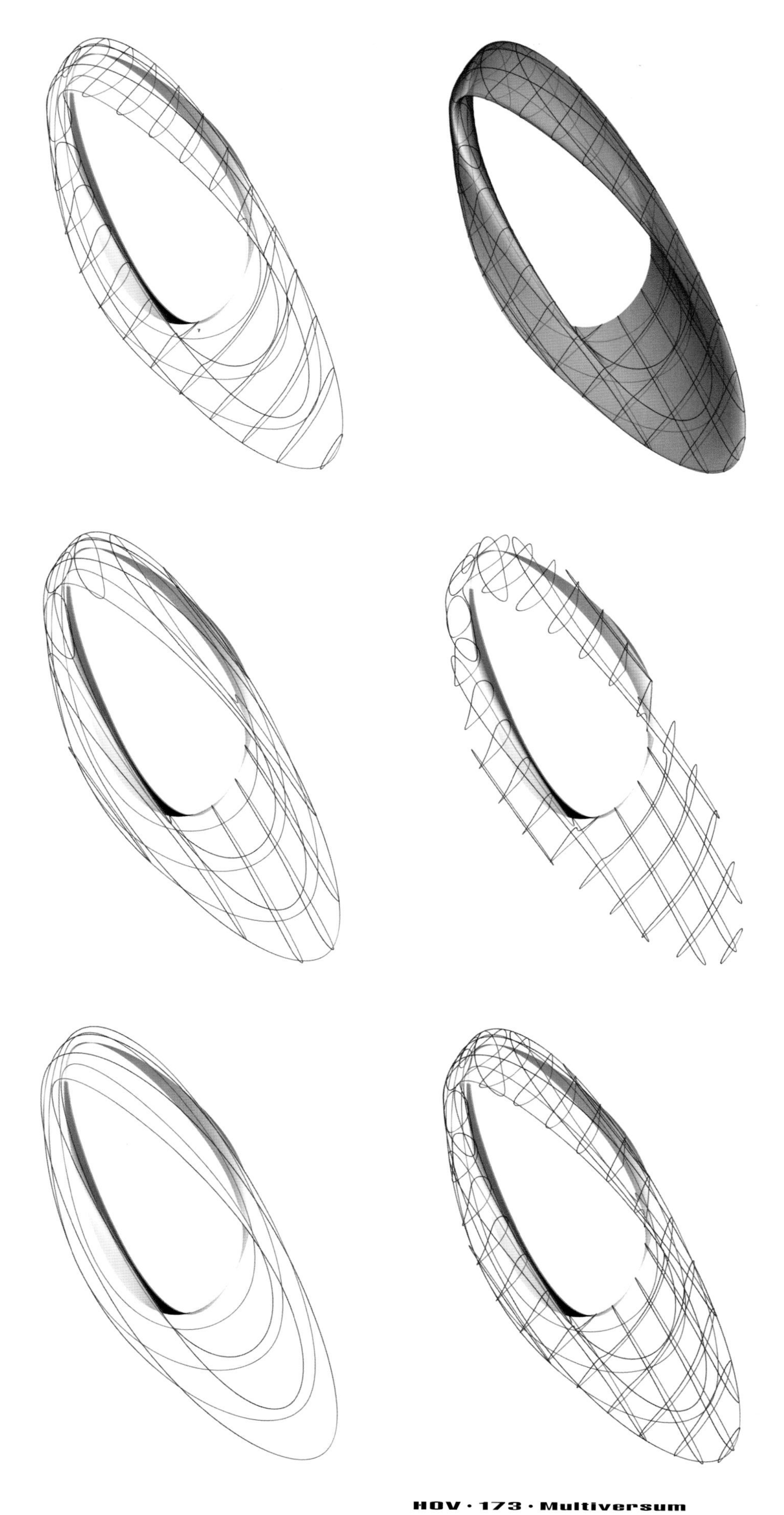

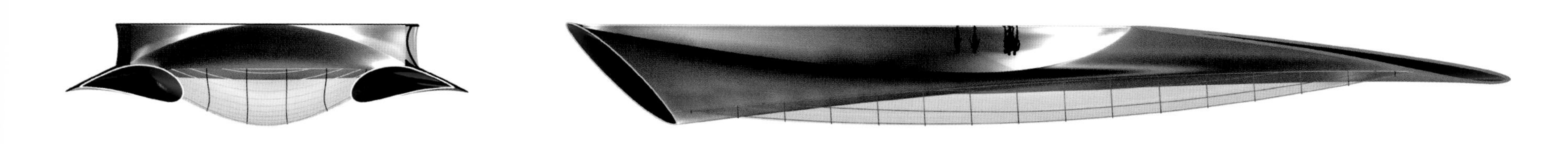

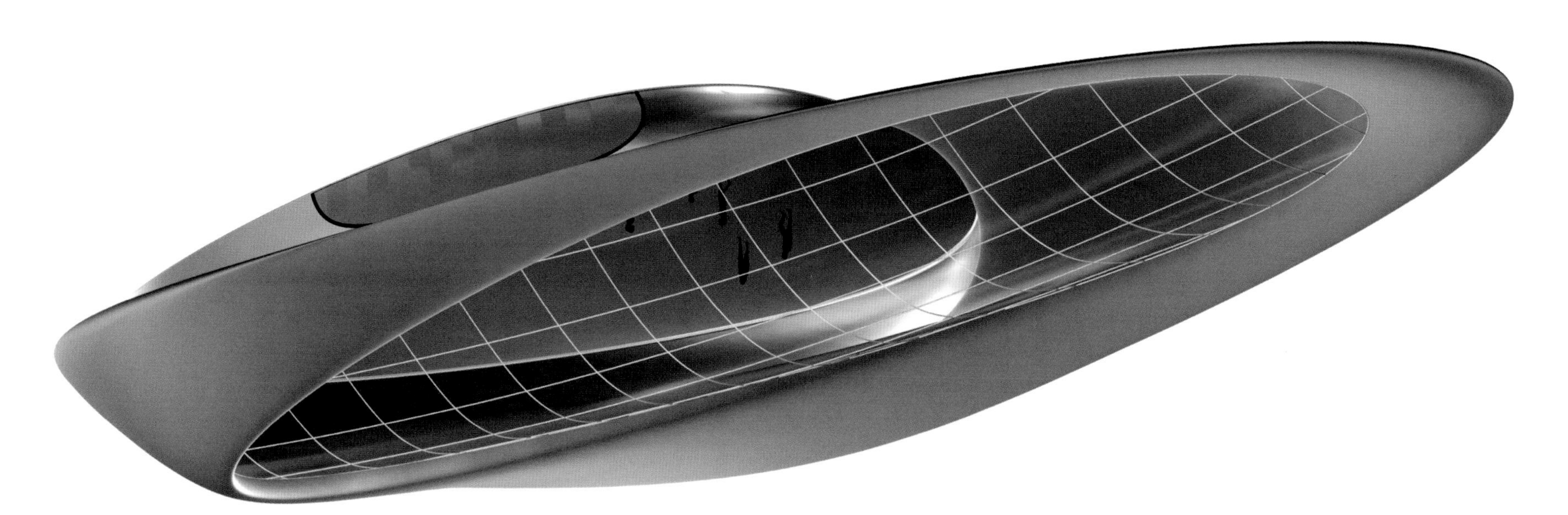

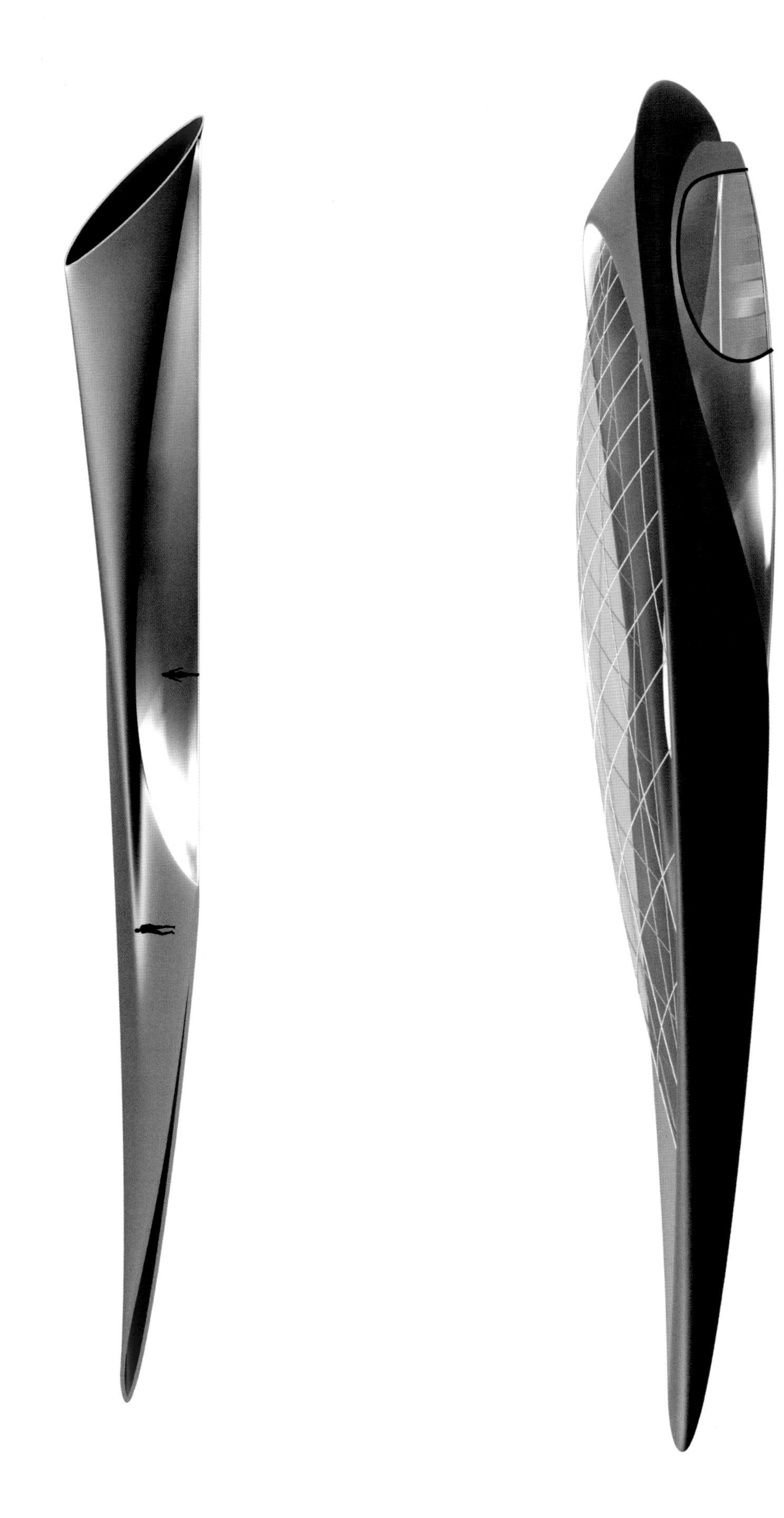

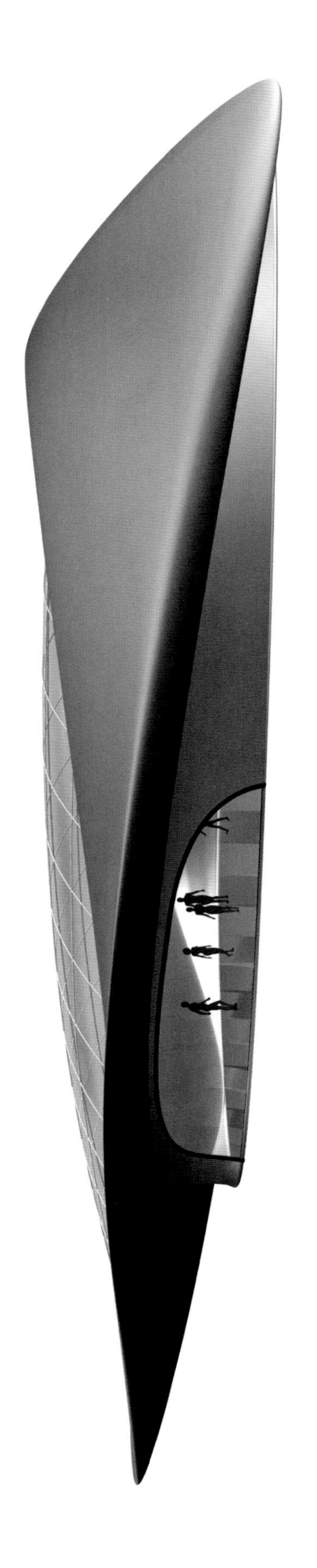

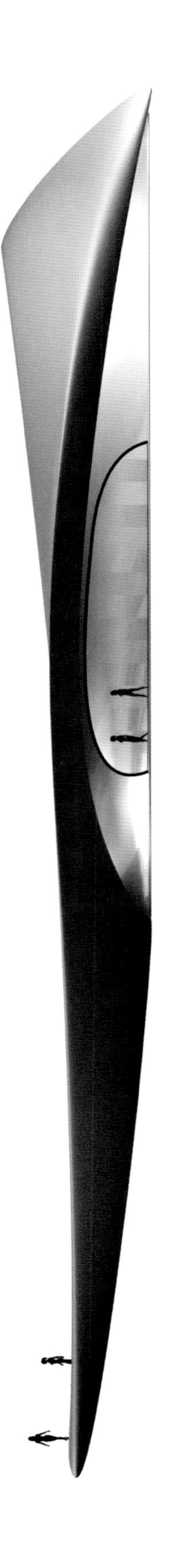

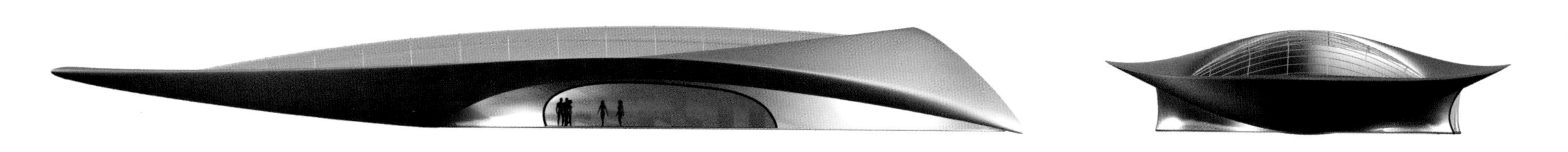

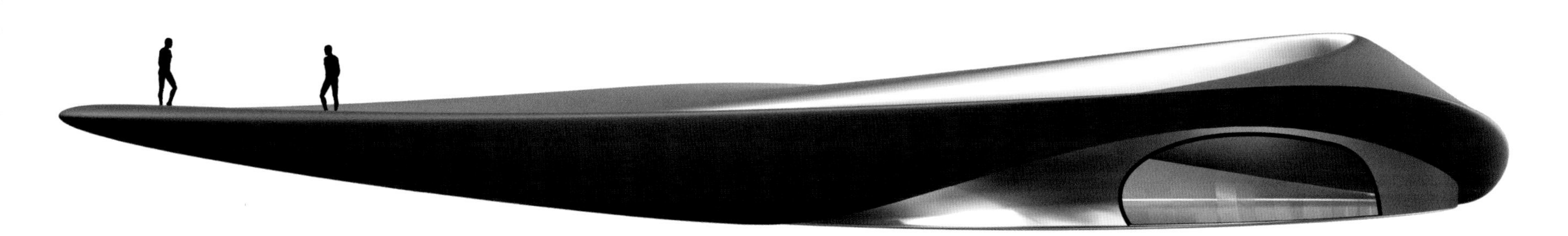

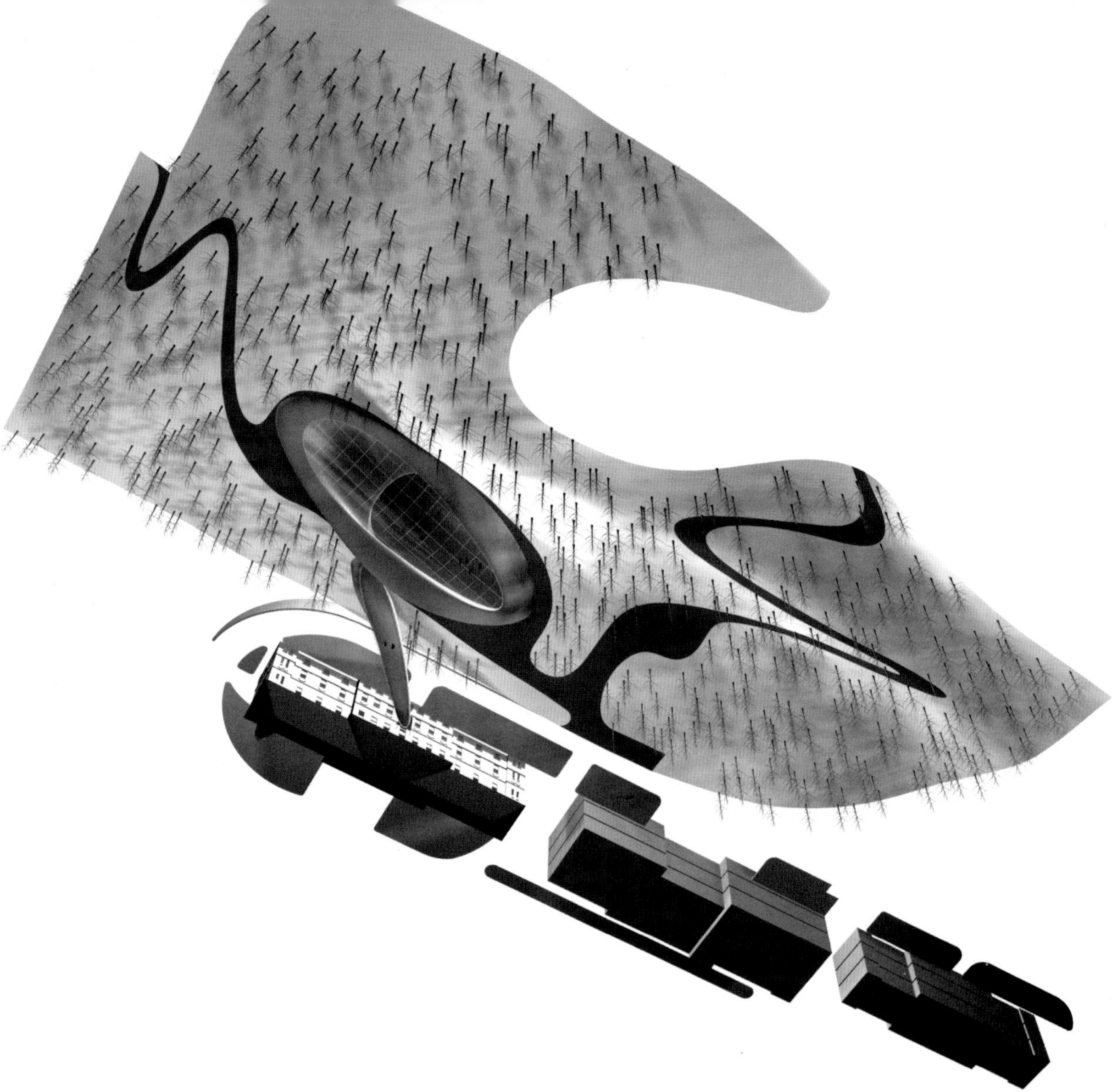

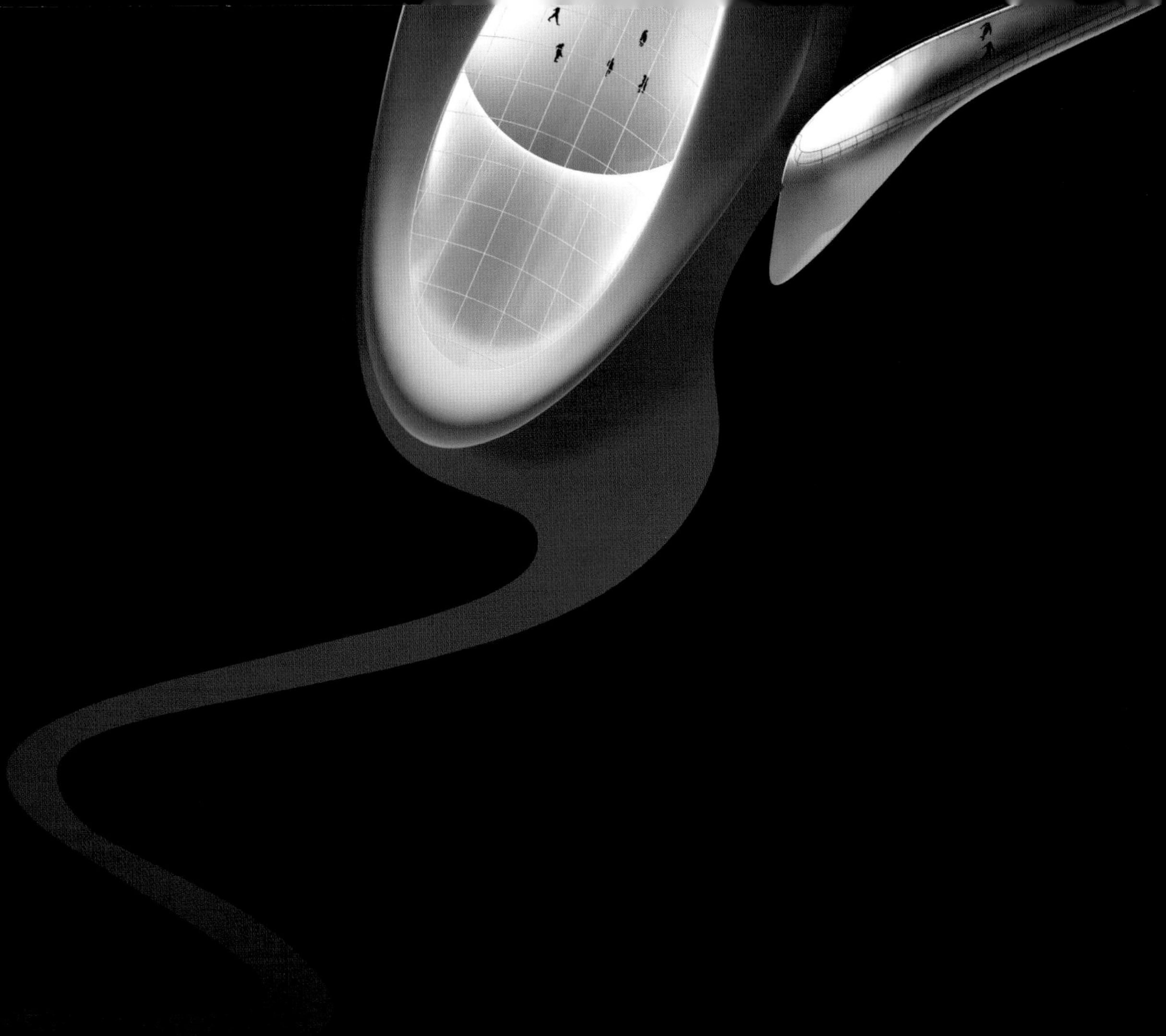

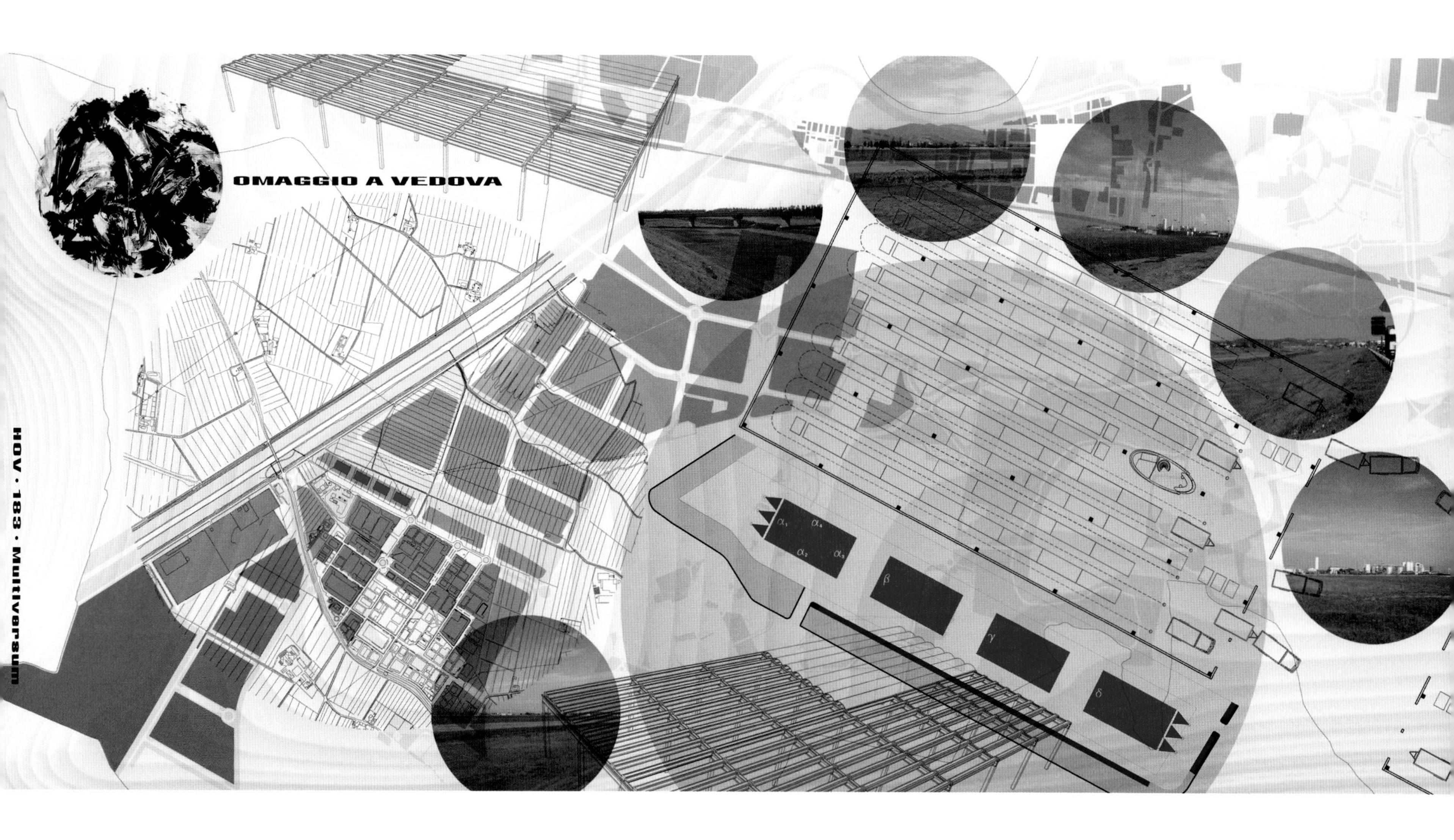
OMAGGIO A VEDOVA
α1
α4
α2
α3
β
γ
δ

Scene 1 - Setting

Standard industrial building with a surface of about 3000 square metres to be used as an automated depot with two movement operators. Development of the suitability of the chosen lot through four distinct buildings (α,β,γ,δ).

Scene 2 - Theory

Identifying a generative lay-out of random surfaces which can be translated into distinguished geometries of façade (exemplified in α1_4, β1_4, γ1_4, δ1_4).

Scene 3 - Construction

Division of the image selected by the customer (for one or more sides of the building) on the partial surfaces of the autoclaved concrete module panel (mm. 625 x 6000). Production by linear development milling unit of average dimensions. Post-processing colouring.

Scene 4 - Image

Automatic projection of the formation process (starting at a pre-established level of brightness) through 3 + 3 large screen stations on the short fronts of the façade α1 and δ4.

Scene 5 - Dedication

(ANSA press agency) – Venice, October 25th, 2006 – " Emilio Vedova died, he was one of the most famous Italian present-day artists. Vedova was born on August 9th, 1919 and he died this afternoon in his house in Venice. Some weeks ago also his wife Anna Maria, to whom he was very much attached, died. It seems that Vedova died during his sleep. In the afternoon he said he was tired and that he would go to his room to rest."

Scene 6 – No Conclusion

场景1–背景

一个标准的工业厂房，表面积约3000平方米，将要被用作仓库，里面有四个操作人员。通过四幢分离的建筑单体(α，β，γ，δ)，发展适宜性的多重选择。

场景2–理论

把一种随机表面生成的布局定义为可以转化的几何形立面。（以α1_4，β1_4，γ1_4，δ1_4为例）

场景3–建筑

由客户选择图像，分隔开放在建筑的一面或几面上。建筑的这部分表面为高压混凝土模板制成（模板尺寸为625*6000毫米）。

场景4–图像

运用自动投影来形成图像，从预设明度开始。将投影通过3+3大型投影仪打到α1 和 δ4立面上。

场景5-贡献

安莎通讯社-威尼斯，2006年10月25日——“诶米留·威斗瓦去世了，他是当今意大利最著名的艺术家之一。威斗瓦出生于1919年8月9日，今天下午在他威尼斯的住所里离开人世。几周前，他挚爱的妻子安娜·玛丽亚也去世了。威斗瓦仿佛是在睡梦中离开人世的。下午的时候他说他累了，他要去他的房间休息一下。”

场景6-没有结论

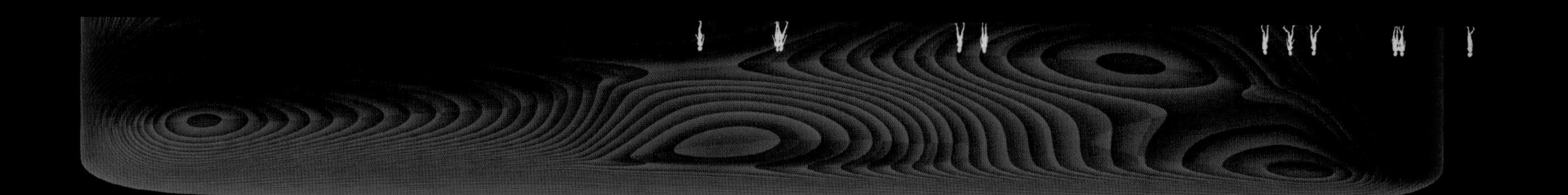

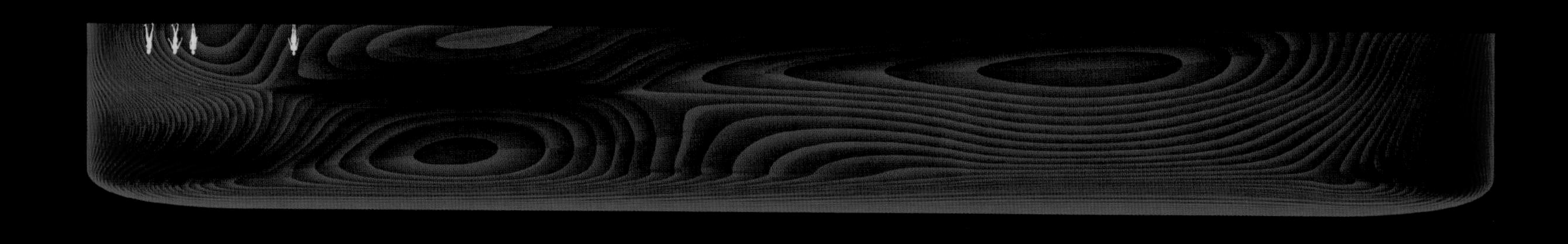

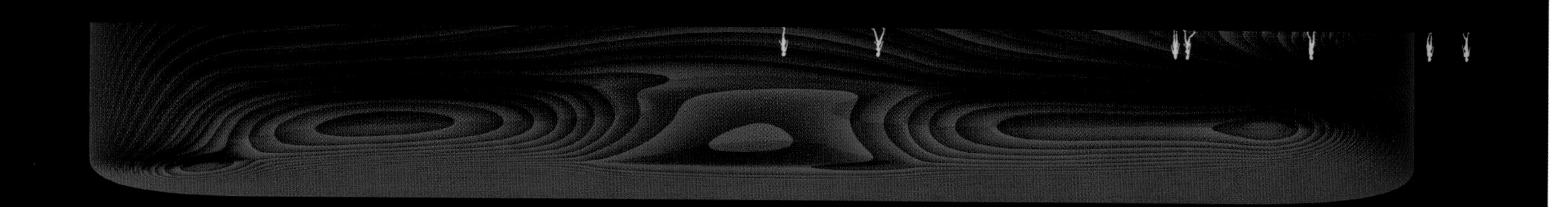

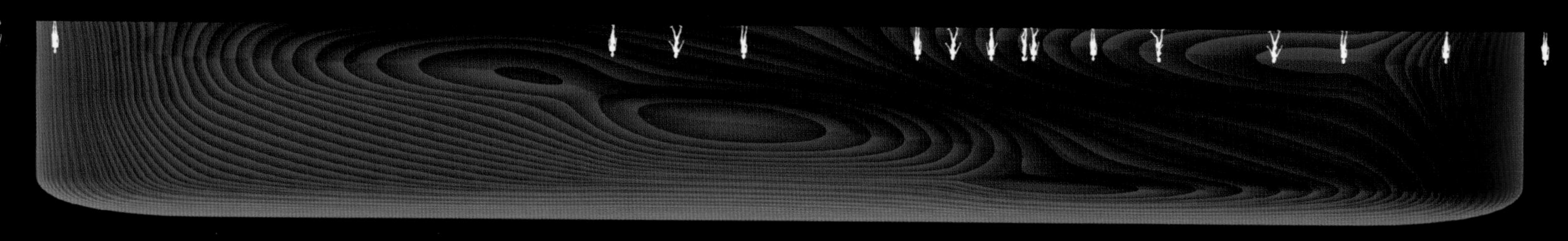

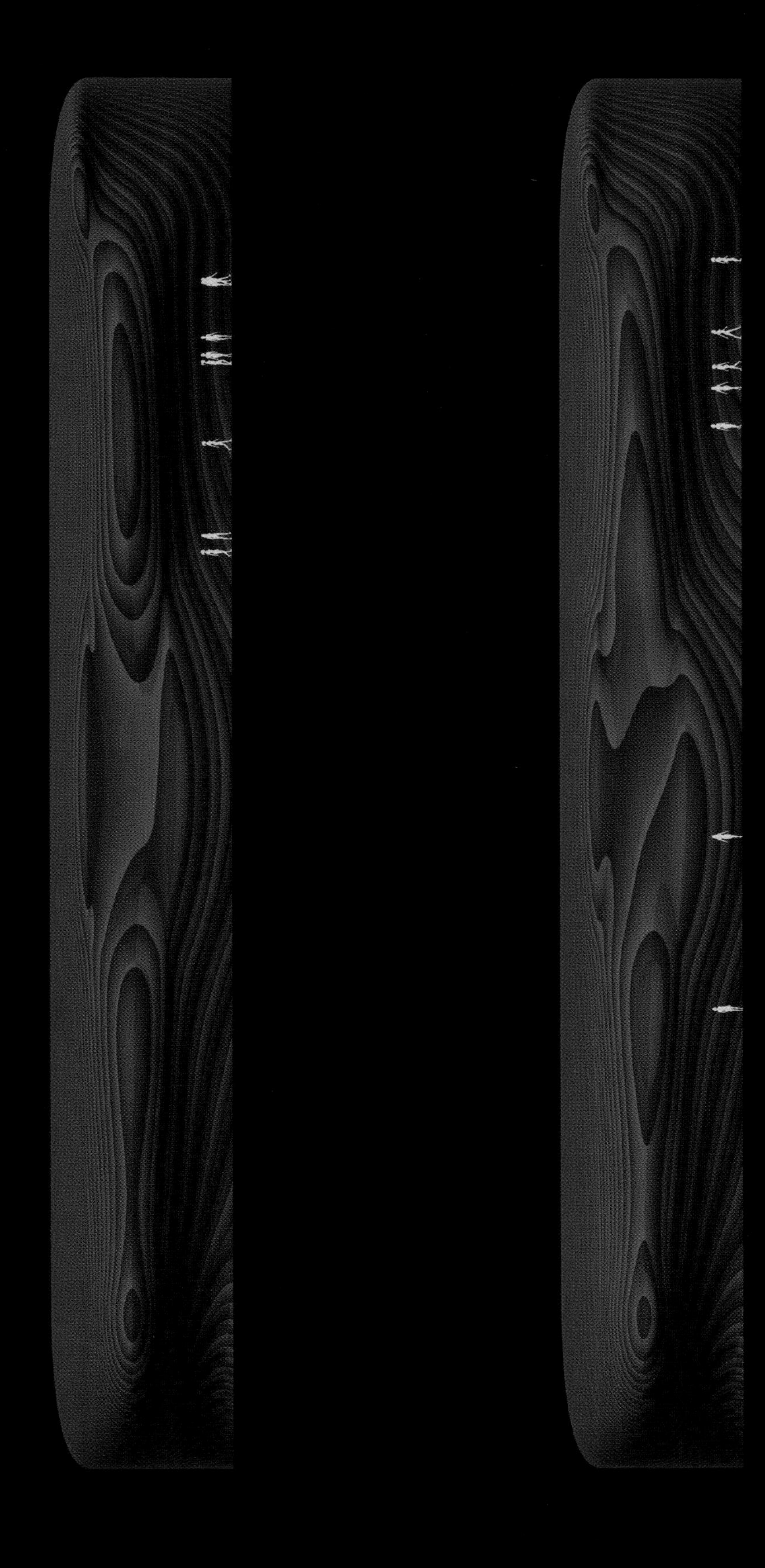

INSTALLATIONS

[The Gallery], 2004　　画廊

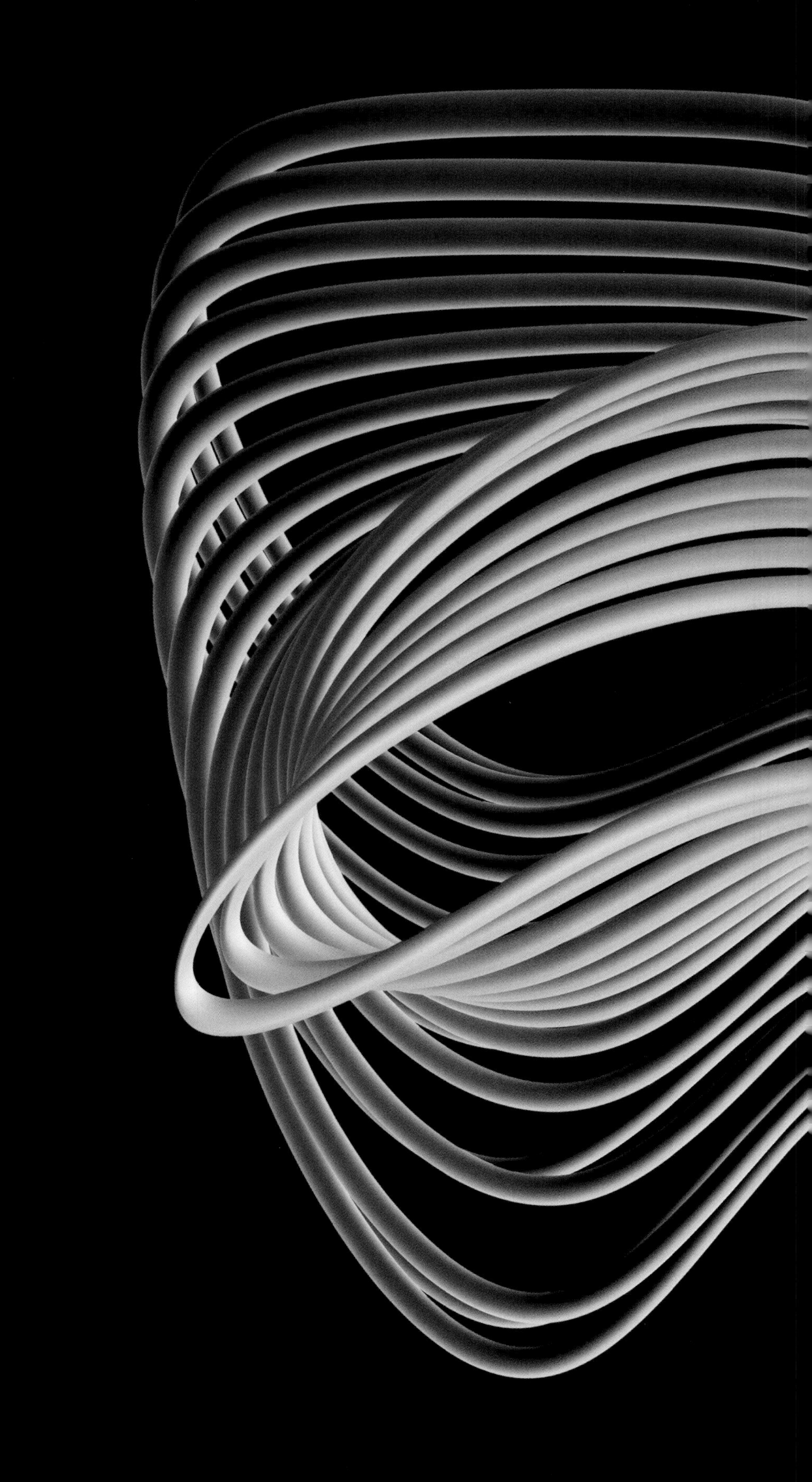

The Gallery is a setting up for a fashion show composed of a series of very light air tubular tyres maintained by air pressure (which can vary depending on the rigidity demanded) through an external compressed-air device.
The sensibility to even weak air currents which can be typical of big closed spaces (like unused industrial containers, deposits, laboratories, etc.) gives the structure a variable configuration with the extremes of kinematical features linked with the elastic resistance of the material.
The fixing at the floor is obtained through a special support – a metal plate – which keeps the structure in the base shape thanks to its own weight.

画廊是为一个时装展览而设计的，展览包含一系列轻质的空气轮胎。空气轮胎由气压维持，而气压用一个外置的气压装置控制，可以根据对刚度的需求进行调节。
设计师给了这个结构一个可变的外观，工业大型封闭空间对于平稳弱气流有一定敏感度，比如闲置工业容器、储藏室、实验室等都有这样的特性，加上材料极佳的弹力，使得结构本身外形可以发生变化。
结构依靠一个金属盘样的特别的支托固定在地板上，这样它就能靠它本身的重量保持它的基本形状。

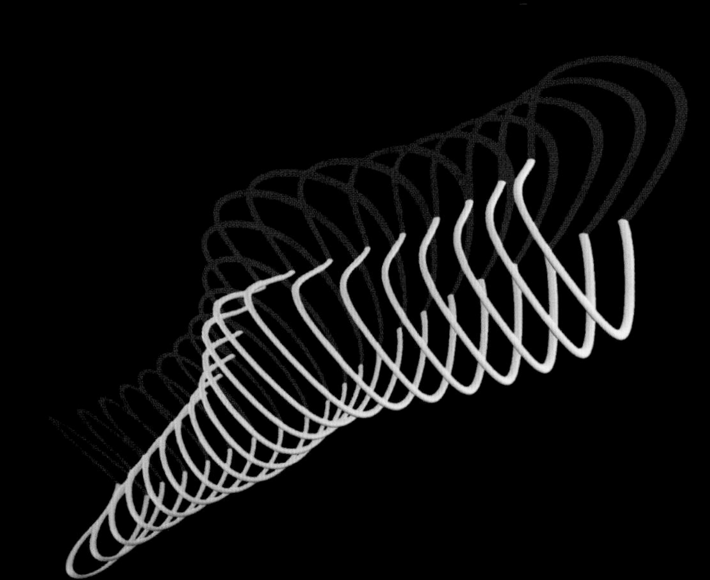

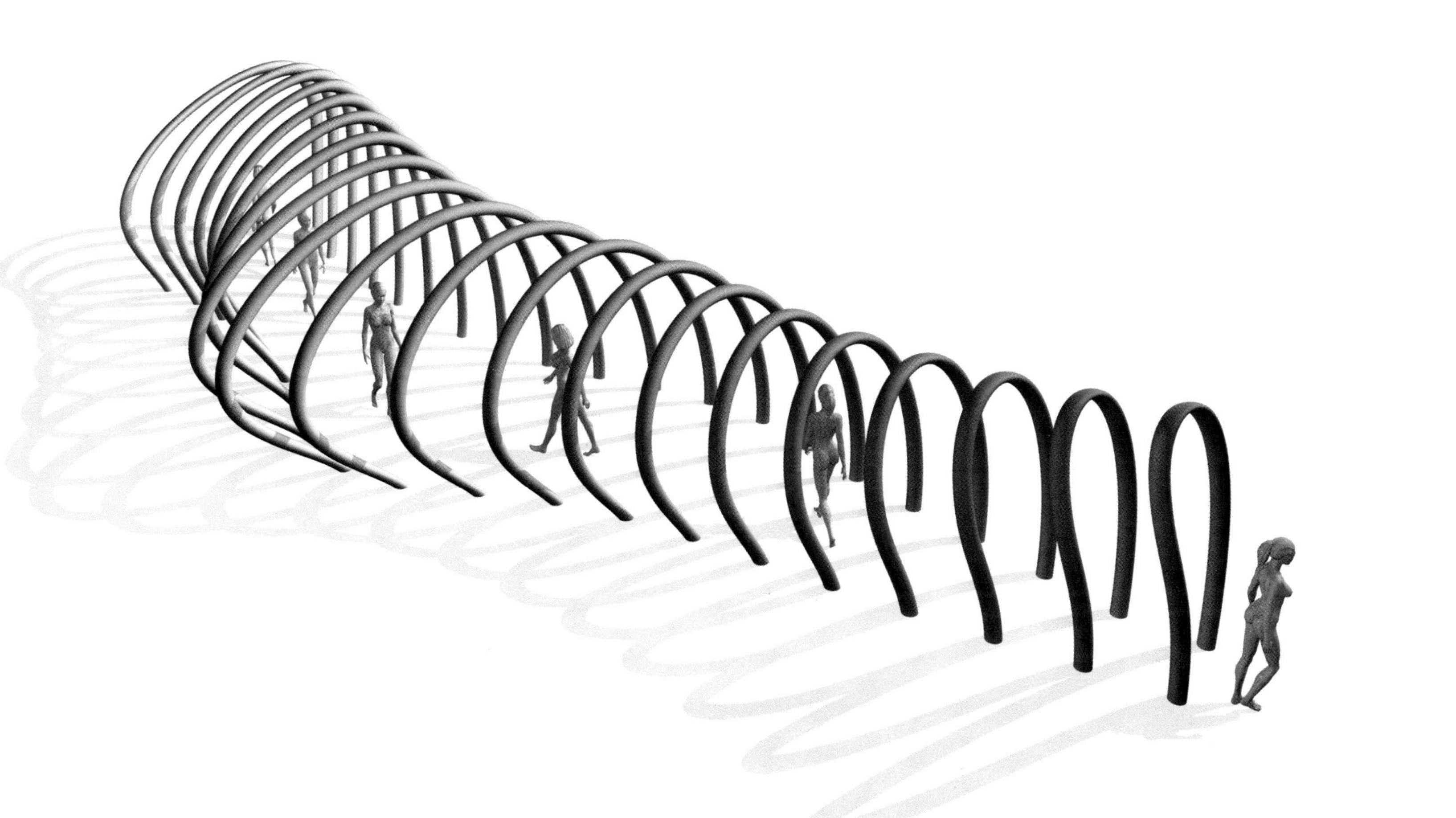

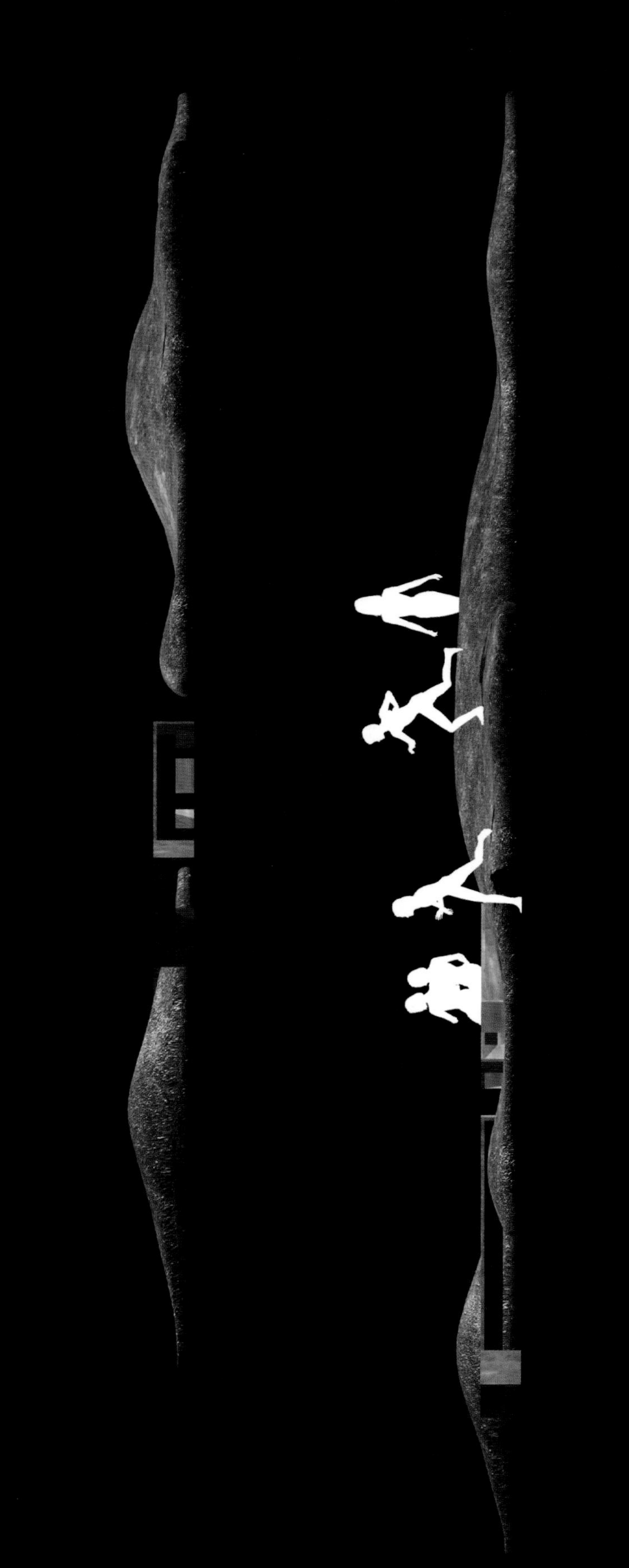

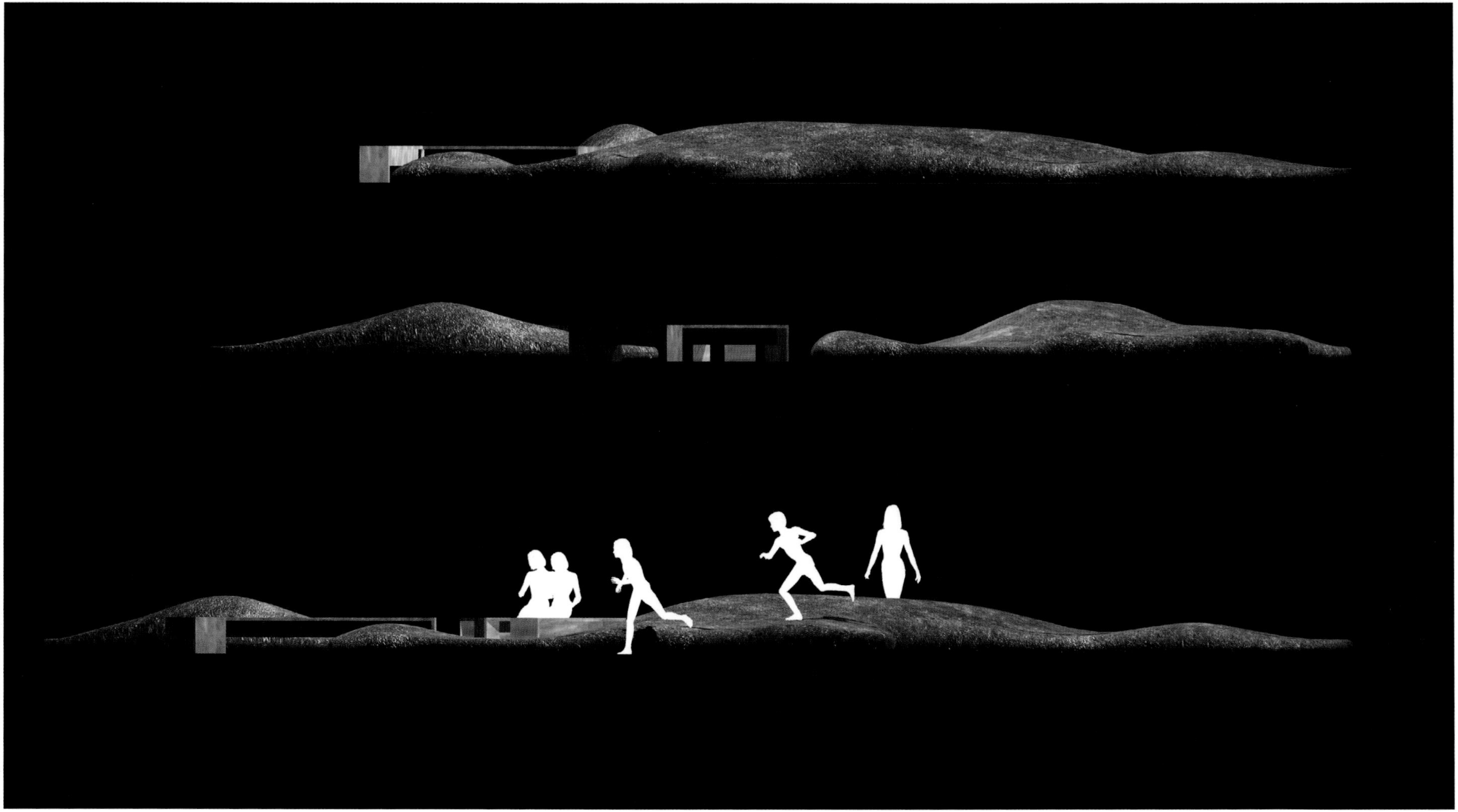

Happy Islands is an unusual installation ready to complete the open space of a city garden. A friendly and curious presence, a non-aggressive one, which is able itself to create interest and involvement, is introduced in the garden area through a minimized landscape. The configuration of the whole has not to be necessarily the same as in the graphics, since it is possibile to shape it during the installation. The execution includes the preparation of the drain/flooring made with fine river gravel and rubble, after the existing material has been removed. Thus, watertighting is prevented and a base for the floating islands is created. The islands are made of a geo-net shell, set on the ground, filled up with compact vegetable soil and closed by natural fibre strings. In a future phase the rough soil mixture is sown and in the end of the taking root, it will be thick and full-bodied thanks to the rooting system (and especially to the pioneer plant agrofyron repens), even not requiring frequent irrigation or mowing.
The total cost of the installation, including the simple accessory benches, is kept under 2,500 euros.

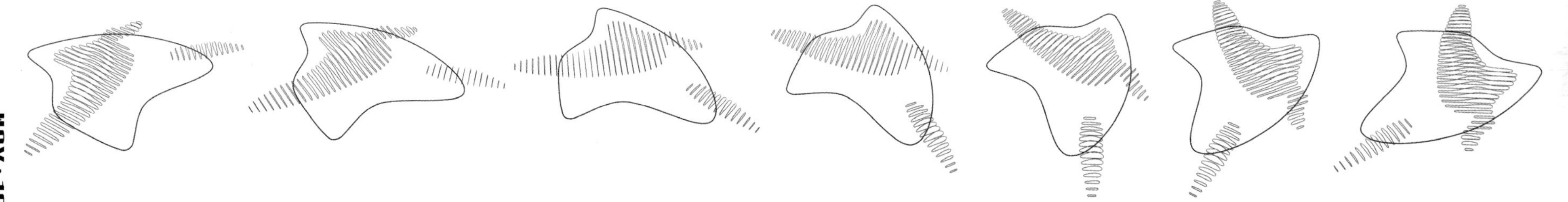

幸福岛是某个城市花园里的一个不同寻常的装置。它显得很友好、古怪而又温和，能依靠自身的魅力激起人的兴趣，让人参与进来。它由一个小型的景观介入这个花园。整体结构的形状并不一定要和图表中所显示的一样，因为它可以在安装过程中改变形状。安装过程要准备排水系统，还要把现有的地面铺装改为用细小的沙砾和碎石来做铺装。这样一来，漂浮岛的基础就建好了，而且有良好的防透水性。岛屿是由土工网壳制成，安置在地面上，立面填满紧密的植物土壤，用自然纤维绳盖在表面。安装完成后，要在土壤混合物里播种。在植物扎根的后期，土壤会变得很厚。植物甚至不需要经常浇灌护理。
加上附加的简单的长凳，整个装置的价格控制在2，500欧元以下。

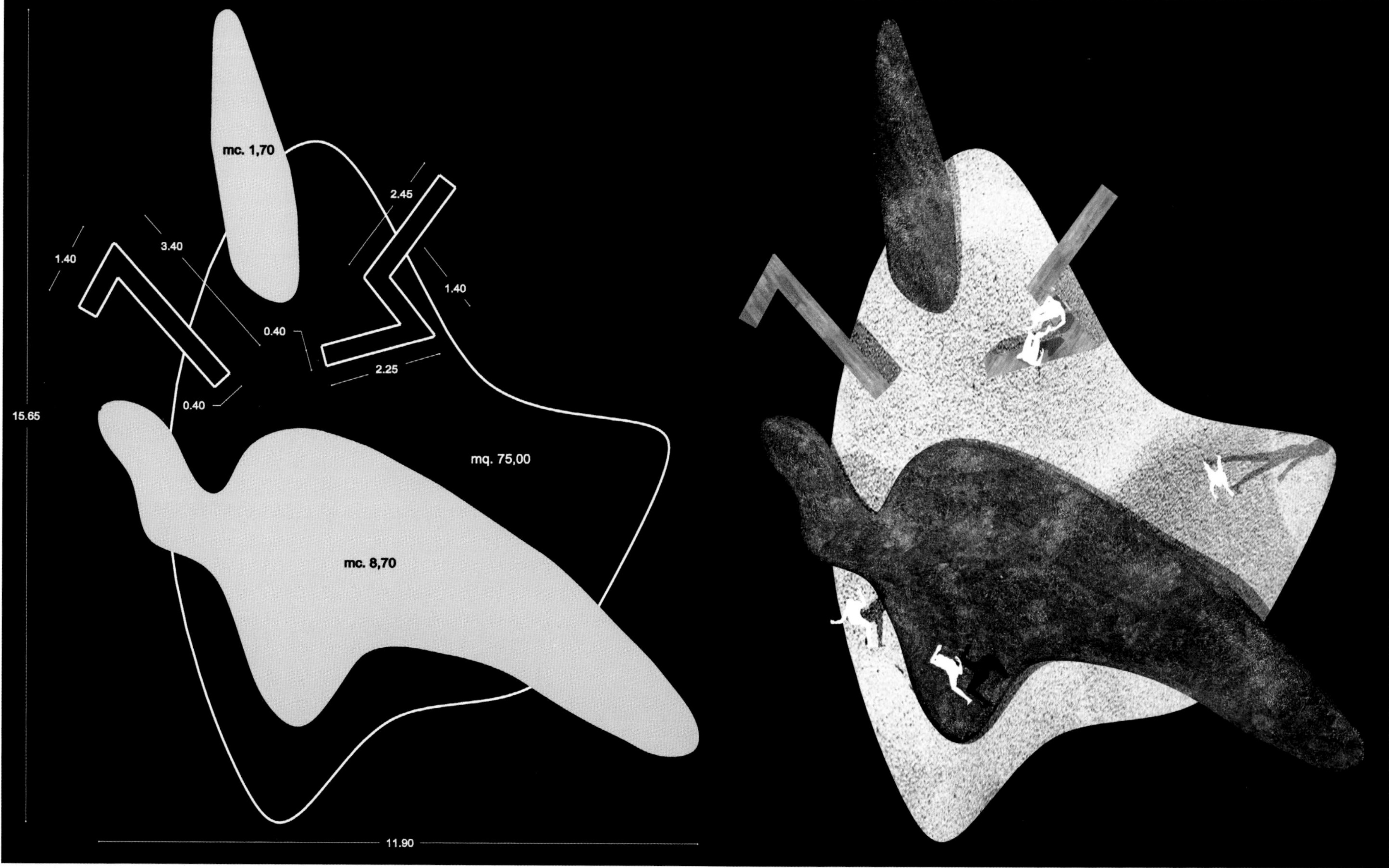
mc. 1,70
2.45
3.40
1.40
1.40
0.40
2.25
0.40
15.65
mq. 75,00
mc. 8,70
11.90

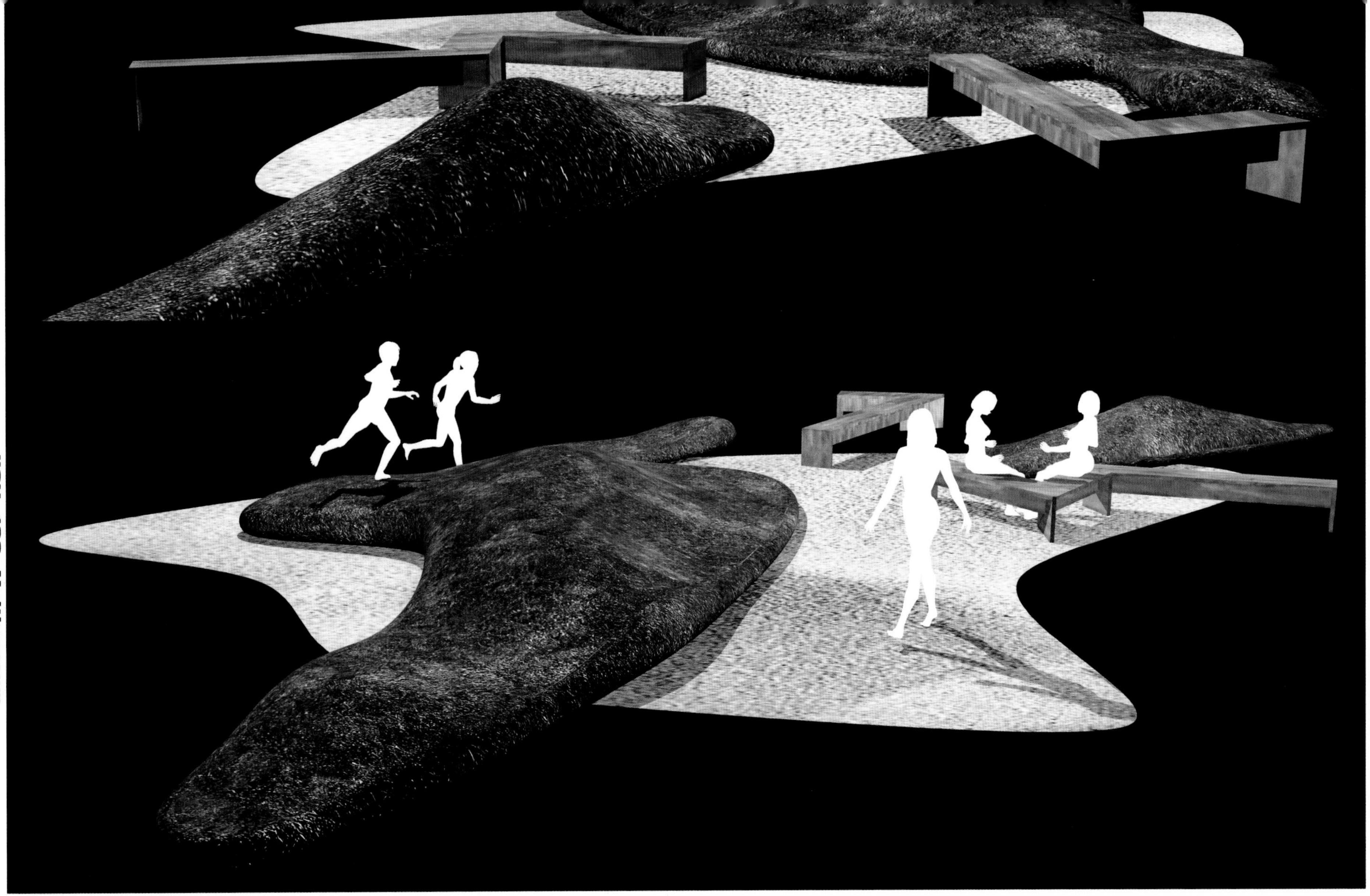

The project defines a space estranging from an imaginary atmosphere by shapes created from the tranformation of unusual and impalpable geometries. The introduction to the fashion event is made through an emotional discard.

The images evoked are not immediately referable to common experience and, within the flow bringing us from a dominion over actions to another one, the scene interferes in the actions of the visitor since its first appearance. This is where and when the involvement is expected: in the very moment of cognition of the surrounding space.

The images are neither optical/holographic simulations nor volumetrical tridimensional projections (that is something lying outside a moderate cost temporary dressing programme), but they are associated with sounds – a 'sound scene' cyclically reproduces – which allude to something else and do not represent well defined or directly accessible elements. The space creates a process of detachment from a reality lived instead of another one, even if tightly held within the short time of the way through the gallery itself. A reality which is exclusive and 'closed' for every observer.

The soft black coloured moquette detaches the bright orange gum carpet from the existing floor and marks the regular perimeter of the gallery, which is delimited by modular panels vertically assembled.

The printing – divided into sectors – featuring the original drawing 'holo III' by HOV (computer generated) is bound to a rigid support and it is made of non-reflecting plasticized paper. The various sectors complete the image making it as a whole.

A black plastic fabric, streched between the two longitudinal sides, forms the upper screen. Dotted with opaque policarbonate discs – corresponding to as many holes in the fabric – it allows the room light to spread. An equipment of projectors set above the discs will provide the light source.

The delimitation of the way to step in the two versions (strings and spheres) is pointed out by plastic material rejection strings (cut and strained by heat) and blown up seats, respectively.

这个项目创造了一种远离想象气氛的空间，运用了非寻常几何体变形而来的形状。它通过一种情感遗忘来展示时尚事件。

所激起的影像并不能马上和平常的经验联系在一起。场景在它一出现的时候就会影响参观者的行为，支配了他们一个又一个的行为。参观者对周围空间有了认识的那一刻，正是他们参与进来的时刻。

图像既不是光学或全息的成像，也不是三维投影（他们不符合低价临时装置的需要），而是和声音有关的图像。这里的图像是一种循环的“声音场景”，不代表容易理解或容易解释的元素，而是暗指了其他。这个空间创造了一种远离生活现实的过程，而让观众身处于另外一个现实，虽然这个现实仅限于穿过画廊本身的短短的那段时间。这个现实对每个观众都是独特而“封闭”的。

柔软的黑色厚地毯夹在明亮的橙色树脂地毯和现存的地板之间，标明了画廊的周长。周长由竖直安装的模版限定。把HOV工作室电脑生成原创画《holo III》印刷在不反光的塑性纸上，再将印刷品分成几部分固定在刚性支撑上。印刷品的不同部分使图像成为一个整体。

黑色的塑性织物在拉在纵向的两边之间形成了上层的屏幕。屏幕上点状地布置不透明聚碳酸酯碟片，和织物里的孔洞相对应，而且这些碟片使得房间的光线散布开来。碟片上方的一个投影机提供了光源。

用热加工的塑料绳和各自吹起的椅子指明了通往两个版本（分别是线和球体）的道路的界限。

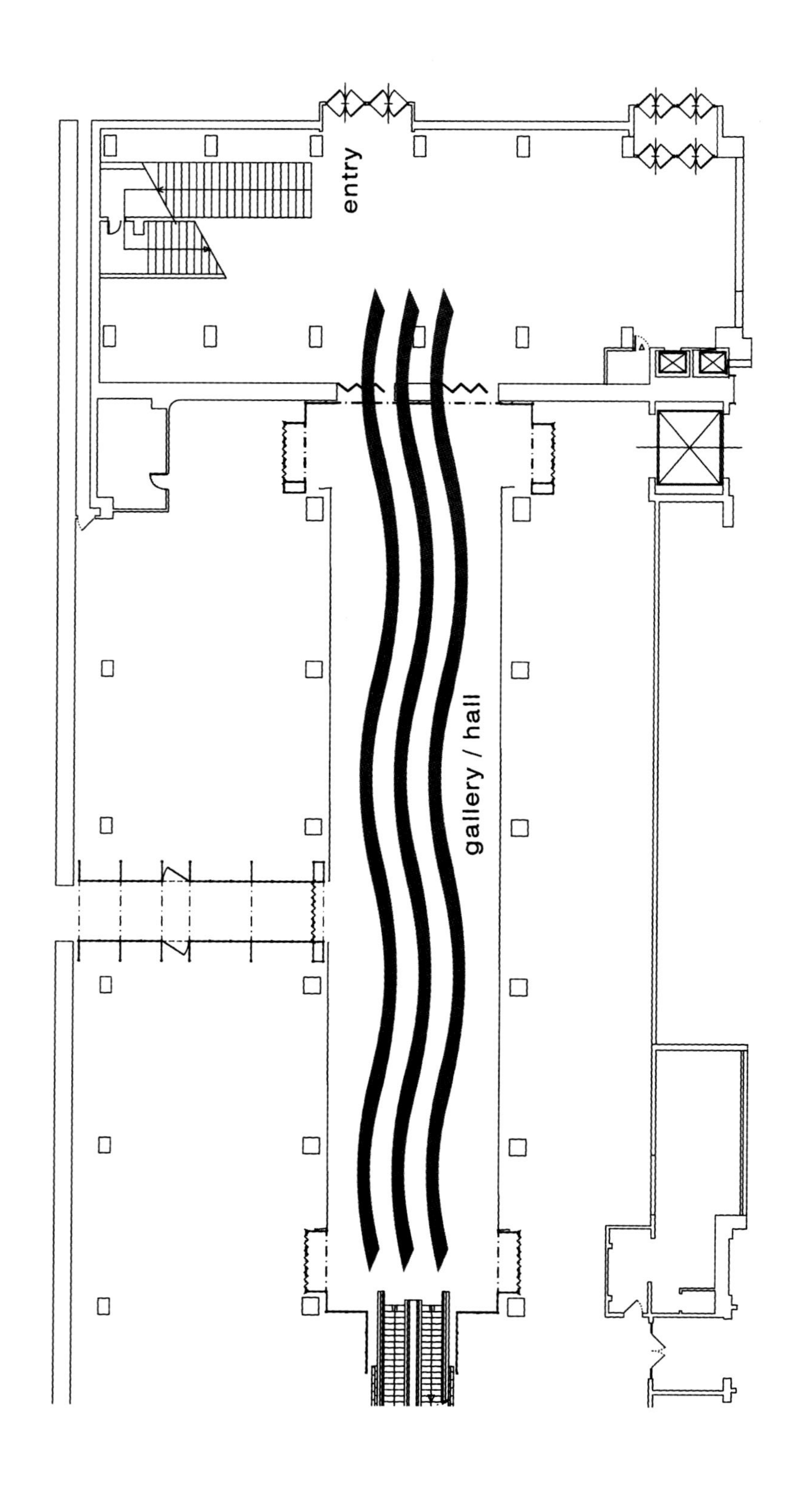
entry
gallery / hall

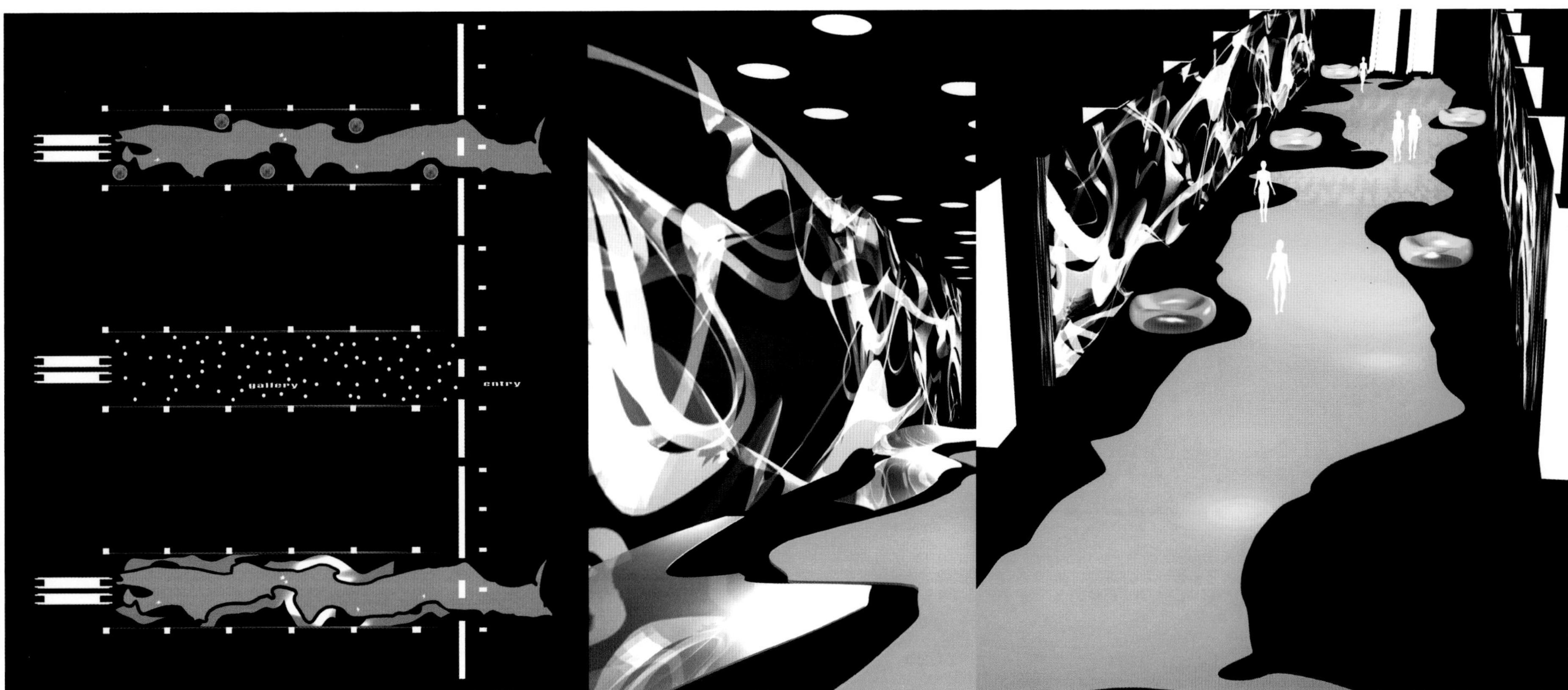
gallery
entry

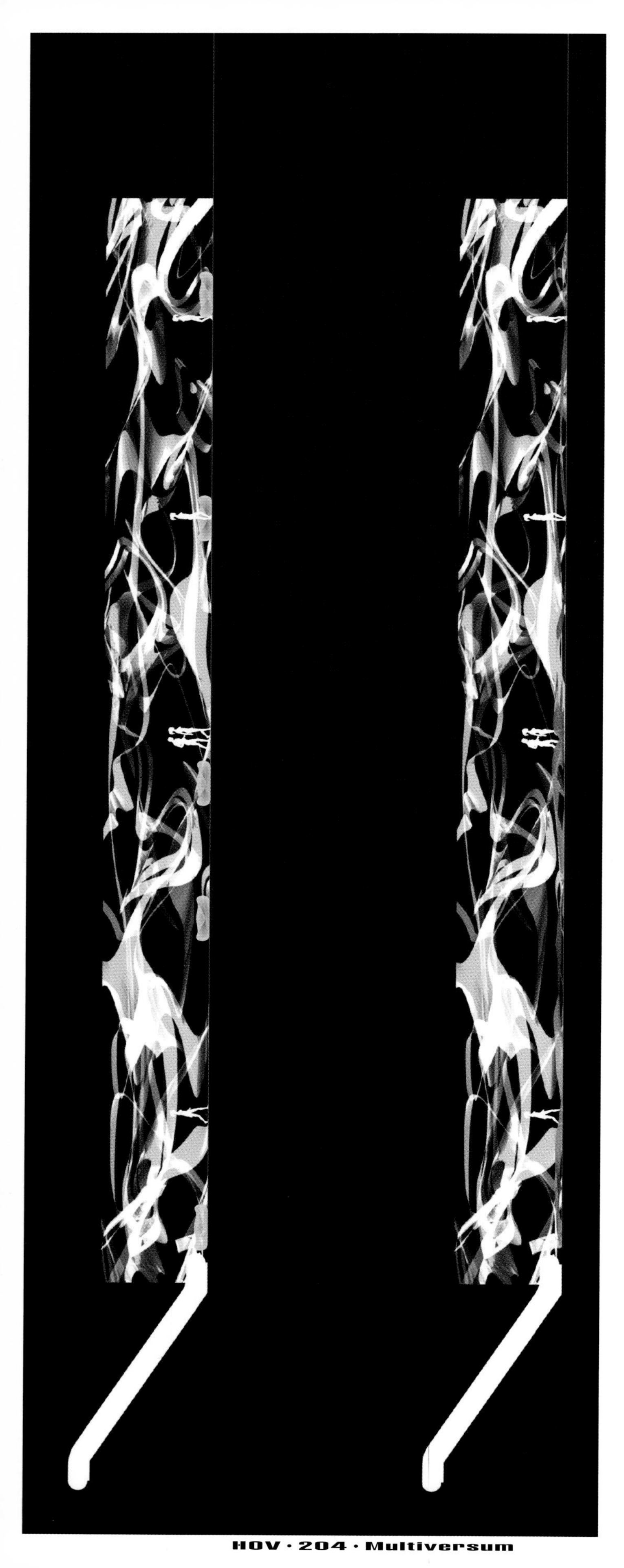

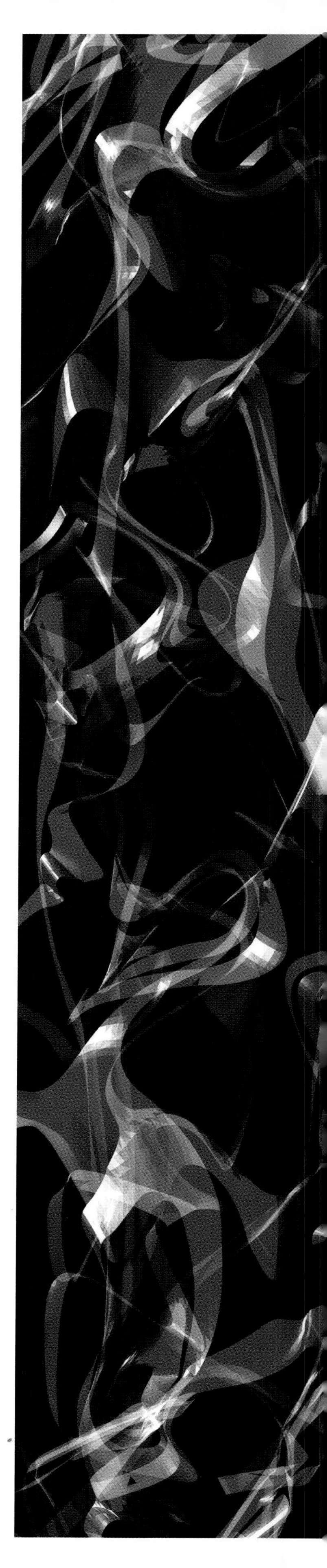

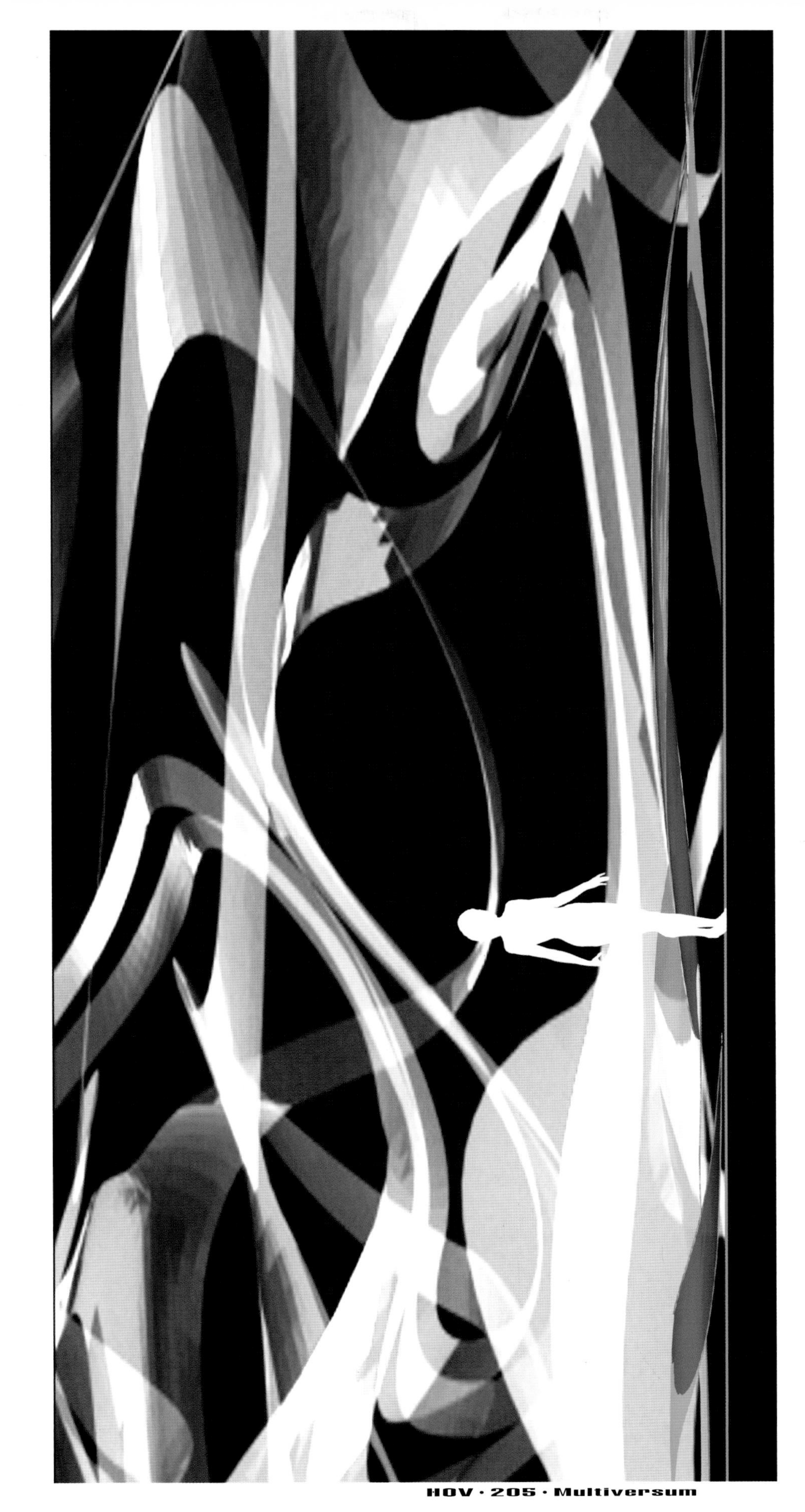

HOV · 208 · Multiversum

The presentation of a new line is the right occasion for this scenography, the placing of which is not bound to the characteristics of an existing space-container. Through the straining and soldering of two concentrical bands a geometry is generated by two isolated rings that do not communicate. During the fashion parade/ representation some models stay tight within the inner 'no-way-out' ring and they 'cope with' the stylist in action who expresses him/herself directly on the dresses tranforming them or changing them in real time.

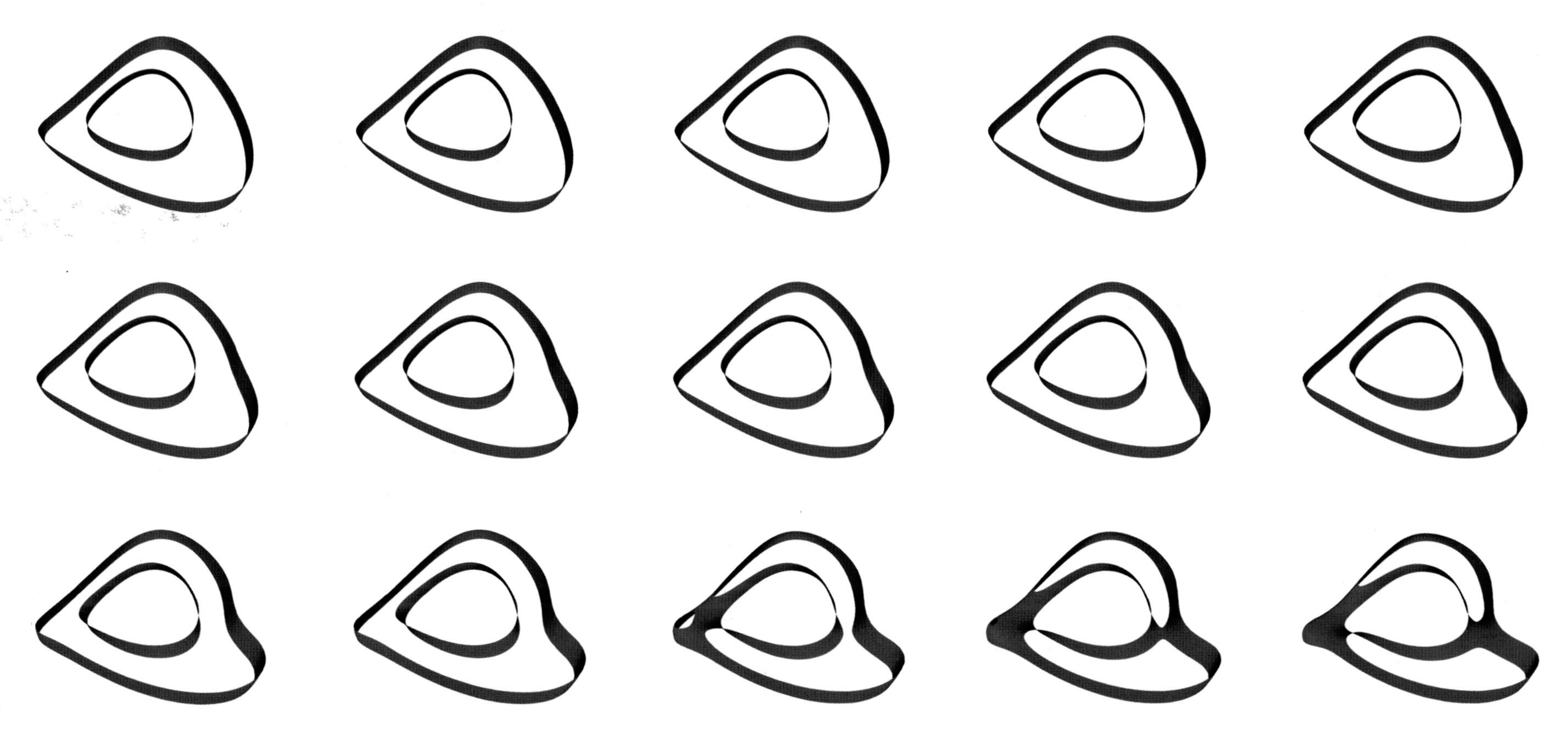

这幅透视图最佳的场景是一条新的流线，这不是空间容器的基本特征。把两条带子进行变形并焊接，两个共中心的独立圆环组成了一个几何体。在时装展览过程中，有些模特站在内层的“没有出口”的圈里，并在那里和设计师一起工作。设计师直接用服饰表达他或她的想法，那些服饰在真实的时间里改变了这些模特。

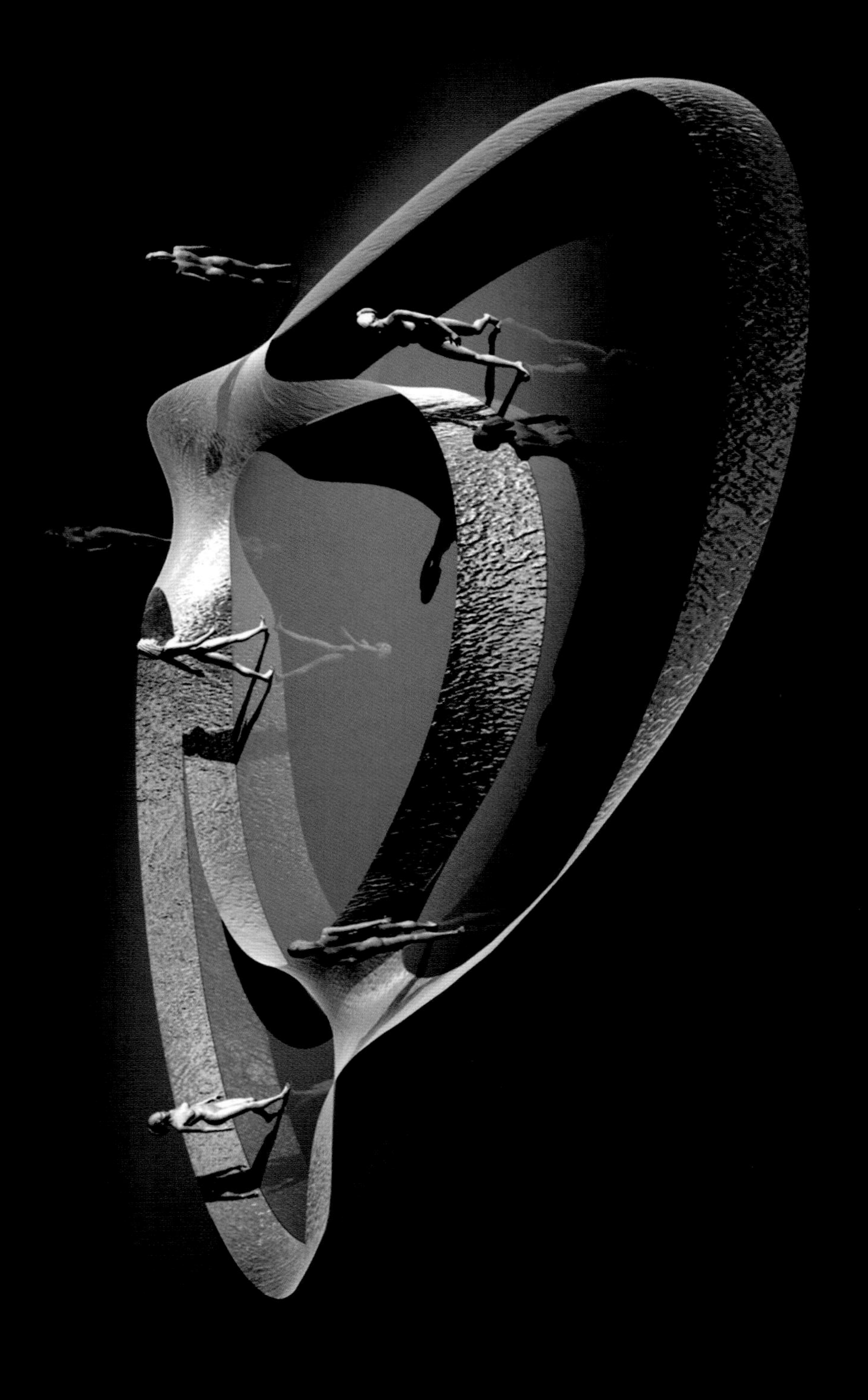

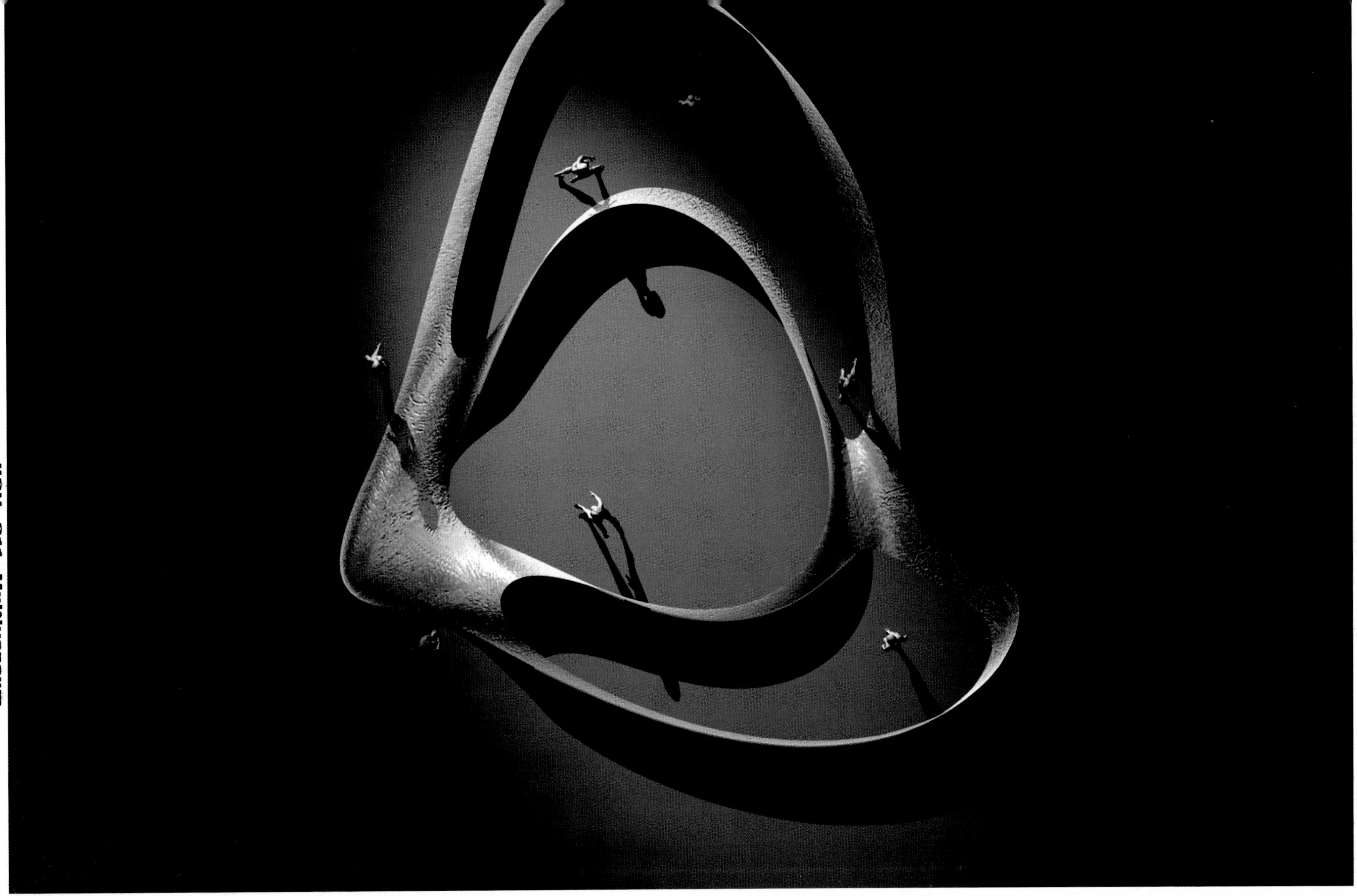

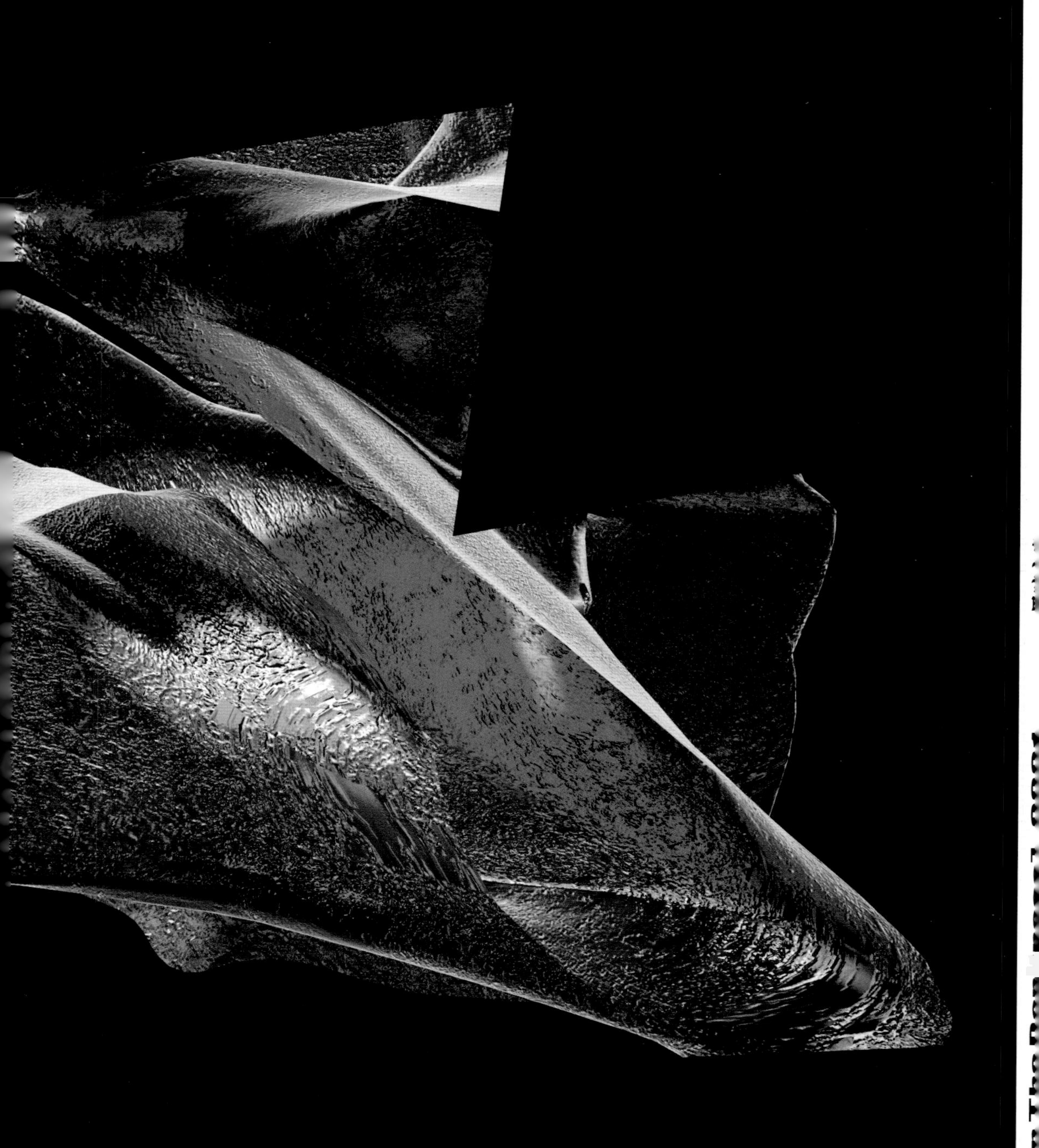

LID distributes heat and water. It also receives emergency calls.
The metallic surface, covered with coal and resin, is heated in winter time through a connection to earth. It gives therefore warmth, when touched.
It is possible to drink or to get cold / hot water, the latter to be collected into small containers to warm up. If it is raining, the covered part will offer a temporary shelter.
Here you will find an emergency button in case of extreme difficulty.
The structure shows uninterrupted and it requires no staff. Neither are there technologies or screens to operate with: all the needs are primary.
The volunteers do not receive beyond a bar or a window, but among the people they are giving information, help, little food to.
The structure is just a datum-point.
"What's that? Nobody's here!"
"They'll come early in the morning", they answer me.

黑暗里的一束光可以分配热量和水，它也可以接受紧急呼叫。
覆盖有煤和树脂的金属表面，冬天它能通过和地面的连接装置而提高温度。所以人可以靠触摸它来取暖。
可以从装置里取用冷水或热水，热水收集到小的容器里加热。如果下雨，它的盖子可以起到临时遮蔽的作用。
这里你可以看见一个紧急呼叫按钮，以防止出现困难情况。
这个结构可以独立工作，不需要员工操作；也没有技术和屏幕来进行操作，所用都很简单。
志愿者不用在服务台或窗口服务，他们站在人群中，提供信息、帮助和一些食物。
这个构筑物只是一个基准点。
"那是什么东西？没有人在那里！"
"他们一大早会来的。"他们回答我说。

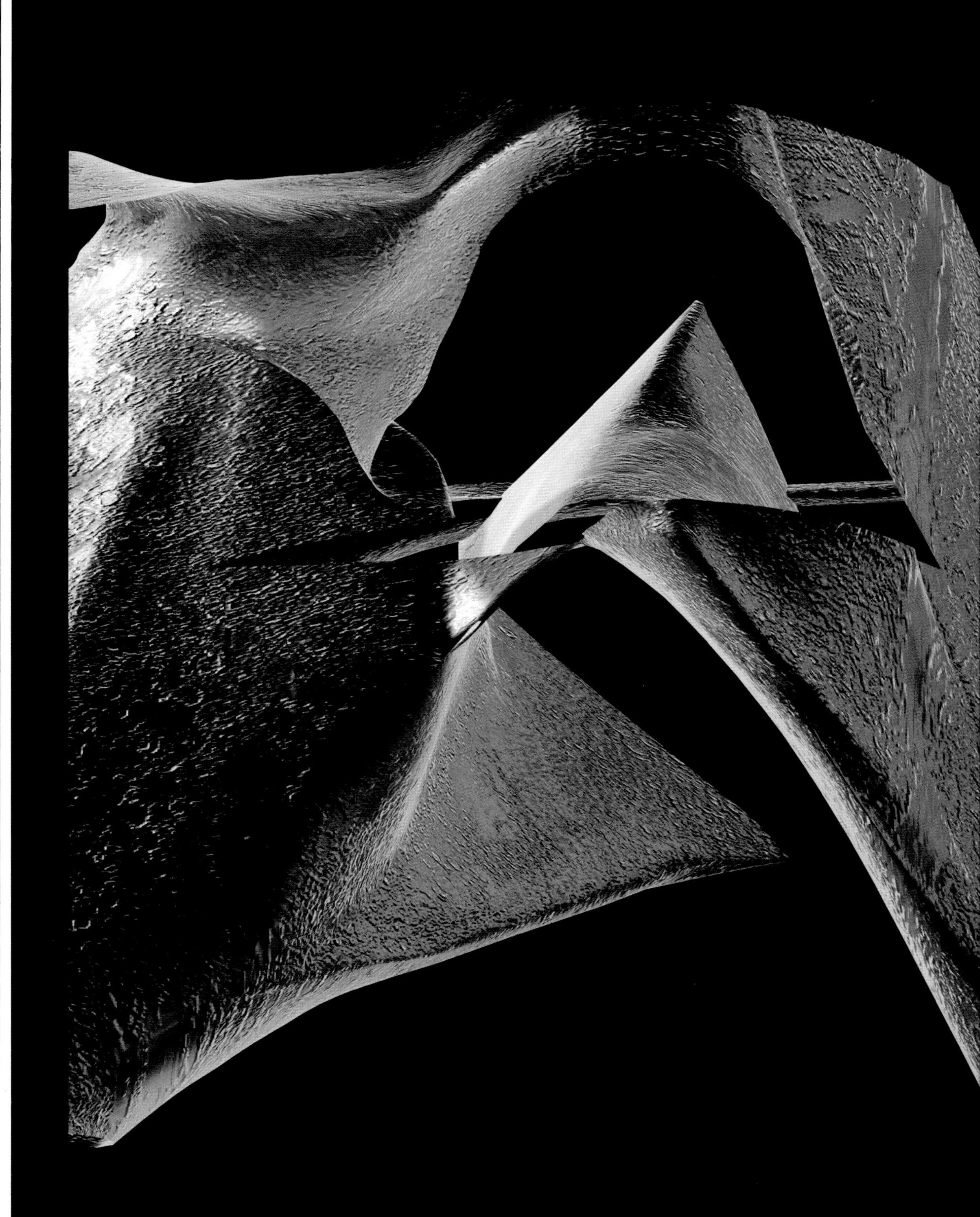

DESIGN

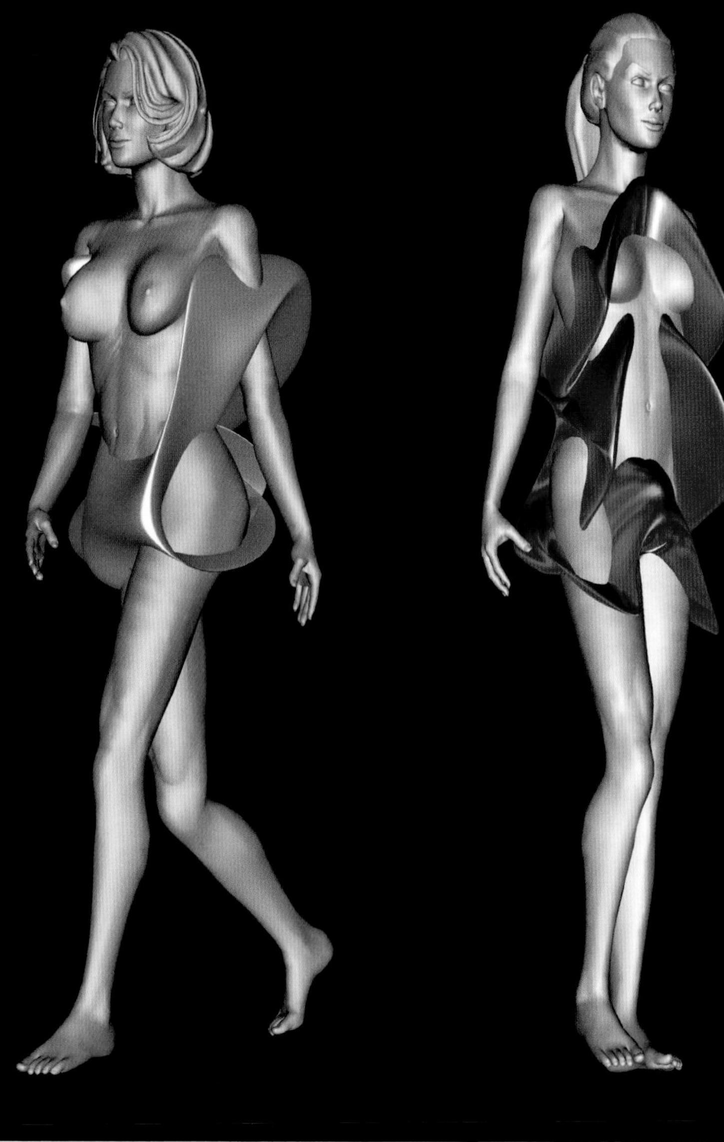

Pictures Notes

This dress takes its origin from the coupling of two figures obtained from the distortion of a geometrical figure known as "Venere Etrusca" (Etruscan Venus). The research for interesting sections of minimal surfaces is one of the basic elements of this series of studies.

图片说明：

把著名的伊特鲁里亚的维纳斯进行变形，接合所得两个形状，形成了这件衣服。是这一系列研究中基本的一条，是研究最小表面里一些有趣的部分。

Work dress

It allows for an integration of technological elements in the different fields of work, where for example memorisation or data availability are as important as the independence and the liberty of action of the operator.

工作服：

它可以综合不同工作领域的技术元素。举例而言，在工作中，工作人员的独立自由与记录、数据的实效性同样重要。

These timeless clay, plaster and resin date back up to 1994, partly anticipating HOV's current researches.
Conceived for some of Michele Gabbanelli's theatrical works, most of these objects, also of great dimensions and made of wood or polystyrene, went lost.
They were part of a world, where all that we regard as accessory and useful is a semi-organic element with which the living organism has a symbiotic relationship.
It was not a question of a direct connection with the nerve ganglions but of an impalpable continuity like that of the higher dimensions where time is just one (not very important) of the parameters
On occasion of a collaboration with fashion stylists these concepts were taken again in consideration. New ones were designed and, because of their differences from normal fashion objects, were also called "timeless."
Since I had no experience of couture, my unusual but workable projects were only a source of inspiration that stylist's sensibility would put into practice.
Now such dresses, differently conceived and without being strictly timeless, clothes young women in their everyday life.
Made of silicon rubber and covered in thick silk, they lie on the bodies wrapping them sweetly.

这些永恒的粘土、石膏和树脂可以追溯到1994年，它们也部分参与到HOV现在的研究。
作品的大部分是为米雪儿·加巴内利的戏剧构思的，同样是用木头和聚苯乙烯做的大尺度的物件，现在已经丢失了。
他们是世界的一部分，我们都认为有用的附属物品是半有机的，而生命体和它们有一种共生关系。
这不是与一个神经元直接联系的问题，　而是一种有更高的尺度的、感触不到的连续性。时间只是一个不是很重要的参量。在和时装设计师合作的场合，这些概念是不作考虑的。现在需要一些新的概念，因为它们和平常的时尚物品不同，这些概念也被称作为“永恒的”。
由于我没有和服装设计师共事的经验，我那些不同寻常但是可使用的物品只是设计师灵感的一个来源，他们会以他们的敏感把这些灵感运用到实践中。
现在这些有不同设计的服装并没有严格的永恒性，年轻的女士日常生活里就可以穿着。
这些服装用硅橡胶制成，覆盖以厚丝绸，它们把模特衬托地甜美可爱。

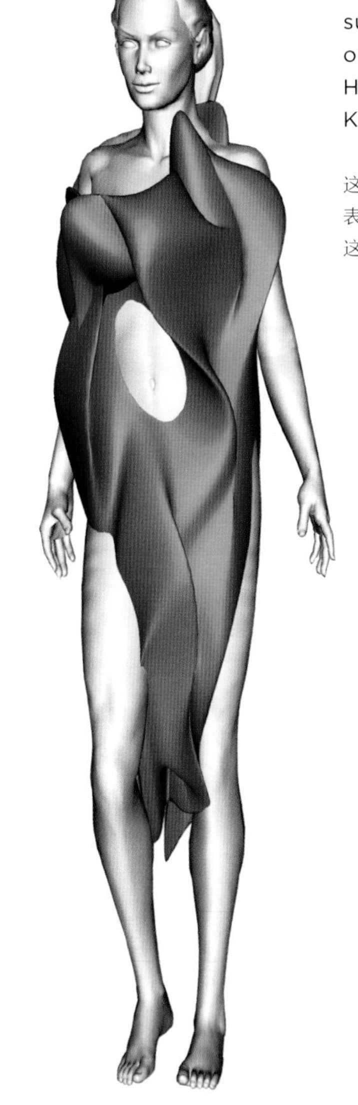

This model derives from
a series of studies about
surfaces that cannot be
orientated.
Here, a strong deformation of
Klein's bottle.

这个模特取自一系列有关不能转向的
表面的研究。
这是一个强烈的克莱因瓶的变形。

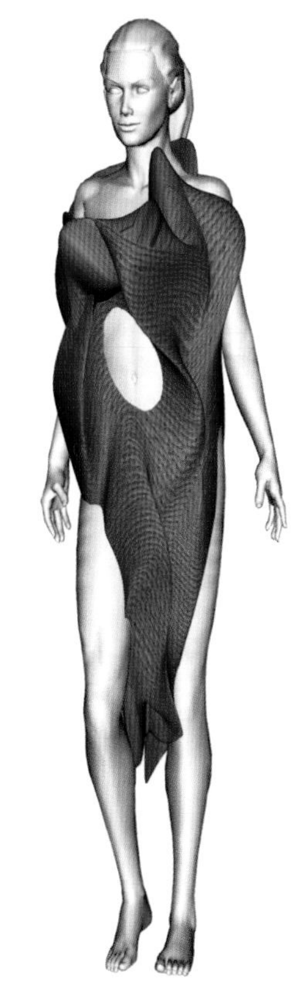

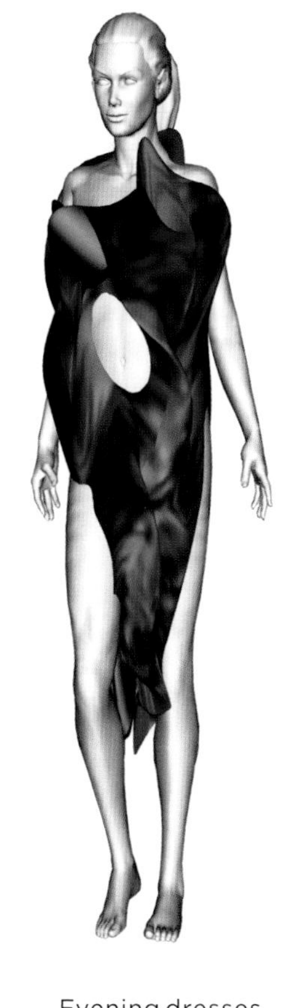

Evening dresses
晚装

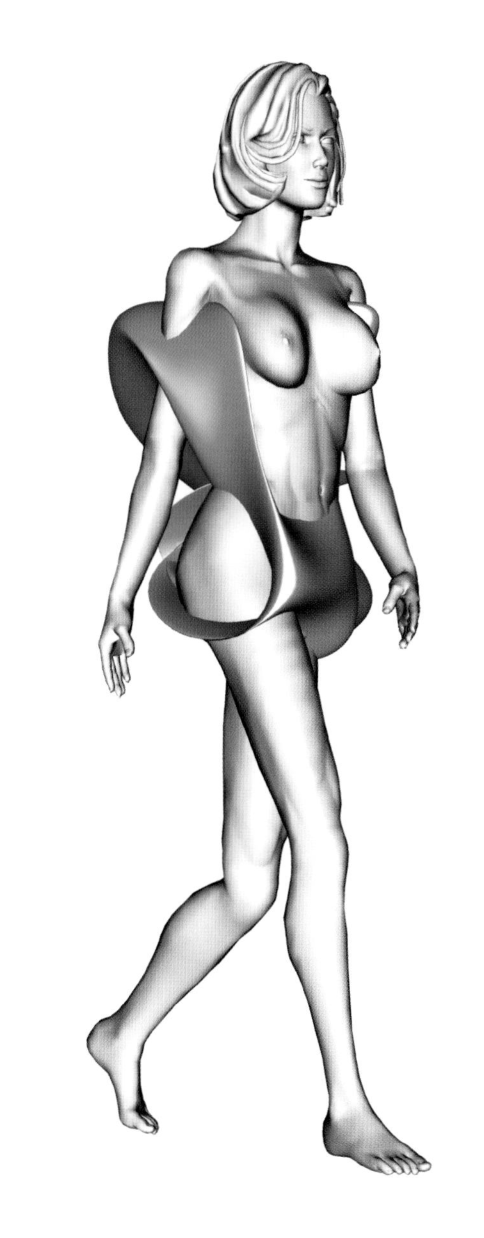

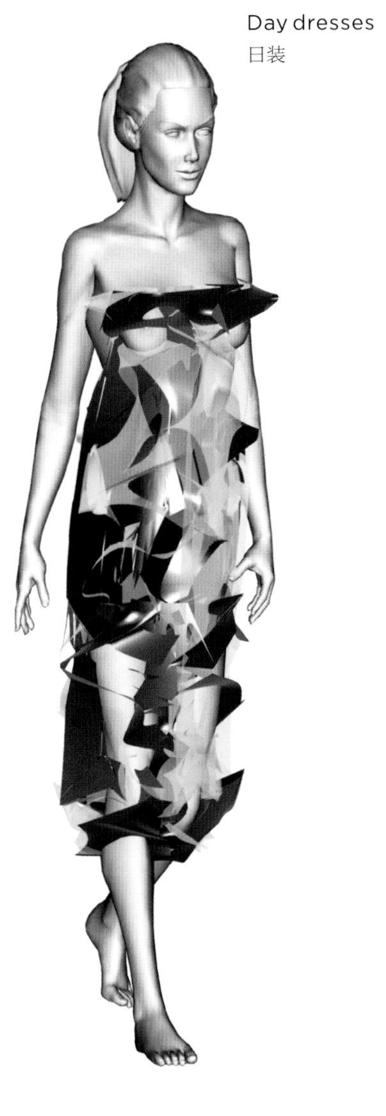

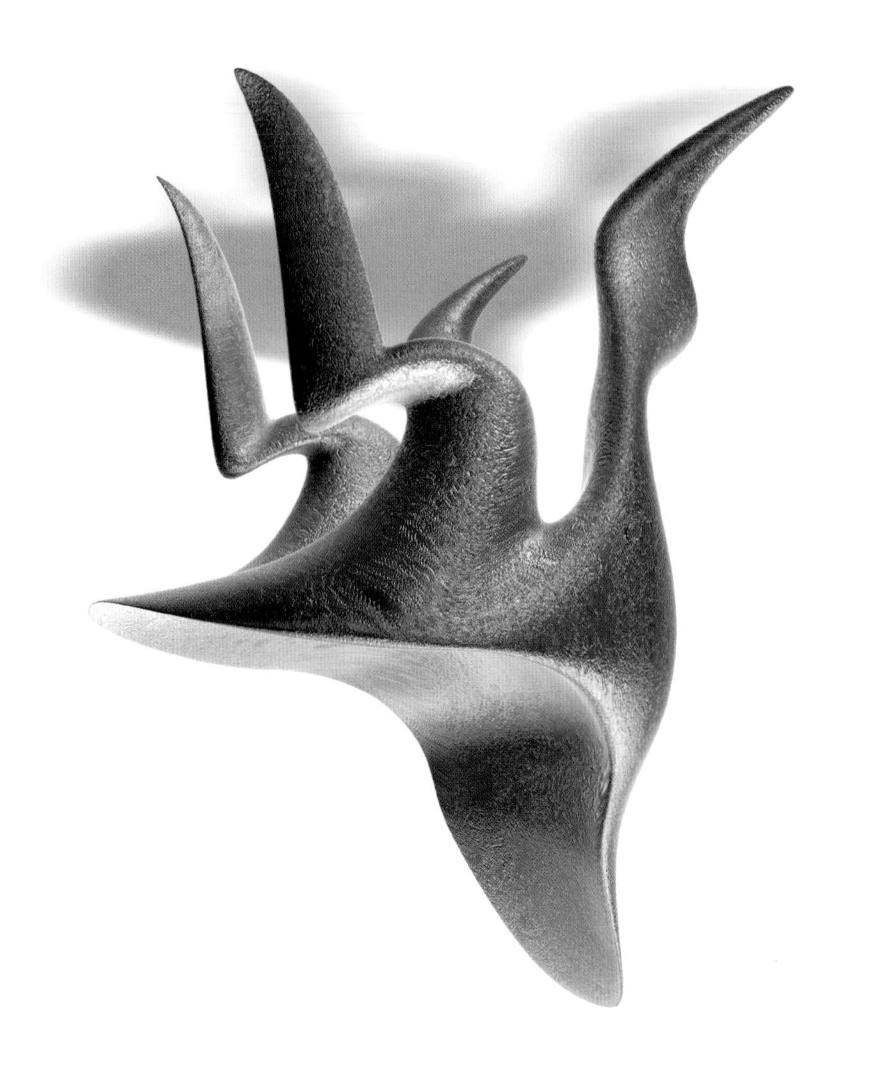

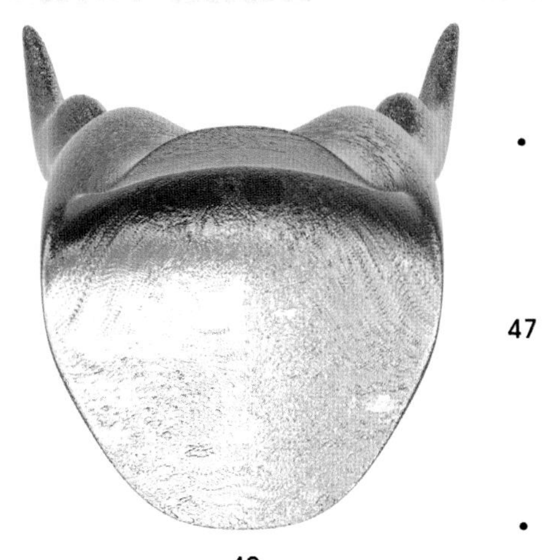

Kix is a chair realized in polypropylene whose conceptual biological reminiscences clearly show in its final perspective. It can awake in the observer/user an imaginary evolutionistic dimension or evoke unconscious, dark and mysterious thoughts. The object is an extreme and out of time element. The uneven surface of contact, with its metallic effect, is uniform the whole development long. It takes its origin from the direct pressing as well as from the possibility of differentiating the density of the material during the production according to the greater or smaller structural importance of the section of the model.

Kix是一把聚丙烯制成的椅子，它最终的效果能显示出它概念上的生物学经历。它能让使用者想象出进化的过程，或者唤起人潜意识的、秘密的想法。这个椅子是极端的、不合时间的。不平坦的表面接触，以及它的金属效果在整个过程中都始终如一。根据模型各部分结构上不同的重要性，在生产过程中对材料进行挤压、改变密度，形成了椅子最终的形象。

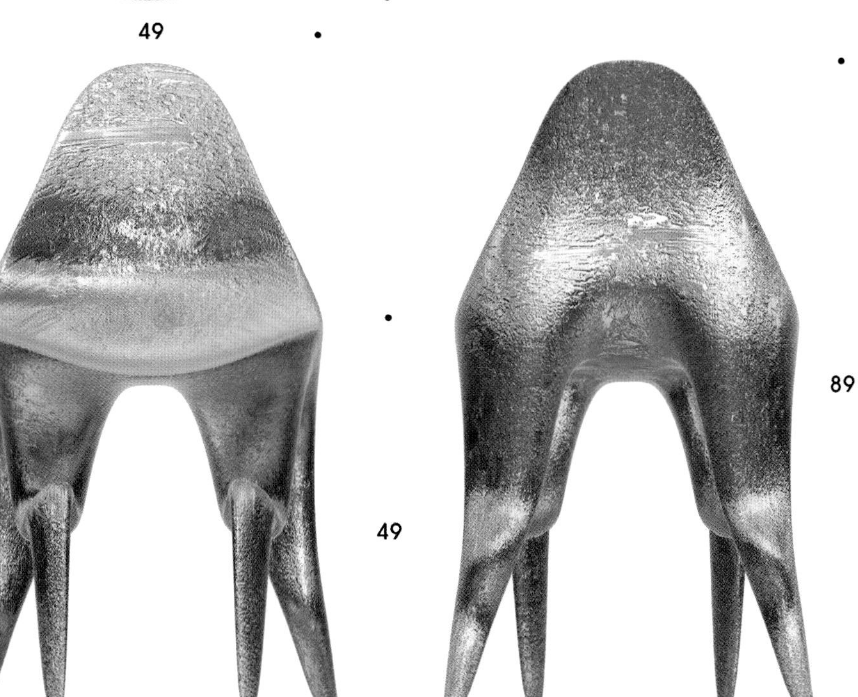

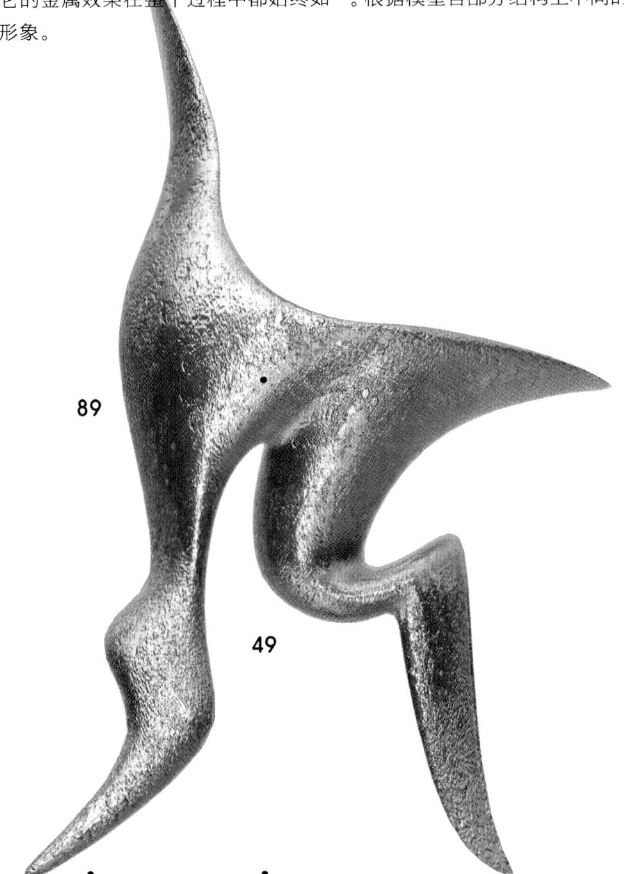

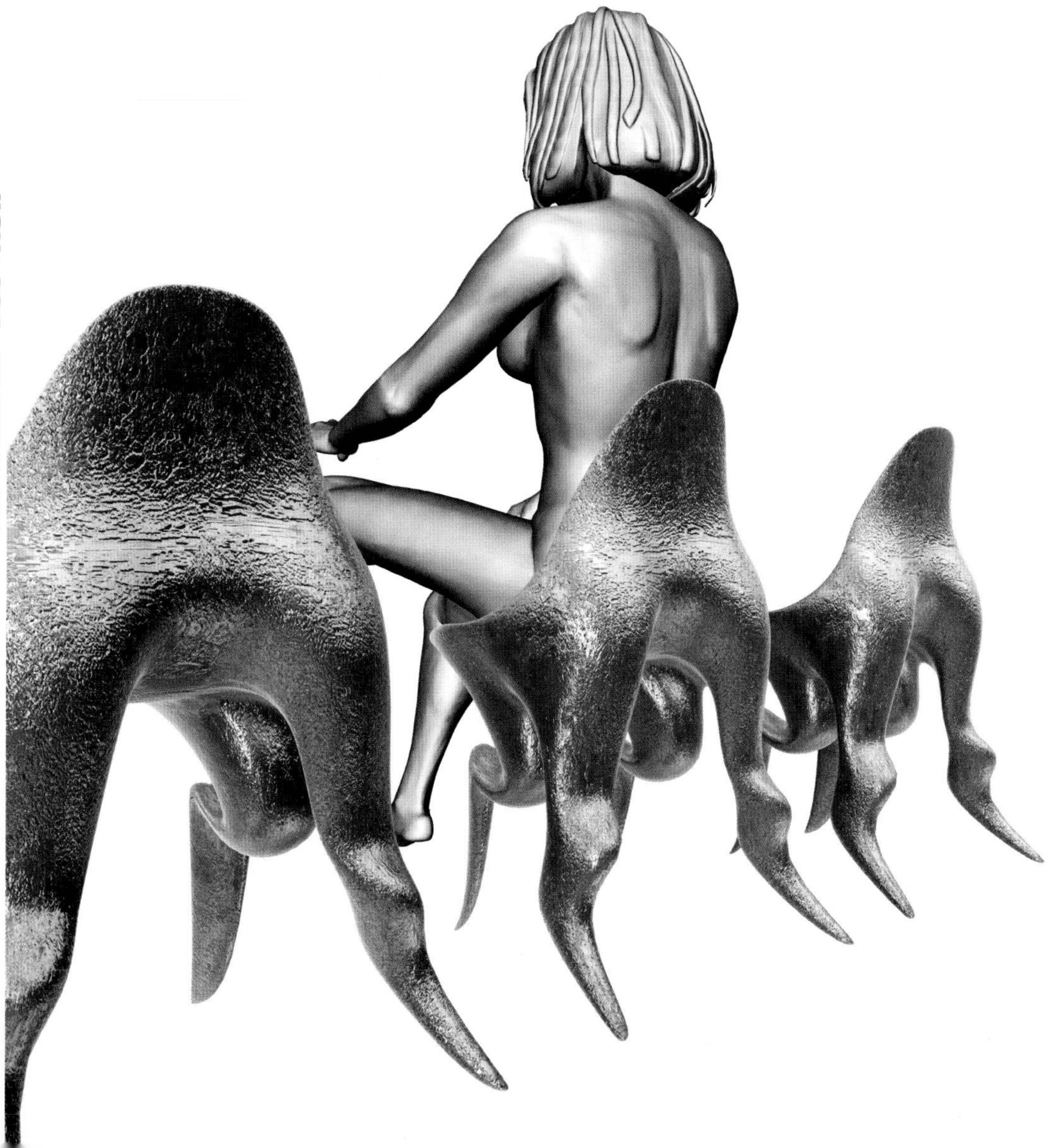

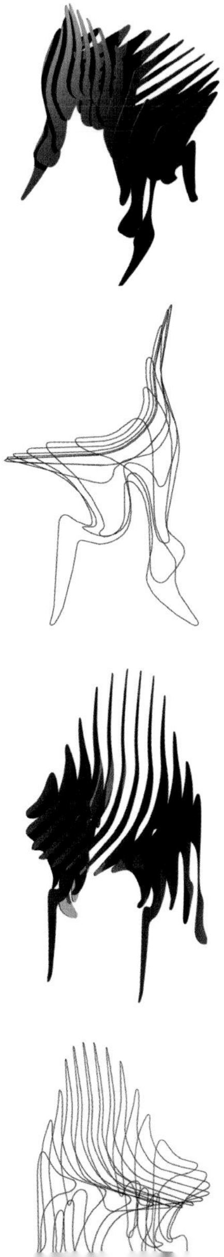

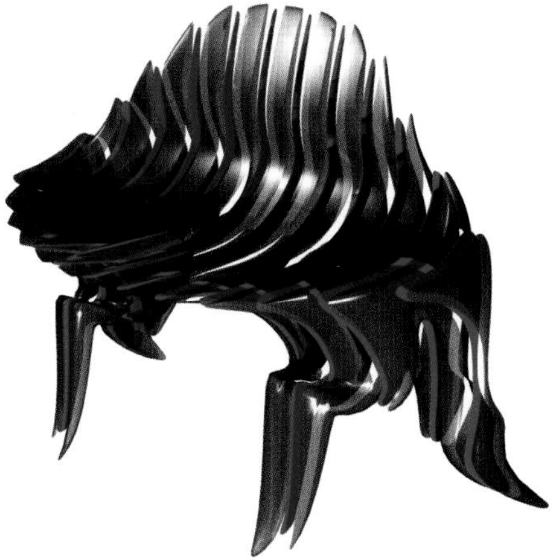

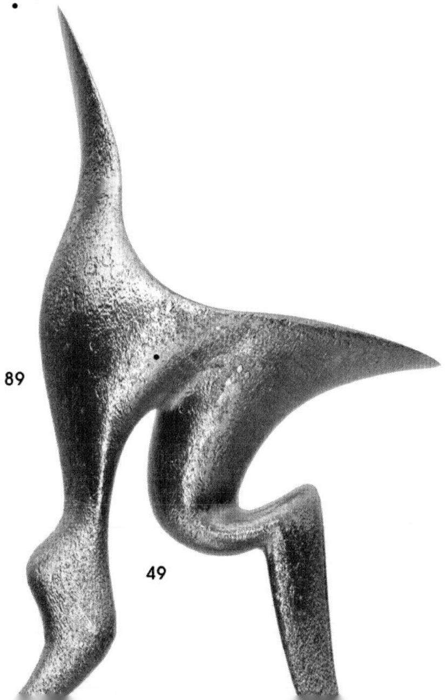

89

49

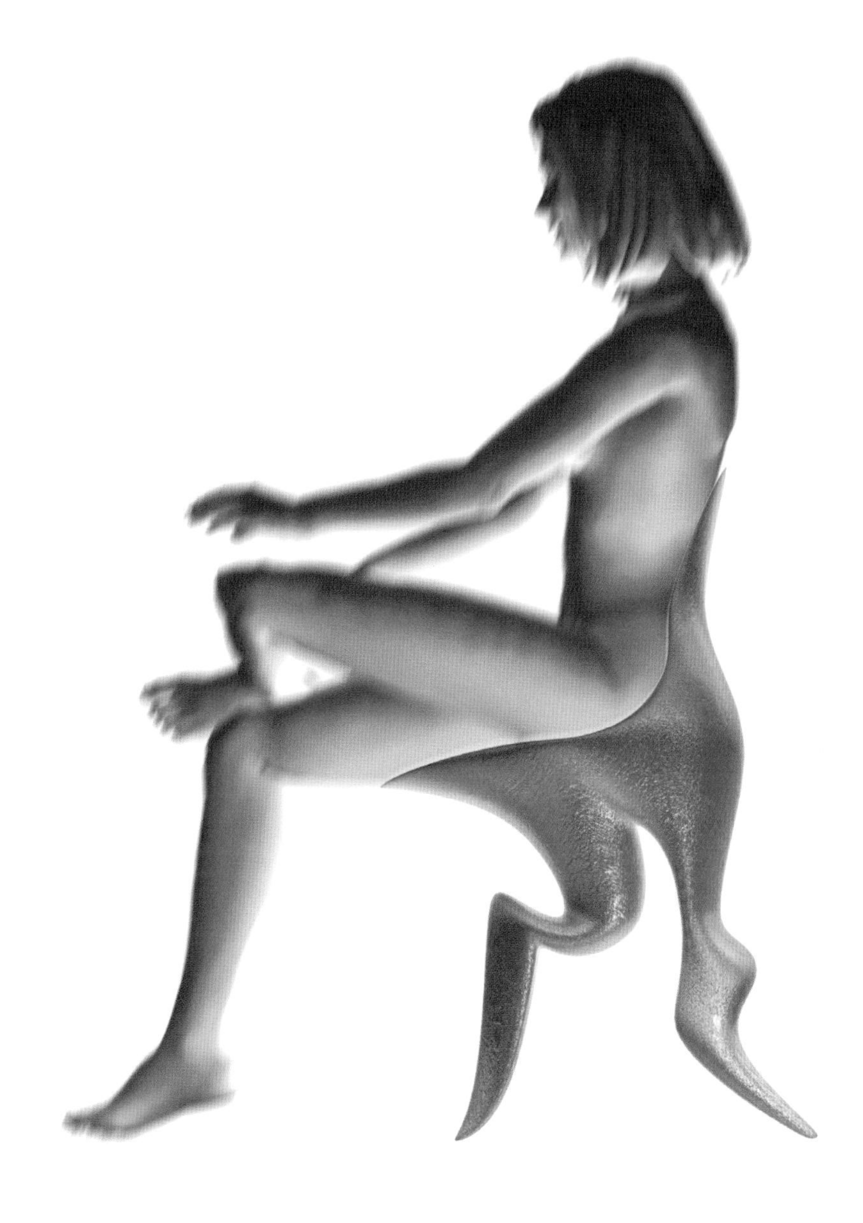

THE ARCHITECTURE OF THE ORGANIC-DIGITAL FUTURE

The digital era has modified our lifestyle and our way of inhabiting our territories - we are more and more hyper-connected navigators in the shapeless and fluid space of bits - it has also changed the conception of architecture and the behaviour of man in the physical space and in the universe-space. Also the discoveries of NASA have contributed to the change that, since the Sixties, has interested the artistic disciplines: from cinema – Kubrick's Odissea 2001 is an example - to architecture and architectonic projects for future houses – think of the Wichita House by Buckminster Fuller, a shining flying object in aluminium, Plexiglas and steel. In England Archigram, with the "plug-in city", the "living pod" and the "walking city", face the topic of the future living of the metropolis taking advantage of the interstices between the highways and the demolition areas, creating a contrast between the structures planned as true spaceships and the existing context: be it a consolidated city landscape or the edge and margin of the city.
The topic of future - also described by science fiction literature - has been a cultural platform for many architects who verified their own researches and experimented constructive technologies and new languages. The digital, after its boom in the Nineties of last century, suffered a slowing down and today it is recovering force through an increasing number of exhibitions and events, even if mass culture still identifies the digital devices with TV sets or cellular phones from which one could control home electric appliances. The contribution of the digital in our life still remains a utopia, because a few architects have been able to transform the abstract landscape produced by a computer into a real object.
Italian architecture must make further progress in order to fully assimilate the digital nouvelle vague. HOV research experiences are grafted in this context made of conservation and tradition. Experimenting, that is empirically trying to study the shapes and the languages induced by the computer and bring them to the limit, generates a strong connection with sciences: Mathematics, Physics and Biology. The great opportunity offered by the digital is the sensory involvement that causes estrangement in the traditional conception of space, made of straight angles and perpendicular lines: man will interact with sinuous wrapping shapes. David Raponi has been searching for a long time the foundation of a new model of society, partly expressed in Glossity, where the aim is "to produce a series of hypothesis inserting variations to the basic concepts, in order to experience their consequences [...] The project prospers - Raponi continues – in the relation between organism and environment, in the same way as in Maturana's words 'walking is created by a movement of legs in their relation with the ground'. The rules of society change and consequently also the way one lives or works in it changes and new relations are created. At this point architecture defines the new codes that every citizen must respect in a sort of ideal city. But HOV insists on the colonization concept in many projects: from the suicides tower to the Mystery Palace. In both cases the walls of the building are "colonized" by fluid matter, that is a set of living organisms that give shape to the architecture skin, like seaweeds.
HOV activity is concentrated on the determination of future sceneries starting from the residence location – the place of maximum experimentation, as shown in the Block House and the Zebra House - and successively extended to the city. The house is conceived as a succession of open homogenous spaces wrapped by round or sharp shapes without privacy. In this case the hypothesis of a change is about the different way of living the space inhabited, breaking off the tradition of separating the various functions in the house – which is what happens when there is a day zone and a night one. There is therefore a place where all functional hierarchies are cancelled.
HOV uses the mouse like an instrument for formal experimentations, it replaces sketches on paper and defines a separated context on the screen, where geographic and morphologic references do not exist. Therefore in HOV activity the topic of future cannot be irrespective of a connection with natural organic shapes and the various theories on the evolution of the society, such as for example the pre-figuration of small communities inter-logged on through the net. HOV, using the digital media, succeeds in formulating sensitive architectures that are similar to the functioning of the human body and it is just the body-architecture that characterizes most of the research: from the clothing for glossity citizens to the intensive centre for procreation.
The present technological possibilities make the 3D solutions conceived on the screen practicable, both for the covers and for the bearing structures of buildings. True hi-tech city sculptures are therefore created and made possible by the computer.

Another important aspect is linked to the availability of skilled labour capable of providing the qualities demanded for the finish, where the construction of sinuous structures, presumably made of steel - the most flexible material for these kind of architectures - also involves a remarkable economic expense, increasing the construction costs. And that is caused by the lack of a consolidated habit of using building technologies induced by the organic-digital project of the city.

Emanuele Piccardo

有机-数码 未来的建筑

数码时代改变了我们的生活方式和我们的居住方式，我们越来越像是在不成形的流动比特空间里的超连通的航海家。它同时也改变了建筑的概念，也改变了人在实际空间和宇宙空间中的行为方式。美国国家航空和宇宙航行局的发现，使得自20世纪60年代以来艺术界各个领域都对太空产生了兴趣：从影院（比如库布里克的《太空漫游》，2001）到建筑和未来住宅的建筑项目。例如巴克敏斯特·富勒设计的威奇托住宅，就是由铝、树脂玻璃和钢建成的一个闪亮的飞行物。曾创作出“插入城市”、“生活荚”、“行走城市”的阿基格拉姆在英格兰研究了一项有关在摩天大楼里未来生活方式的课题，摩天大楼处于高架与遗迹地区之间的缝隙里，这给宇宙飞船式的建筑与现有文脉之间创造了一个对比的机会：使它与城市景观结合为一个整体或是成为城市的边界。

被科幻小说所描述过的未来这个主题，成为了很多建筑师的创作文化平台。他们证实了他们自己的研究，并实验了新的建造技术和新的语言。20世纪90年代数码科技曾一度繁荣，之后衰弱下来。现在，它又通过不断增长的展览重新开始繁荣，虽然大众文化仍然认为电视机、手机等数码设备并不是那种可以控制家庭生活的电子设备。数码对我们生活的贡献仍然只是乌托邦式的，因为没有几个建筑师把电脑所描绘的微缩景观变成了实物。

意大利建筑必须再有更多的进步，这样才能吸收掉数码小说里的不确定性。HOV的研究经历是和这种保存与传统的背景相联系的。

那些实验试图研究电脑生成的形状和语言，并把它们带向一个极致。这使它们和科学之间产生了强烈的联系：数学、物理和生物。数码所提供的机遇是一种情感参与，远离传统的直角和平行线组成的空间的概念：人会和复杂的包装形状相互作用。大卫拉普尼花了很多时间研究社会新模型的基础。其中部分以平滑性表现。它的目的是创造一系列嵌入基本概念的假想变化，从而验证它们的结果。拉普尼继续研究生物体和环境之间的关系，这个项目进行得越来越好。他们的实验和玛吐拉那那句话是同样的方式“走路是来自双腿和地面之间关系的运动”。社会标准发生了变化，一个人在社会中生活工作的方式也发生了变化，新的关系已经建立了起来。在这一点上，建筑定义了一种新的代码，在理想城市里每个市民都要遵守这种代码。但是HOV在很多项目中都坚持殖民的概念：从自杀塔到神秘宫。在这两个例子里，建筑的墙体都被流动性的材料“殖民化”，建筑的表皮形状来自一系列的生物体，比如海草。

HOV的活动是以未来景象为目标，从居住场所开始——正如在金属块房屋和斑马房屋中，那是一些最大极限实验的场所——现在已成功地扩展到城市里去。这个房屋被构想为由一连串同质的开敞空间组成，这些空间没有私密性，被圆形或尖形的形状包裹起来。在这个案例中，假想产生的变化是在居住空间里体现不同的生活方式，打破把房屋中不同的功能分开的传统——有白天活动区和夜晚活动区的传统。因此就出现了取消所有功能分层的场所。

HOV把鼠标作为正式实验中的一个仪器，它代替了徒手草图，在屏幕上定义了一个单独的背景，这个背景里不存在地理学和形态学的参考。所以在HOV的活动中，有关未来的课题不能不考虑其与自然有机体形状的联系，以及和各种社会进化理论的联系，例如有小团体通过网络日志相互集结的先兆。HOV利用数码媒体，成功地表达了与人体机能相似的灵敏性高的建筑，而且大多数研究正是以人体-建筑为特色：从为glossity市民设计的服装到生殖中心都是如此。

现有的技术可以使屏幕上出现3d画面，也可以表现建筑的表面和支撑结构。由此就可以用电脑创造出真实的高科技城市雕塑。

另外一个重要的方面技术劳动力的使用，他们能为完成复杂结构建造的质量提供保证。结构材料估计是钢，它是此类建筑最灵活的一种材料，使用这样的材料需要很高的费用，这会增加整个建筑的成本。而这是由于没有整体运用有机-数码城市项目中的建筑技术所造成的。

Emanuele Piccardo

HOV BIBLIOGRAPHY

HOV

[Architecture firm founded in 1998 by David Raponi__Ancona__Italy]
[David Raponi_born 08_01_1965] [Licensed architect_1991_University of Florence]
[Theatre (1993_1996) Scenography, models, sculptures]
[Yacht Design (1997_1998) Interior designer_CRN Yachts and Perini Navi]

Exhibitions

15th July – 15th August 1995, Binomio Artistico Autonomo (Autonomous Artistic Binomial) , Palazzo Simonetti Gallery, Osimo (AN);
24th January – 7th February 1999, Tesi di laurea della Facoltà di Architettura per Firenze (Graduation Thesis at the Faculty of Architecture of Florence), Design Accademy Hall in S. Marco's Square, Florence;
29th May – 20th June 1999, IX Biennale dei Giovani Artisti dell'Europa e del Mediterraneo. Sarajevo Concert Hall (IX Biennial Exhibition of European and Mediterranean Young Artists. Sarajevo concert Hall), Architecture Pavilion Ex-Slaughter House, Rome;
29th - 31st March 2000, Sarajevo Concert Hall Stripes, Tapestries Hall / S.Michele's Structure, Rome;
26th August – 6th September 2001, Biennale di Arte Contemporanea Porto Ercole (Porto Ercole Contemporary Art Biennial Exhibition), Forte Stella, Porto Ercole (GR)
1st – 13th October 2001, Possibile Futures, Biennial Exhibition of Architecture of Miami, Miami - FL (USA)
2nd – 5th May 2002, Image, Innocents' Hospital, Brunelleschi Hall, Florence;
18th May – 30th June 2002, A_Factor – Dimensioni Artificiali Variabili (Variable Artificial Dimensions), Contemporary Art Borromini, Ozzano Monferrato (AL);
25th May – 30th June 2002, A_Factor – Dimensioni Artificiali Variabili (Variable Artificial Dimensions), Solicitor's Office Gallery, Caserta;
21st – 30th July 2002, Atlante dell'Architettura del futuro (Atlas of Future Architecture) – XXI Congress of Architecture UIA, Berlin (Germany);
6th – 9th September 2002, Premio Macef Design (Macef Design Award), Fair District, Milan;
2nd – 24th November 2002, Premio Internazionale di Arti Visive "Espoarte 2002" (International Award for Visual Arts "Expoarte 2002), Civic Museum of Contemporary Art, Albissola Marina (SV);
13th – 20th April 2003, Dal cucchiaio alla città (From the Spoon to the City), Via Pepe, Isola District, Milan;
2nd – 5th October 2003, Image, Innocents' Hospital, Brunelleschi Hall, Florence;
2nd – 12th October 2003, Intimacy, Ex-Leopolda Station, Florence;
15th – 18th September 2005, Attraversamenti, Umbria 05, Biennale Diffusa di Architettura contemporanea (Crossings, Umbria 05, Diffuse Contemporary Architecture Biennial Exhibition), Town Picture-Gallery Museum, Todi (PG);
19th – 25th September 2005, Nuovi Laici (New Laymen), Festival of Architecture, S. Ludovico's Church, Parma;
15th May – 27th August 2006, GOOD N.E.W.S., Palace of Art – Foundation "La Triennale di Milano", Milan;
25th – 29th May 2006, Mixedmedia Festival – Hangar Bicocca, Milan.

Lectures

4th October 2002, Meetings for Italian Architecture, IUAV Tolentini, Venice
8th May 2003, Faculty of Architecture, University of Trieste
24th October 2004, Frame & Mutations, National Museum Square, Naples
23rd February 2005, Format-C frequency, answer, question, IUAV Tolentini, Venice
24th October 2005, Turn up the Volume! Architecture and Future, Rome
8th April 2006, Visions of Architecture, Maschio Angioino, Naples
25th May 2006, Mixedmedia Festival – Hangar Bicocca, Milan.

Books

Matter and Geometry, Didactics of Design, Publication of graduation Thesis
AA.VV., University of Florence, Designing Department, Alinea Ed., 1994, pages 106-119
The Citadel of Clean Energy, Ideas for the new seat of Gas Rimini Society
AA.VV.,Maggioli, 1995, p. 137
Beyond Media, M. Brizzi and P. Diaconia, Compositori Ed., 2002, p. 63
A Factor, Variable Artificial Dimensions, L. Beatrice and M. Rainò, 2002, pages 18-19
Defining Digital Architecture, 2001 Feidad Award, Yu-Tung Liu, BirkHauser, 2002, p. 85

Developing Digital Architecture, 2002 Feidad Award, Yu-Tung Liu, BirkHauser, 2003, p. 97
GR – the Net Generation, Experimentations in Italian Architecture - 2A+P, M. Brizzi and L. Prestinenza Pugliesi, Cooper & Castelvecchi, 2003, pages 106-119 and 248-249
Intimacy, Drastic Architectures, M. Brizzi and P. Diaconia, Mandragora, 2004, pages 79-80
Format c, Frequency Answer Question 02, Format C Research Group, 2004, pages 32-87
Frame & Mutations, Visions of Architecture, L. Affuso, Dracme Ed. s.r.l., 2005, pages 63-71

Magazine Reviews
Avant Garde, Profile by G. Grandi, 2001 n. 12, p. 72
d'Architettura, One Hundred Projects, 2002 n. 17, p. 63
EDGE Collections, Architecture & Design by A. Carloni, Spring-Summer 2002 n. 121, pages 166-171
Next Exit, Rice Hi-Tech by M. Bastante, Aprile 2002 n. 6, p. 44
L'Arca, I-(m)possible architecture by Luigi Centola, June 2002 n. 171, pages 2-4
l'Arca, Agora Dreams and Visions by L. Centola, October 2002 n. 174, pages 36-47
d' Architettura, One Hundred Projects, 2003 n. 20, p. 59
d'Architettura, One Hundred Projects, 2003 n. 21, p. 57
l'Arca Plus, Trespassings and Strategies by L. Centola, 2003 n. 36, pages 40-51
Parametro 14_02, Between the Digital and the Organic by E. Piccardo, January-February 2003 n. 243, pages 32-37
Garden Design Journal, The italian job by R. Cattano, February-March 2003, pages 16-17
L'Arca, The Adriatic Sea Gate, Ancona by M. Gabbanelli, 2004 n. 190, pages 70-73
Arcvision, Emotional Spaces by D. Raponi, January 2004 n. 10, pages 64-71
Parametro, Projects and Conversations - by D. Raponi, November-December 2004 n. 254, pages 68-77
d'Architettura, New Laymen by L. Gelmini, September-December 2005 n. 28, pages 90-98
l'Arca Plus, Found space Theatre by M. Gabbanelli, 2005 n. 44, pages 20-23

TV Programmes
CULT TV – Millepiani - Everybody Home / Interview with HOV - by Emanuele Piccardo - January 2005

HOV Team
Principal
David Raponi

Office coordination
Eleonora Moscardi

HOV_team and partner - in reverse order of appearence, 2006 - 1998

- FIMA Engineering*
- Raffaella Valverde*
- Paolo Baroni*
- Stefano Morelli
- Daniele Feriozzi
- Serenella Ottone
- Donatella Magni
- Enrico Baroni*
- Michele Gabbanelli*
- Raul Raponi*

Authorship
Cesare Maria Casati
Michele Gabbanelli
Luigi Centola
Emanuele Piccardo
Filippo Forzato
Federica Bianconi
Andrea Carloni

图书在版编目(CIP)数据

全息建筑形态学一HOV作品 / 蓝青 主编
-武汉:华中科技大学出版社,2008.4
ISBN 978-7-5609-4464-7
I.全... II.蓝... III.建筑设计—造型设计 IV.TU2
中国版本图书馆CIP数据核字(2008)第034690号

全息建筑形态学一HOV作品
主 编:蓝青
美国亚洲艺术与设计协作联盟(AADCU)

出版发行:华中科技大学出版社
地 址:武汉市珞瑜路1037号(邮编:430074)
出 版 人:阮海洪
责任编辑:杨睿
责任监印:张正林
制版印刷:北京画中画印刷有限公司
开 本:889mmx1194mm 1/16
印 张:14.5
字 数:169千字
版 次:2008年4月第1版
印 次:2008年4月第1次印刷
ISBN 978-7-5609-4464-7/TU·322
定 价:228.00元

出品-经 销:北京哲匠之门文化有限责任公司
联 系 人:黄琴
电 话:010-64154182 邮 箱:hgy_huang@yahoo.com.cn
地 址:北京市海淀区云会里远流清园5号楼2单元101室
(如图书凡属有印刷装帧错误,可向经销商调换)